C0-CDD-807

MIDLAND

Twenty-five Years of Fiction and Poetry Selected fr

MIDLAND

e Writing Workshops of the State University of Iowa

EDITED BY *Paul Engle*

ASSISTED BY *Henri Coulette* AND *Donald Justice*

RANDOM HOUSE · NEW YORK

PS
536
E55

FIRST PRINTING

© *Copyright, 1961, by State University of Iowa*

All rights reserved under International and Pan-American Copyright Conventions. Published in New York by Random House, Inc., and simultaneously in Toronto, Canada, by Random House of Canada, Limited.

Library of Congress Catalog Card Number: 60-12132

MANUFACTURED IN THE UNITED STATES OF AMERICA BY
THE COLONIAL PRESS INC.

54932

ACKNOWLEDGMENTS

Permission has been obtained from authors and publishers for items used in this book. Grateful acknowledgment is made as follows:

WILLIAM BELVIN: "Palermo, Mother's Day, 1943" © 1951 by Kenyon College, from *The Kenyon Review;* "The Geographers" © 1954 by *Botteghe Oscure*

WILLIAM BERGE: "That Lovely Green Boat" © 1951 by Reed Whittemore, from *Furioso*

GEORGE BLUESTONE: "The Ascent of Corey" © 1944 by *Epoch*

FREDERICK BOCK: "A Return from the Wars" © 1956 by Yale University Press, Inc., from *The Yale Review;* "Winter: The Statue of Pomona" © 1956 by The Modern Poetry Association, from *Poetry*

DONNA BOWEN: "The Eggs" © 1961 by Donna Bowen; "Pursuit" © 1956 by *Botteghe Oscure*

JAMES BUECHLER: "The Proud Suitor" © 1958 by Street & Smith Publications, Inc., from *Mademoiselle*

R. V. CASSILL: "The Prize" © 1955 by Perspective, Inc., from *Perspective*

JANE COOPER: "The Faithful" © 1957 by Jane Cooper, from *New World Writing #11;* "Morning on the St. John's" © 1957 by Jane Cooper, from *The New Yorker*

HENRI COULETTE: "The Trophies" © 1961 by Henri Coulette; "Intaglio" © 1957 by The Hudson Review, Inc., from *The Hudson Review;* "Cygnets House" © 1961 by Henri Coulette; and "The Attic" © 1957 by Street & Smith Publications, Inc., from *Mademoiselle*

ALEXANDER CRAIG: "John Smith" © 1958 by Alexander Craig, published in Australian quarterly, *Meanjin*

BRUCE CUTLER: "The Language of Yes" © 1960 by the University of Nebraska Press, from *The Year of the Green Wave* and first published in *The Friends Journal*

ROBERT PATRICK DANA: "Goodbye. Goodbye." and "For Sister Mary Apolline" © 1957 by Robert Patrick Dana, the latter poem from *Poetry*, both published in *My Glass Brother and Other Poems* by Constance Press (now Stonewall Press)

RICAREDO DEMETILLO: "You Laugh Within the House of Me" © 1961 by Ricaredo Demetillo; "The God My Father Chiseled with His Tongue" © 1955 by Ricaredo Demetillo, from *No Uncertain Weather*

WILLIAM DICKEY: "The Plot" © 1957 by The Hudson Review, Inc., from *The Hudson Review;* later published in *Of the Festivity* by Yale University Press, Inc.; "Part Song, with Concert of Recorders" © 1959 by Yale University Press, Inc., from *Of the Festivity;* "To His Companions in Exile" © 1959 by *Chicago Review;* "Twenty Years Gone, She Returns to the Nunnery" © 1957 by The Hudson Review, Inc., from *The Hudson Review*, later published in *Of the Festivity*

HARRY DUNCAN: "The Answer" © 1961 by Harry Duncan, from *The Daily Iowan*

JOHN ENGELS: "The Experimenters" © 1960 by The Commonweal Publishing Co., Inc., from *The Commonweal*

PAUL ENGLE: "You Can't Be Wise" © 1959 by Paul Engle, published in *Poems in Praise* by Random House, Inc.; from "For the Iowa Dead" (XIII © 1957 by *Botteghe Oscure*, XV © 1956 by Paul Engle, from *Life*) published in *Poems in Praise* by Random House, Inc.; "Beasts" © 1950 by Paul Engle, from *Poetry* and published in *The Word of Love* by Random House, Inc., in 1951

PETER EVERWINE: "Soldiers' Woods: Occupied Germany" © 1959 by *December;* "To My Father's Ghost" © 1959 by The Paris Review, Inc., from *The Paris Review;* "On a Photograph of My Grandfather, Paolo Castelnuovo" © 1961 by Peter

Everwine, published in *The Broken Frieze* by Hilltop Press in 1958; "Winter Stop-over" © 1959 by *Spectrum*

DONALD FINKEL: "Braille" and "Danger Is the Pivot of the Sublime Life" © 1959 by Donald Finkel, "The Clothing's New Emperor" © 1956 by Donald Finkel; all three poems reprinted with permission of Charles Scribner's Sons from *The Clothing's New Emperor and Other Poems*, POETS OF TODAY VI

E. S. FORGOTSON: "Poem at the Hour of Surveyance" and "Colloquy" © 1939 by Louisiana State University, from *The Southern Review;* "St. Anthony 1960" © 1961 by E. S. Forgotson

KIMON FRIAR: "Greek Transfiguration" © 1961 by Kimon Friar

JEAN GARRIGUE: "A Fable of Berries" © 1959 by Jean Garrigue, from *A Water Walk by the Villa d'Este*, published by St. Martin's Press, Inc., and first published in *The Hudson Review*

WALKER GIBSON: "Advice to Travelers" © 1956 by Saturday Review, Inc., from *Saturday Review;* "Come Off It" © 1958 by Walker Gibson; both poems published in *Come As You Are* by Hastings House, Inc., in 1958

WILLIAM GOODREAU: "The Father" © 1961 by William Goodreau

MARTHA GRIMES: "The Haunted House" © 1959 by John Calder (Publishers) Ltd., published by Criterion Books Inc.

JAMES B. HALL: "A Spot in History" © 1952 by *Epoch*, published in *Fifteen by Three* by New Directions in 1953

CARL HARTMAN: "A Season of Mists" © 1952 by Garrett Publications, from *Tomorrow*

ANTHONY HECHT: "Upon the Death of George Santayana" © 1954 by Kenyon College, from *The Kenyon Review;* "The Vow" © 1957 by The Hudson Review, Inc., from *The Hudson Review;* "A Poem for Julia" and "Samuel Sewall" © 1954 by Anthony Hecht, both poems published in *A Summoning of Stones* and used by permission of The Macmillan Company

ALBERT HERZING: "Canticle I" © 1952 by The Modern Poetry Association, from *Poetry;* "The Candy-Man's Art Is the Sweetest Art I Know" © 1956 by *Partisan Review*

THEODORE HOLMES: "Journeys" © 1957 by Theodore Holmes, from *The Kenyon Review*, published that year under the title "Poem" in *The Harvest and the Scythe: Poems*, POETS OF TODAY IV, reprinted with permission of Charles Scribner's Sons; "The Life of the Estate" © 1956 by Theodore Holmes, from *The Kenyon Review;* reprinted with permission of Charles Scribner's Sons from *The Harvest and the Scythe: Poems*, POETS OF TODAY IV

DOMINADOR I. ILIO: "Diplomat Listening to Speech of Another Diplomat" © 1952 by The Modern Poetry Association, from *Poetry;* later published in *Six Filipino Poets* edited by Leonard Casper © 1955 by the Benipayo Press

DAVID CLAY JENKINS: "Summer: Sun and Shade" © 1952 by The New Yorker Magazine, Inc., from *The New Yorker* and used here in a slightly different version

CAROL JOHNSON: "Sonnet" © 1954 by The Commonweal Publishing Co., Inc.; "From a Book of Hours" © 1960 by The Commonweal Publishing Co., Inc.; both from *The Commonweal*

DONALD JUSTICE: "Beyond the Hunting Woods" © 1956 by Donald Justice; "Tales from a Family Album" © 1957 by Donald Justice; "Sonnet" © 1957 by Donald Justice; "On a Painting by Patient B of the Independence State Hospital for the Insane" © 1954 by Donald Justice; "Anniversaries" © 1957, 1960, by Donald Justice; all five poems reprinted from the book *The Summer Anniversaries* by Donald Justice, published by Wesleyan University Press

CALVIN KENTFIELD: "The Bell of Charity" © 1955 by The New Yorker Magazine, Inc., from *The New Yorker*

KIM YONG IK: "The Wedding Shoes" © 1952 by The New Yorker Magazine, Inc., from *The New Yorker*

JOSEPH LANGLAND: "Pruners: Conca di Marini" © 1957 by Meridian Books, Inc., published in *New Poets of England and America;* "The Amalfi Grotto" © 1957 by The New American Library of World Literature, Inc., from *New World Writing #11*

ALFRED M. LEE: "Beside My Grandmother" © 1961 by Alfred M. Lee

PHILIP LEGLER: "Landscape for a Wife" © 1959 by The Modern Poetry Association, from *Poetry*

PHILIP LEVINE: "Mad Day in March" © 1958 by Philip Levine, from *The New Yorker;* "Green Thumb" © 1961 by Philip Levine, from *The New Orleans Poetry Journal;* "Small Game" © 1961 by Philip Levine; "Night Thoughts over a Sick Child" © 1958 by The Modern Poetry Association, from *Poetry*

ROBIE MACAULEY: "A Nest of Gentlefolk" © 1957 by Robie Macauley, from *Furioso* and later published in *The End of Pity and Other Stories* by McDowell, Obolensky, Inc.

WILLARD MARSH: "Mexican Hayride" © 1960 by Esquire, Inc., from *Esquire*, March, 1960

E. L. MAYO: "Joy of Man's Desiring" © 1958 by University of Nebraska Press, from *Prairie Schooner* and later published in *Summer Unbound and Other Poems* © 1958 by University of Minnesota; "Three Ladies" © 1958 by University of Minnesota, published in *Summer Unbound and Other Poems;* "The Factory" © 1958 by The Modern Poetry Association, from *Poetry*

KARL KIMBER MERKER: "Poem for Con" © 1959 by The Modern Poetry Association, from *Poetry*

ROBERT MEZEY: "Pakim Pond, New Jersey" © 1954 by Kenyon College, from *The Kenyon Review;* "The Funeral Home" © 1956 by Robert Mezey, from *The Paris Review;* "Against Seasons" © 1959 by The New Yorker Magazine, Inc., from *The New Yorker;* "The Lovemaker © 1960 by *Partisan Review*

RAEBURN MILLER: "For Megan Hall Merker, Newly Born" © 1961 by Raeburn Miller

WARREN MILLER: "Man Waiting" © 1959 by Warren Miller, from *The New Yorker*

JOHN MONTAGUE: "Speech for an Ideal Irish Election" © 1958 by John Montague, published in *Forms of Exile* by The Dolmen Press, Dublin, later in *Poetry*

WILLIAM M. MURRAY: "Little Boy Blue's Father Speaks" © 1960 by Angel Island Publications, Inc., from *Contact 4*

DOUGLAS NICHOLS: "The Island Queen" © 1952 by Kenyon College; "Of Spinster Ladies and Flowers" © 1956 by Kenyon College; both poems from *The Kenyon Review*

Flannery O'Connor: "The Artificial Nigger" © 1955 by Flannery O'Connor; reprinted from *A Good Man Is Hard to Find and Other Stories* by permission of Harcourt, Brace and Company, Inc.

YOSHIE OSADA: from "Hiroshima" © 1961 by Yoshie Osada

DONALD PETERSEN: "Going Back" © 1959 by The Paris Review, Inc., from *The Paris Review;* "On Several Landscapes by Van Gogh" © 1952 by *Western Review* (now *Contact*)

PAUL PETRIE: "In Defense of Colds" © 1957 by The Modern Poetry Association, from *Poetry;* "Elegy for an Unrelated Cousin" © 1958 by The Modern Poetry Association, from *Poetry;* "Bridge Park" © 1957 by The New Yorker Magazine, Inc., from *The New Yorker*

CYNTHIA PICKARD: "Light on the Water" © 1951 by The University of the South, from *The Sewanee Review;* reprinted from *Woman in Apartment* by permission of the publisher, Alan Swallow, © 1957 by Cynthia Pickard

RICHARD POWER: "The Rebels" © 1959 by Richard Power, from *The Dial*

VERN RUTSALA: "The Institution" © 1961 by Vern Rutsala

BIENVENIDO N. SANTOS: "The Transfer" © 1959 by Capitol Publishing House, Inc., from *Kislap-Graphic*

SATORU SATO: "On the Bridge" © 1961 by Satoru Sato, from *Poetry*

ROBERT SHELLEY: "Harvest" © 1952 by The Modern Poetry Association, from *Poetry;* "Evening in the Park" © 1951 by Reed Whittemore, from *Furioso;* "On My Twenty-first Birthday" © 1949 by *Western Review* (now *Contact*)

KNUTE SKINNER: "An Athlete Dying Old" © 1958 by Knute Skinner, from *A Houyhnhnm's Scrapbook*

W. D. SNODGRASS: "These Trees Stand . . ." and "April Inventory" © 1956, 1957, 1959 by William Snodgrass, both from *Epoch* and *The Hudson Review;* from "Heart's Needle"

© 1959 by William Snodgrass; all three poems reprinted from *Heart's Needle* by permission of Alfred A. Knopf, Inc.

JEAN STAFFORD: "In the Zoo" © 1953 by The New Yorker Magazine, Inc., from *The New Yorker;* published in *Stories* by Farrar, Straus & Cudahy, Inc., in 1956

WILLIAM STAFFORD: "For the Grave of Daniel Boone" © 1957 by *Botteghe Oscure;* "Walking West" © 1954 by William Stafford, from *The Hudson Review;* "Along Highway 40" and "Written on the Stub of a Paycheck" © 1957 by William Stafford, both from a longer poem entitled "The Move to California" in *Poetry;* the latter three poems to appear in a book *West of Your City* published by The Talisman Press

WALLACE STEGNER: "The Blue-Winged Teal" © 1950 by Wallace Stegner, from *Harper's*

RICHARD G. STERN: "Arrangements at the Gulf" © 1956 by Richard G. Stern, from *Epoch*

LAWRENCE STURHAHN: "The Democrat" © 1956 by The Paris Review, Inc., from *The Paris Review*

HOLLIS SUMMERS: "The Prayer Meeting" © 1956 by The University of the South, from *The Sewanee Review*

BETTY SUNWALL: "Things Changed" © 1956 by The University of the South, from *The Sewanee Review*

ROBERT S. SWARD: "The Poetry Workshop" © 1959 by *The Beloit Poetry Journal*

JOHN A. TAYLOR: "The Bat" © 1959 by John A. Taylor

EDITH TIEMPO: "Lament for the Littlest Fellow" © 1952 by The Modern Poetry Association, from *Poetry*

ROLANDO S. TINIO: "Gentle My Song" © 1956 by *Botteghe Oscure*

EMMANUEL TORRES: "Song for a Dry Season" © 1957 by Bantam Books, Inc., from *New Campus Writing, No. 2*

LEWIS TURCO: "Raceway" © 1959 by The Mid-Century Book Society, Inc., from *The Mid-Century*

LEONARD UNGER: "Forgetful" © 1942 by Louisiana State University, from *The Southern Review*

Constance Urdang: "The Madman" © 1956 by The Paris Review, Inc., from *The Paris Review*

Mona Van Duyn: "Three Valentines to the Wide World" © 1959 by Mona Van Duyn, from *Poetry* and later published in *Valentines to the Wide World* by The Cummington Press in 1958

Tennessee Williams: "Little Horse" © 1956 by Tennessee Williams, reprinted from *In the Winter of Cities* by permission of New Directions

Thomas Williams: "The Buck in Trotevale's" © 1958 by Thomas Williams, from *Esquire*

Herbert Wilner: "The Passion for Silver's Arm" © 1957 by The University of the South, from *The Sewanee Review*

Christopher Wiseman: "Magnets" © 1961 by Christopher Wiseman

Leonard Wolf: "Florentine Easter III © 1957 by The Hudson Review, Inc., from *The Hudson Review*

John Woods: "On Genius, Interrupted" © 1959 by *Poetry Northwest;* "In My Darkest Age" © 1957 by University of Nebraska Press, from *Prairie Schooner;* "When Senses Fled" © 1958 by The Paris Review, Inc., from *The Paris Review*

Rex Worthington: "A Kind of Scandal" © 1953 by *Accent*

The song quotation in "The Blue-Winged Teal" by Wallace Stegner is from "Annie Doesn't Live Here Any More" © 1933 by Bourne, Inc., New York, N. Y., and is used by kind permission of the copyright owner.

To the State University of Iowa

As a PATRON, *you are not the Medici. Although as gracious to all of the arts, you rely less on poison. Nor are you merely the audience, the buyer of books. You are more stable, more varied, more indulgent. Nor are you the national state, that benevolent buzzard, spreading its wide wings over a nestful of young, protecting from weather but shutting out sunlight. Nor are you simply the depository of the ages, an immense shelf where the wisdom and folly, the beauty and horror, of the past wait to be touched by a living hand.*

You are something more difficult and honorable than any of these: a creating source.

You have believed in the imagination as a family believes in a child, as a new thing, an exciting hope, a charming violence, an unpredictable risk.

The writer has come to you from the far corners of this wide country and from the farthest curves of the round world. In winter, your walks have sparkled with snow, sunlight and talent. In summer, your walks have glowed with green leaves, sunlight and talent. Your black nights and dark days have been luminous with the intense presence of talent.

The limit of your campus is not street or building, but whatever outermost space the creative mind can reach in its remotest flight. Once having reached there, it will of course look ahead to the next unimaginable leap.

xiii

Contents

Introduction by Paul Engle   x x i

I. Short Stories

William Berge · that lovely green boat   3

George Bluestone · the ascent of corey   2 4

James Buechler · the proud suitor   4 2

R. V. Cassill · the prize   6 1

James B. Hall · a spot in history   7 9

Carl Hartman · a season of mists   9 3

David Clay Jenkins · summer: sun and shade   1 0 8

Calvin Kentfield · the bell of charity   1 1 8

Kim Yong Ik · the wedding shoes   1 4 0

Robie Macauley · a nest of gentlefolk   1 5 4

Willard Marsh · mexican hayride   1 7 1

Warren Miller · man waiting   1 8 5

Flannery O'Connor · the artificial nigger   2 0 9

Richard Power · the rebels   2 3 3

Bienvenido N. Santos · the transfer   2 5 0

Jean Stafford · in the zoo   2 6 1

Wallace Stegner · THE BLUE-WINGED TEAL 285
Richard G. Stern · ARRANGEMENTS AT THE GULF 305
Lawrence Sturhahn · THE DEMOCRAT 313
Hollis Summers · THE PRAYER MEETING 322
Betty Sunwall · THINGS CHANGED 334
Thomas Williams · THE BUCK IN TROTEVALE'S 351
Herbert Wilner · THE PASSION FOR SILVER'S ARM 377
Rex Worthington · A KIND OF SCANDAL 406

II. Poems

William Belvin · PALERMO, MOTHER'S DAY, 1943 419
THE GEOGRAPHERS 420
Frederick Bock · A RETURN FROM THE WARS 421
WINTER: THE STATUE OF POMONA 421
Donna Bowen · THE EGGS 423
PURSUIT 423
Jane Cooper · THE FAITHFUL 424
MORNING ON THE ST. JOHN'S 424
Henri Coulette · THE TROPHIES 428
INTAGLIO 429
CYGNETS HOUSE 430
THE ATTIC 431
Alexander Craig · JOHN SMITH 433
Bruce Cutler · THE LANGUAGE OF YES 435
Robert Patrick Dana · GOODBYE. GOODBYE. 436
FOR SISTER MARY APOLLINE 436
Ricaredo Demetillo · YOU LAUGH WITHIN THE HOUSE
OF ME 439
THE GOD MY FATHER CHISELED
WITH HIS TONGUE 439

xvi

William Dickey · THE PLOT 441

PART SONG, WITH CONCERT OF
RECORDERS 441

TO HIS COMPANIONS IN EXILE 443

TWENTY YEARS GONE, SHE RETURNS
TO THE NUNNERY 444

Harry Duncan · THE ANSWER 446

John Engels · THE EXPERIMENTERS 446

Paul Engle · YOU CAN'T BE WISE 448

from FOR THE IOWA DEAD, XIII, XV 448

BEASTS 449

Peter Everwine · SOLDIERS' WOODS: OCCUPIED GER-
MANY 452

ON A PHOTOGRAPH OF MY GRAND-
FATHER, PAOLO CASTELNUOVO 452

TO MY FATHER'S GHOST 454

WINTER STOP-OVER 454

Donald Finkel · BRAILLE 457

THE CLOTHING'S NEW EMPEROR 457

"DANGER IS THE PIVOT OF THE SUB-
LIME LIFE" 458

E. S. Forgotson · POEM AT THE HOUR OF SURVEYANCE 460

COLLOQUY 461

ST. ANTHONY 1960 462

Kimon Friar · GREEK TRANSFIGURATION 464

Jean Garrigue · A FABLE OF BERRIES 467

Walker Gibson · ADVICE TO TRAVELERS 472

COME OFF IT 472

William Goodreau · THE FATHER 473

Martha Grimes · THE HAUNTED HOUSE 474

Anthony Hecht · A POEM FOR JULIA 475

SAMUEL SEWALL 478

UPON THE DEATH OF GEORGE SAN-
TAYANA 479

THE VOW 480

xvii

Albert Herzing · CANTICLE I   482
THE CANDY-MAN'S ART IS THE
SWEETEST ART I KNOW   483
Theodore Holmes · JOURNEYS   484
THE LIFE OF THE ESTATE   486
Dominador I. Ilio · DIPLOMAT LISTENING TO SPEECH
OF ANOTHER DIPLOMAT   488
Carol Johnson · SONNET   489
FROM A BOOK OF HOURS   489
Donald Justice · BEYOND THE HUNTING WOODS   491
TALES FROM A FAMILY ALBUM   492
SONNET   493
ON A PAINTING BY PATIENT B OF THE
INDEPENDENCE STATE HOSPITAL
FOR THE INSANE   494
ANNIVERSARIES   495
Joseph Langland · PRUNERS: CONCA DI MARINI   497
THE AMALFI GROTTO   498
Alfred M. Lee · BESIDE MY GRANDMOTHER   500
Philip Legler · LANDSCAPE FOR A WIFE   501
Philip Levine · MAD DAY IN MARCH   503
GREEN THUMB   504
SMALL GAME   505
NIGHT THOUGHTS OVER A SICK CHILD   507
E. L. Mayo · JOY OF MAN'S DESIRING   509
THREE LADIES   510
THE FACTORY   511
Karl Kimber Merker · POEM FOR CON   512
Robert Mezey · THE LOVEMAKER   514
PAKIM POND, NEW JERSEY   515
THE FUNERAL HOME   516
AGAINST SEASONS   517
Raeburn Miller · FOR MEGAN HALL MERKER, NEWLY
BORN   519

xviii

John Montague · SPEECH FOR AN IDEAL IRISH ELEC-
TION   5 2 2

William M. Murray · LITTLE BOY BLUE'S FATHER
SPEAKS   5 2 4

Douglas Nichols · OF SPINSTER LADIES AND FLOWERS   5 2 5
THE ISLAND QUEEN   5 2 6

Yoshie Osada · *from* HIROSHIMA   5 2 7

Donald Petersen · GOING BACK   5 2 8
ON SEVERAL LANDSCAPES BY VAN
GOGH   5 2 9

Paul Petrie · IN DEFENSE OF COLDS   5 3 0
ELEGY FOR AN UNRELATED COUSIN   5 3 1
BRIDGE PARK   5 3 2

Cynthia Pickard · LIGHT ON THE WATER   5 3 4

Vern Rutsala · THE INSTITUTION   5 3 5

Satoru Sato · ON THE BRIDGE   5 3 6

Robert Shelley · HARVEST   5 3 8
EVENING IN THE PARK   5 3 8
ON MY TWENTY-FIRST BIRTHDAY   5 3 9

Knute Skinner · AN ATHLETE DYING OLD   5 4 0

W. D. Snodgrass · THESE TREES STAND . . .   5 4 2
APRIL INVENTORY   5 4 2
from HEART'S NEEDLE, II, VI, VII,
IX, X   5 4 4

William Stafford · FOR THE GRAVE OF DANIEL BOONE   5 5 3
WALKING WEST   5 5 4
ALONG HIGHWAY 40   5 5 4
WRITTEN ON THE STUB OF A PAY-
CHECK   5 5 5

Robert S. Sward · THE POETRY WORKSHOP   5 5 6

John A. Taylor · THE BAT   5 5 9

Edith Tiempo · LAMENT FOR THE LITTLEST FELLOW   5 6 1

Rolando S. Tinio · GENTLE MY SONG   5 6 2

Emmanuel Torres · SONG FOR A DRY SEASON   5 6 4

Lewis Turco · RACEWAY   5 6 5

Leonard Unger · FORGETFUL   5 6 7

Constance Urdang · THE MADMAN   5 6 8

Mona Van Duyn · THREE VALENTINES TO THE WIDE

WORLD   5 6 9

Tennessee Williams · LITTLE HORSE   5 7 3

Christopher Wiseman · MAGNETS   5 7 4

Leonard Wolf · FLORENTINE EASTER III   5 7 5

John Woods · ON GENIUS, INTERRUPTED   5 7 9

IN MY DARKEST AGE   5 7 9

WHEN SENSES FLED   5 8 0

Biographies   5 8 2

Introduction

THE WRITER AND THE PLACE

by Paul Engle

THIS BOOK IS THE RESULT OF A VISION.

By vision, I do not mean the abrupt and ecstatic experience of Saul on the road to Damascus, blinded by a light "above the brightness of the sun," and startled by a voice speaking from heaven.

By vision, I mean the steady development at the University of Iowa of the conviction that the creative imagination in all of the arts is as important, as congenial, and as necessary, as the historical study of all the arts. How simple, and yet how reckless.

This gradual revelation was quite as astonishing as a sudden idea seen, for the first time, in a flash of light. It took imagination, some years ago, for an educational institution to put its trust in the imaginative arts. Logical as the theory that it is as proper to encourage the writing of a good poem as the study of a bad one (or even of a good one) might sound, what would really happen when the poets arrived? Were they not traditionally doubtful types, likely to turn up wearing a nest of robins in their hair?

Universities are not famous for taking chances, but the University of Iowa took one. There were doubts at the start. Could the writer keep his native frenzy in an academic air? Would not the place be overrun with aesthetes come not to work but to dabble their delicate fingers in the Iowa River, which flows through the campus? (The answer to this was an easy "No!" for the River is frozen hard all winter and it is too muddy all summer, although with the finest mud in the world.) Would there not be fire, violence in the streets, and, most criminal of all, loafing in the classroom? If you gave young writers enough rope, would they hang decency and honor instead of, as might be hoped, hanging each other?

The French novelist Gustave Flaubert said, "The sight of a nude woman makes me think of her skeleton." Similarly, the University looked beyond the superficial image of these doubts and thought of the solid talent beneath, although perhaps not with Flaubert's analytical enthusiasm. By doing so, it recognized a powerful new direction in this country's culture, the writer everywhere on the campus, the older as teacher, the younger as student. For the first time in the sad and enchanting history of literature, for the first time in the glorious and dreadful history of the world, the writer was welcome in the academic place. If the mind could be honored there, why not the imagination?

One can understand why European universities would find this distasteful, with their ancient and rigid structures, although young writers are increasingly found at English institutions today. It was the flexibility of the American university, with its effort to roam over all areas of human activity, which made possible, if not easy, the addition of the creative person to the campus. If it is proper to teach chicken-sexing, which calls for extreme acuteness of eye, and weaving, which can be a matter of the most gracious taste in design, then why is it not appropriate to teach originality in writing? To say that the creative has no part in education is to argue that a university should not be universal.

There is still a fair question to be asked—however pleasant this may sound, will it really work in practice? Here are a few facts from the University of Iowa in the last couple of years: In the anthology *New Poets of England and America* (edited by Hall, Pack and Simpson), one third of the whole American section consisted of poets who were then, or had recently been, at the Poetry Workshop, surpassing in number those at any university in this country or in England. In 1959 the Lamont Poetry Award given by The Academy of American Poets was won by Donald Justice for *The Summer Anniversaries*. In 1960 it was won by Robert Mezey for *The Lovemakers*. In 1960 the Pulitzer Prize for poetry was given to W. D. Snodgrass for *Heart's Needle*. The Yale Series of Younger Poets volume for 1959 was William Dickey's *Of the Festivity*. Winner of the first University of Nebraska Press First-Book publication prize for a new manuscript of American verses was Bruce Cutler's *The Year of the Green Wave*. The Scribner's annual series, *Poets of Today*, has included five Iowa Workshop poets in the first six volumes: Harry Duncan, Murray Noss, Joseph Langland, Theodore Holmes, Donald Finkel. The National Book Award for fiction, 1959, went to Philip Roth, now teaching at the Fiction Workshop, for his book of stories *Goodbye, Columbus;* in 1960 the National Book Award for poetry went to Robert Lowell, a former teacher in the Poetry Workshop, for his *Life Studies*. The *Esquire Reader*, a collection of ten new writers of fiction, 1960, includes five who are either students or teachers at the Fiction Workshop.

These are works from the middle of the imagination by people who have been a part of this creative effort in the middle of the country. They represent only the most recent of the scores of books of fiction and poetry published by members of the writing program, and hardly a fraction of the hundreds of poems and stories which have appeared in every magazine of consequence in this country, and in some from Europe. I would rather not resort to this sort of obvious cataloguing of successes, but they are unassailable facts proving objectively that the university today is an honest and helpful place for the writer to be.

When President Lincoln was ill one time he said, "Now let the office-seekers come, for at last I have something I can give all of them." The writing program at the University of Iowa, more modest and less infectious than the President, does not offer something to all seekers. We believe that you can only teach where something in a mind is waiting to be taught. We do not pretend to grow blonde curls on an autumn pumpkin (alas, for what a triumph that would be in a farm state; when this happens, Iowa will be first). When Shelley wrote Keats, after reading some of his early and unrestrained poetry, that he should load every rift with ore, he was engaged in the sort of teaching we try to do; that is, he was identifying talent, and then saying what he could to make it better. Indeed, if Shelley turned up at the University of Iowa today, as English poets now do, his talent would be recognized and encouraged, and it is inconceivable that he would be thrown out as he was at Oxford. Maxwell Perkins editing the massive manuscripts of Thomas Wolfe into presentable shape is the sort of teaching we believe can be done.

After all, has the painter not always gone to an art school, or at least to an established master, for instruction? And the composer, the sculptor, the architect? Then why not the writer? Good poets, like good hybrid corn, are both born and made. Right criticism can speed up the maturing of a poet by years. More than that, tough and detailed criticism of a young writer can help him become his own shrewd critic so that, when he publishes, the critics will not have to be tough on him. In the process of original writing, every word and every attitude is subject to a constant scrutiny, or should be, and much of what we do is to heighten the sense of awareness which this requires. We knock, or persuade, or terrify, the false tenderness toward his own work out of the beginning writer. This is the beginning of wisdom.

As so often, Flaubert has said it wisely. "Beware of that intellectual overheating called inspiration," he wrote, and this is our warning too. Learn that it is not the intensity of emotion in the writer that matters, but the intensity of the shaped language (to paraphrase T. S. Eliot). Unless the writer keeps his aesthetic distance from the object he is creating, it may well overwhelm him in an excess of self-commitment. Flaubert said it: "You can depict wine, love, and women on the condition that you are not a drunkard, a lover, or a husband. If you are involved in life, you see it badly; your sight is affected either by suffering or by enjoyment." This is not to argue for coldness in the writer, but only for that minimum level of calmness without which the work will not have the control necessary to achieve form, without which the moving cry becomes only screaming.

Flaubert knew the emotional risks of the writer, and only urged an objective stare at the subjective scene because he was so greatly in danger of drowning in his own subjectivity. "When I was describing the poisoning of Emma Bovary," he commented, "I had such a taste of arsenic in my mouth and was poisoned so effectively myself, that I had two attacks of indigestion, one after the other—two real attacks, for I vomited my entire dinner." What young writer could be harmed by discovering such an example? He is more likely to be harmed by looking at writing as the spontaneous outpouring of immediate feeling, like a patient on the psychiatrist's couch, the sodium amytal in his blood dissolving his inhibitions. The typewriter seems to act as the hypodermic syringe, releasing his babble of language. This writing then goes to the printer unrevised, lively perhaps, with the immediacy of its memories, but turgid in its unshaped prose. This delusion, that writing is not a formed art, but that it falls naturally onto the page like sudden rain, we try to persuade out of any heads which have it thundering and raging inside.

In a country with so ranging a landscape, with its concentrations of culture so widely diffused, the problem of where a young writer is to feel at home becomes far more urgent than in England, where London is in easy reach. There must be an alternative between Hollywood and New York, between those places psychically as well as geographically. The University of Iowa tries to offer such a community, congenial to the young writer, with his uneasiness about writing as an honorable career, or with his excess of ego about calling himself a writer. To them, we offer hard criticism and decent sympathy. More than that, our way of mimeographing poetry and fiction for the Workshops offers everyone a hearing. To have your work read by all of the members of the Workshop, and publicly criticized and praised by your instructors in the weekly meetings, represents a helpful and at the same time less hazardous form of publication.

The system offers proof that writing can be seriously regarded, and that it is a difficult art not only worth an absolute commitment of faith, time and energy, but demanding it. The writer finds that the students around him are alert to his faults and quick to praise his virtues. In brief, he is, while practicing a completely private art, reassured by a sense of belonging to a group which gives him a decent regard. For as long as he is a part of this community, he has a useful competition with those around him, and at the same time is freed from the imperatives of the market place, as he may never be again. He can have a manner of publication without losing too much blood.

This matter of place is of tremendous importance to the writer in the U.S.A. We do not have that intense concentration of talent in one city, as certainly exists in Paris, London and Rome, where writers either know each other or know a good deal about each other. Our plan gives the writer a place where he can be himself, confronting the hazards and hopes of his own talent, and at the same time he can measure his capacity against a variety of others, some better, some worse. He grows up rapidly. He becomes his own self-critic. He discovers that learning to write is not a mere acquiring of "techniques," as if he were learning to be a laboratory assistant or an appliance repairman, but in part a learning of his own nature. The criticism of a manuscript may be directed less to the prose than to the personality who wrote it. Sometime the young writer must understand that writing is a hard and solitary occupation, accomplished only by the old and bitter way of sitting down in fear and trembling to confront the most terrifying thing in the world—a blank sheet of paper. It is heartening to be able to do this in a place where you know that others are facing the same ordeal.

Place does not mean simply the boundaries of the United States. We have found that the creative imagination is wonderfully alert in breaking down the barriers of nationality and language. The Workshops have heard the voices of poets and fiction writers speaking English (and writing it) in a charming and original way, which varied according to whether the speakers were from Japan, Formosa, South Korea, the Philippines, Ireland, England, Canada, Sweden, India. A former officer in the Imperial Japanese Navy has heard his poems on the fall of Japan criticized by a former yeoman in the American Navy. A girl from India, looking as if she had stepped down from her usual job of holding up the corner of a temple roof just to attend this class for an hour, has heard with shock the story of an American boy's anxieties and bafflement in his relationship with women. "But why all of this fuss about sex?" she asked in a voice British in enunciation but gently, beautifully songlike.

The man who wrote the story, a former Marine sergeant with shoulders which looked as if they could have held up the temple alone, glared at her and demanded with a luminous suspicion, "OK, so what's wrong with sex?"

"Oh, nothing," she replied, dropping the words into the air as if they were carved in stone, "but why do so much worrying about it? We settled all of that thousands of years ago."

For a moment all discussion stopped while the calm-out-of-violence of ancient India hung in the troubled atmosphere of a hot August afternoon in a modest-sized Iowa town just about to become one hundred years old.

The strength of this international quality in the Workshops is an example to us all of the power which the creative impetus has. Kim Yong Ik, probably the leading South Korean fiction writer in English, describes his widowed mother diving far down in the freezing waters of a Korean island to gather edible plants to feed her family. The place is strange to us, the customs are stranger, the language spoken by the family is strangest of all. Yet in a plain room in Iowa City, with the closest salt water over one thousand miles away, in the presence of young writers from the red earth hills of Georgia, the green counties of the English Midlands, the brown width of Texas, the granite-gouged valleys of New Hampshire, the deep Minnesota woods, the shallow Louisiana swamps, the California coast sun-brilliant below Los Angeles, the northern fog of Dublin and the southern jungle of Negros Island in the Philippines, the story of that diving woman and her family was as close as the air they breathed. Reason: it was told with imagination.

For such a community, home is not the place where, when you have to go there, they have to take you in, as the Frost poem accurately says of its people. Home is the one place where the creative energy finds that, once it has come there, they are glad to take it in. The benefit to the whole United States of giving these articulate people from the far islands and continents of the earth a conviction that this country cherishes their talent (as their own countries often do not) is beyond measuring. For those seeking a true image of America, it is lucky that they come not to a seacoast city but to an interior town in the midst of the fat land that feeds the nation. Here they have a direct look at the daily life of the U.S.A. in its most typical manner.

Of course there are those in the academic life of the U.S.A. who either suspect us, deplore us, or hate us. In certain cases, we are proud to have them as enemies. In other cases, we regret the misunderstandings spoken about our beliefs or intentions. Let us be definite about this. There seems to us no reason for hostility between the study of literature and its creation. There are those who feel that writing is better done by the inspired ignoramus, uncorrupted by the weakening influences of the university. To us, it makes no difference what grows on the wall outside the writer's house, whether it is English ivy, poison ivy, hops, morning glories or gourd vines. F. Scott Fitzgerald said once that there are no second chapters in American lives. Too often there are no second books, or at least there are second books no better (often worse) than the first. We think that the critical study of past literature will give the writer a maturity and an awareness of all the infinite variety of forms and attitudes, and that this will give bone and tendon to the soft flesh of his feelings.

A very important help here is that scholarship has never been so congenial to the writer as today. In much of their work, many scholars make literary insights which sometimes equal in perception the insights contained in the text they are studying. There has been a good deal of criticism today which surpasses in imaginative texture some of what is taken for literature. (The work of Harry Levin and Perry Miller, for example.)

It would be folly to deny that there are often reasons for hostility. Never in the world's cultural history has the study of literature been so minutely organized into Departments of English, with numbered courses and named degrees. How can this immense apparatus really find enough fresh material to equal its massive arrangements? Will there not be several scholars converging through the tall grass of the library's meadow, all aiming for the one poor little rabbit-fact? New interpretations there will always be, but as of now the scholarly pattern is set up as if there really would be a place for the textual scholar as there had been in the past, when we needed a definitive text of Shakespeare and Chaucer. Here is where the writer becomes useful. Why should he not be a small, indeed a very small, part of this academic scene? After all, creative talent is more limited than academic intelligence. But it has its value, wanting to teach the writers of the past from the writer's point of view, as imaginative expressions of his agony and delight, rather than as historical instances. If the creative writer is a menace to scholarship, then take a cold look at what that scholarship truly is. All too often it lacks the substance and power, not to mention the decent prose, of even minor writing.

The future looks hopeful. The Boylston Professor of Rhetoric at Harvard is now, superbly and rightly, a poet, Archibald MacLeish. The number of writers at colleges and universities from coast to coast is too great to list here. They have found the campus a suitable combination of security with time for work. For better or worse, the direction of American writing is going to be moving across the academic air. More places are realizing, as we long ago realized here, that the future of American literature can be deeply affected by giving young talent a clear and critical grasp of modern literature, from Flaubert, Joyce, Camus in the novel, from Rimbaud, Rilke, Eliot in poetry. They see that for the writer, it is more important to read Rimbaud's *The Drunken Boat* than the King Alfred version of *The Voyages of Ohthere and Wulfstan*, to read the diamond imagery at the beginning of Valéry's *The Cemetery by the Sea* than *The Pearl*.

We do not pretend to have produced the writers included in this book. Their talent was inevitably shaped by the genes rattling in the ancestral closets. We did give them a community in which to try out the quality of their gift, as New Englanders used to speak of trying out the oil from whale blubber. Much of this writing was done in Iowa City and received our criticism. Some of it was written far away. In either case, the writer was for a while part of the community we have made here where the University has stood in the position of friend and, to a slighter degree than we would wish, of patron. It is conceivable that by the end of the twentieth century the American university will have proved a more understanding and helpful aid to literature than ever the old families of Europe. That sort of patronage had its doubtful aspects too. Franz Joseph Haydn, radiant in his talent, was counted in the lower ranks of the domestics by the great Esterhazy family of Hungary. He wore a blue uniform and ate down at the end of the table. He composed much of his sunlit music while living with that family, whose idea of fun was to have in the music room a big chair which, when sat in, played a cheerful flute solo.

We believe in the solitary genius, not in the agreeable average. Art may turn out to be the last refuge of the individual in our time. The one man raging in his terrible talent may be worth more than the sum of one hundred thousand bland mediocrities. When Flaubert wrote the word "hysterics," he says that he was so swept away, was bellowing so loudly and feeling so deeply what his little Bovary was going through, that he was afraid of having hysterics himself. This is seldom, I would guess, the way of scholarship. The bellowing of scholars I have been happy enough to observe was not out of sympathy with the characters they were studying. Such conduct indicates a different disposition in the sort of people coming to a writing program. To our delight and astonishment, they can adapt, they can be at home, they can find a heartening help.

Of course there are risks. The mild frost of a university air can kill the tender plant. Excess of self-consciousness can slow down a talent which has little momentum. An English novelist, V. S. Pritchett, laments that the American university may induce "an unnatural hostility to vulgarity" in the writer. I have seen twenty-five years of American writers at a university. Have no fear. They will not lose their vulgarity.

For some, the university will never be the right place, and this is right. They should remain on the road or on the beach or up in the attic or down in the cellar. It's a big country, mister. There's a place for everybody, in or out of the university, in or out of the house, in or out of jail.

Three groups of people deserve particular mention.

Bravest of all are the wives and children of the married

writers who have been at the University of Iowa. While the husband and father kept his typewriter smoking with one hand and heated the pablum with the other, his family has stoically endured the fate of living with a writing man. Remember the woman in the story who groped for the most hideous term she could throw at the object of her temper. Rejecting all known profanities and obscenities as too mild, she finally shouted, "You, you *writer!*" The wives have come to the Workshops and suffered through criticism of their husband's manuscript. Babies have waited for shoes until papa sold a story. Sometimes we have followed an entire affair, from the first tentative love poems of a boy and a girl, both in the Workshop, to the inevitable quarrels, to the inevitable reconciliations, to the abandoned verse of approaching marriage, and then stood up for them at the altar, later receiving poems on an expected child, both from the father's point of view and the mother's. And many of them have been fine poems. And fine children.

At the risk of seeming to view a wicked world with too much cheerfulness, I want to list the names of a surprising number of people outside this University who have given good will and time to the writing program. In some cases, they have also contributed money to make this anthology possible (About cheerfulness—this is an old American habit. Certainly I got mine from pioneering and farming ancestors, who were faced with so many disasters and diseases, and so much death, that they either had to keep cheerful or else give up and admit that they did not have the heart and resolution to face the appalling future. Of course they faced it, and in doing so made that future into one deserving cheerfulness. At the risk of moralizing, let me add that this is a state of mind the U.S.A. must keep alive right now.):

The Academy of American Poets and Mrs. Hugh Bullock; Philip Adler, Davenport Newspapers; Curtiss Anderson, *Ladies Home Journal* (formerly of The Meredith Publishing Co.); Virginia M. Anderson, Wyoming,

Iowa; John B. Bishop, *Burlington Hawk-Eye*, Burlington, Iowa; Frank R. Brownell, Montezuma, Iowa; Edward Burchette, Des Moines; Bennett Cerf, Random House, Inc., New York; Arthur A. Collins, Collins Radio Co., Cedar Rapids; S. E. Coquillette, Merchants National Bank, Cedar Rapids; Gardner Cowles, *Look*, and The Cowles Charitable Trust; Mrs. W. Murray Crane, New York; Gordon DeLay, Quaker Oats Co., Cedar Rapids; George Doty, Washington, D.C.; Sutherland Dows, Iowa Electric Light & Power Co., Cedar Rapids; Ogden Dwight, *Des Moines Register;* Mr. and Mrs. Owen Elliott, Cedar Rapids; Frank Eyerly, *Des Moines Register;* Lou Fellman, May Drug Co., Cedar Rapids; J. W. Fisher, Fisher Governor Co., Marshalltown, Iowa; Sterling W. Fisher, The Reader's Digest Foundation; George Foerstner, Amana Refrigeration, Amana, Iowa; Robert S. Gates, Collins Radio Co., Cedar Rapids; Arnold Gingrich, *Esquire;* Howard Hall, Iowa Manufacturing Co., Cedar Rapids; Joyce C. Hall, Hallmark Cards, Kansas City, Missouri; Philip Hampson, Robert R. McCormick Charitable Trust, Chicago; Mr. and Mrs. W. Averell Harriman, New York; Delmar C. Homan, Ames, Iowa; G. W. Hopkins, Iowa National Mutual Insurance Co., Cedar Rapids; George P. Hunt, *Life*, New York; J. Patrick Lannan, Chicago; Kenneth MacDonald, *Des Moines Register;* Mrs. John P. Marquand, Cambridge, Mass.; Harry E. Maule, Random House, Inc., New York; Fred Maytag, The Maytag Co., Newton, Iowa; the late W. S. Merryman, The Messenger Printing Co., Fort Dodge, Iowa; Harlan Miller, *Des Moines Register;* Warren W. Miller, New York; Mr. and Mrs. Robert Montgomery, New York; Ruth Ann Musick, Fairmont, West Virginia; Loran Parker, Iowa Falls, Iowa; William Quarton, WMT, Cedar Rapids; Mr. and Mrs. Joseph Rosenfield, Younkers, Des Moines; Mr. and Mrs. Robert F. Vance, The Maytag Co., Newton, Iowa; Mr. and Mrs. DeWitt Wallace, *The Reader's Digest*, Pleasantville, N. Y.; John

F. Merrian, Northern Natural Gas Company, Omaha, Nebraska.

The world, in its too little information, and many critics of this country, in their too great folly, have said some brutal things about the American businessman. The quantity of these much-maligned people to be found in the above list is a factual refutation.

There were many people behind this writing program. As I said at the beginning, it was an institutional vision, rather than that of a single man. But a university is its individuals, and it was a Swedish immigrant, Carl E. Seashore, who became interested in locating creative talent on this campus. As Dean of the Graduate College, he was the first person in the United States to print in an academic catalogue the startling news that creative work was to be considered as acceptable for advanced degrees. The view that imaginative writing was an honorable activity of the total man, involving his intelligence as well as his sympathetic nervous system, was continued by George D. Stoddard while Dean of the Graduate College (Dr. Stoddard is now Chancellor of New York University), and Norman Foerster, while Director of the School of Letters here; the late Dean Walter F. Loehwing, scientist, was a steady support. Ted McCarrel, Registrar, took bold chances by admitting many writing students with the most melodramatic academic records. Loren Hickerson, Alumni Director, Philip Kruidenier and the State University of Iowa Foundation have been a pillar of cloud by day. James R. Jordan, Gordon Strayer and Ken Donelson, of University Relations, have been a pillar of flame by night.

However enthusiastic the body of a university may be, it has to have a head. We have been fortunate in having administrators who believed in our belief that the writer belongs on the campus, along with others who work with the mortal mind. Sir Charles P. Snow, English novelist and scientist, remarked that "American universities, which have received so much lip from ignorant Englishmen that it makes me blush, are singularly attractive places to live in." The University of Iowa has been an attractive place for poets and fiction writers in great part because the administration, which could have destroyed the writing program with the flourish of a pen (on the golden tablets of the accounting system) has helped bravely. Virgil M. Hancher, President, has been sympathetic, rare enough among Presidents, but also available personally, which is even rarer. Harvey H. Davis, Provost, has given us advice, a building which was odd and just right, frequent aid in exuberant projects which were no necessary part of our program, and some dear dollars. Baldwin Maxwell, Head of the Department of English, distinguished Elizabethan scholar, closest of all to the actual writer-on-the-hoof, has always offered us the firmest support in our hopes and the liveliest compassion in our troubles. Without his friendly help, none of our efforts would have been possible.

The people of the state of Iowa did not have to make the desert blossom as the rose when they came here. This fortunate land was already blooming when they arrived. The Board of Regents for our state institutions have worked devotedly to keep it that way. Without their quiet agreement with our hopes, we would have had quite as rugged a path as some writers have had in less prophetic universities.

We are a tax-supported university, one of those ingenious and at times ungainly institutions which the United States has invented to respond to its varied society, and in turn to help shape it. As a state, we are agriculture and small industry, without great wealth, but without poverty, a pleasant middle place. This does not produce huge taxes, but within the limits of modest resources, the people of the state have been behind us (a little far behind, now and then, but always there). Those taxes, and the hard work of the industrious citizens who paid them, are a sturdy support in our wish to break down the barrier between the artist and society. It

XXXV

should also be mentioned that the valley of the Iowa River, in which the University lives, and the fertile farms along it, keep the student close to the actual world of tree, pig, space, corn, cow, hay, weather and market.

It has been heartening to the writers here to know that all of the arts were busy creating. The theatre, handsomely set on the edge of the Iowa River, as the Shakespeare Theatre at Stratford is set on the bank of the Avon (just above the brewery), is the home of new plays and new playwrights. The Art Department has produced an astonishing variety of painters, sculptors, and printmakers. The Music Department has helped in the composition of new works in every form. Thus the community in which the writer moves is not merely as wide as the limits of literature, or as the broad length of the prairie landscape in which he lives, but extends to the far-ranging horizons of the total artistic imagination, some of whose places are still farther away from our understanding than the most distant exploding star.

Over the difficult and exuberant years, many writers have taught here. Some have been students first, many have been long-established before coming. The following is a list of those who were here for more than a brief visit. Apologies to any who may have been inadvertently omitted:

Wilbur Schramm (who did much to found the writing program), Robert Penn Warren, Ray B. West, Paul Horgan, Eric Knight, Josephine Johnston, Hansford Martin, Walter Van Tilburg Clark, Robie Macauley, Herbert Gold, Harvey Swados, W. D. Snodgrass, Joseph Langland, James B. Hall, Oakley Hall, Thomas Williams, Verlin Cassill, Vance Bourjaily, Philip Roth, George P. Elliott, Henri Coulette, Donald Justice, Hortense Calisher, Curt Harnack, Calvin Kentfield, Philip Levine, Herbert Wilner, Walter Sullivan, Wirt Williams, Robert Lowell, Karl Shapiro, William Stafford, Andrew Lytle.

The curious and extraordinary devices which made this writing program possible in a state university are a part of the lavish variety of the American way of doing everything, including education and literature. It is proper, then, to express our thanks to a country which has given freedom of voice to its own young talent, and to that of many other nations. We have been allowed to run, stumble and jump over the lovely landscape of the imagination. How can writers praise a country more than by saying: Look! In this place we have been free.

I   Short Stories

That Lovely Green Boat

WILLIAM BERGE

S HE WAS A DUCK BOAT, YOU KNOW, LIKE THE KIND YOU'VE seen and hungered after in the catalogues you look through during winter nights when the river's frozen hard and black like granite, and the wind is moaning to come in, and the train whistles are howling like souls come out of Chippahanock Cemetery. Only in the catalogue, her lightness and smoothness don't show, and you can't feel her turn in her own length or guess how fast she'll go upstream against an east wind and the waves chopping at her.

She was made of thin lath, her bow decked over, and she was painted light green—the color of maple leaves in early spring, and varnished with clear varnish and sanded and varnished and sanded again, and worked on with steel wool until the bottom was as smooth as the granite ice in winter that froze without wind. She was swift and light, like a kingfisher, and she seemed blonde in her greenness.

She would have been perfect for a light motor, if the back end had been built up stronger, but we didn't have a motor. But she rowed well, and nothing could touch her. And she looked blonde in her greenness.

We would come down to her by the river early in the morning—the three of us, Carl, his sister Helen, and me— and she would be waiting for us there on the sand that had been left by the June rise of the river, and her greenness and

3

the dry gold sand and Helen's hair all seemed blonde and light and lovely at once.

Helen and Carl and I would come down to the river early in the morning and find it smooth, without a ripple, save where a snag divided the surface or a whiff of wind ruffled it like a ribbon; and we would get in the boat and row out on the dark glass, heading downstream with the sun behind us, for the Mississippi flows from east to west there. We would anchor her on the sandbar that ran down the middle of the river, lining her bow on the trees that stood a breath above the far bend to make sure she was over the center, and then we could get out of the boat in water only up to our knees, and walking toward shore, steadily go deeper until the water was over our heads and as deep as anyone could want.

We wore suits that summer, though it was early in the morning, for Carl was sixteen, and I was fourteen, and Helen was just fourteen, and she didn't have just nipples any more like a boy, but soft round swellings the shape of lemons or young pears. And I wished I was her brother instead of Carl so that her Uncle John would be my uncle too, and then I could stay there on the river all year around, fishing and swimming and skating, and rowing her in the green duck boat.

Then, while we were swimming, the river would begin to break up like a girl's skin that gets wet and cold and then wrinkles; but you would never see it doing this, but all at once you would look up and see that the mirror was shattered and shrivelled the way you find it at noon or any other time of the day; and you would feel just under your skin the peacefulness gone out of the river; and you would know the river's night was over and that it was time for breakfast.

Aunt Jane Springer would have a pile of pancakes as big as plates waiting for us, and after breakfast we would run the trot lines and pull up the fish traps that were longer than a man is tall, and the length of a man's arm across, shaped in a cylinder of strong wire with an entrance like a cone that a fish could come in by but never leave again.

4

And then, if Carl didn't start working in the garage, making something like bird houses or broom holders or anything you could make in the winter when it was too cold to go outside, or if he didn't have chores to do, the three of us would cross to the island and hunt for coon tracks, or stalk the big blue herons, or shoot crows or swim off the bank. It was deep along the shore of the island, so deep in places that you could not touch bottom when you dived—even by holding a rock in your hands when you went down; and you would come up, sometimes, with your chest feeling crushed and then about to explode and then crushed again; and once my nose bled and I could not go down again all day.

But sometimes, when Carl stayed behind, Helen and I would cross the island and lie on the bank on the channel side and watch for the tow boats pushing their barges up or down the river, and if the *Mark Twain* or the *Lone Star* came along, we waved, because their crews always waved back. Sometimes we saw diesels, but we always felt sad about the diesels —both of us—because they were so small and blunt and ugly and work-a-day, and never so nice as the stern-wheelers.

At night, the three of us slept on the sleeping porch—Carl on my left and Helen on my right, if I was lying on my back. Carl always fell asleep immediately, like a stone dropping into the river, but Helen and I would light the lamp between our cots and read until midnight. Sometimes Carl was troubled and talked in his sleep, and once he got up and walked completely around his bed talking in his sleep, and then lay down again without waking up. Helen and I would ask him questions and he would answer the sound of our words but not the sense, saying, "Got to tie up the boat. That lovely green boat's going to float away. Got to tie up the boat."

Things would happen to me at night that summer, and in the morning I would wake and find them and think I had some awful disease until finally I was so worried about other people catching it from me that I told Carl about it, but he said it was regular and natural enough. And he took me out in

5

the green duck boat and talked to me and connected it up with other things I already knew; and then he gave me makings and we smoked and just drifted.

Every day was maple-green and gold and lovely that summer.

II

One day in August as Helen and I sat resting after a swim off the dock, the water drying on us leaving our skins wrinkled as though with age, one of those high-priced, syrup-colored, inboard motorboats came barrelling down the river, passed us, and then made a wide sweeping turn just inside the sandbar, and came back upstream.

"My, that's a fine boat," Helen said.

"Yes, it is," I said.

The motor cut out just then, and the boat coasted over before the dock like a fat mallard hen floating half asleep with the current, but coming upstream and being braked by the current so it could land with just a little bump at the far end of the dock. A brown-haired boy about as old as Carl held the boat to the dock and in a voice just a cut above normal talking said, "Do you want a ride?"

He said it in the way a man with five dollars offers to loan you a dollar just to show you he's got money and can afford to borrow out.

"No, thanks," I said. "We got boats of our own."

"I see you have," he said, as though I had been trying to explain to him an arithmetic problem he had solved the year before. "You got a motor for that green boat?"

"Don't want a motor," I said. "Rowing, she stays on the water. With a motor, she'd fly."

"Do *you* want a ride?" he said again, nodding his head toward Helen.

"I told you once—"

"I don't mean you, I mean your sister."

"He's not my brother," Helen said. She didn't even look at me when she spoke.

"Do you want a ride?" the boy said again.

"No, she doesn't want a ride," I said.

"Yes, I'd like a ride," Helen said, as though she had just been awakened for breakfast.

"Wait a minute, Helen, you don't even know his—"

But she was running down the dock to stop suddenly by the boat and put her hand out, touching and petting the syrup-colored deck as though it was a horse's neck. "Yes, I'd like a ride," she said again, and she stepped down into the boat and settled on the leather seat like a great blue heron feeling for land under her when she's coming in to land big and awkward against a rough skipping wind.

The stranger gunned the motor and they cut away from the dock and up the river. I watched the boat go flying up the river and then go out of sight around the point. And I watched after it was gone until I couldn't hear the motor any more—as if I could watch instead of hear its sound—and I knew they must be up near Andalusia by then.

I sat on the dock and splashed my feet in the water and got cold and shivered and wrote my initials in the oil scum on the barrels that hold up the platform of the dock, and then wrote Helen's initials and then scratched them out and got up and ran and dived off the dock and hit the water wrong so that I was hurt where a boy hurts the worst and felt sick as though I had swallowed too much river water, and then came back to the dock swimming on my back, and crawled up on the platform and banged my shin and lay down on my back with my knees up, watching the sky and the trees change suddenly from blue and green-gold to red to hot white and then to October dun—all in a minute.

Helen was late for supper—so late Aunt Jane Springer got mad and told us to go ahead and eat without Helen, and asked herself out loud where Helen could have gone—clear up to the Rock Point dam, certainly not much farther. And then, as we were sitting down, we heard the motor faintly like a fly buzzing outside the screen door, and then it commenced to get louder and pretty soon it sounded like a nighthawk coming out of a dive, and we knew that the stranger had cut his motor and was coasting upstream to the dock. Then the motor gunned up again and in a few seconds it began to die away up the river. Helen came in then with her cheeks showing red even under her sunburn, and she was pretty and breathless and a little nervous and she asked Aunt Jane's pardon for being late. She would have been pretty any other day but this—her hair the color of dry gold sand and her skin blushing red under the color of wet gold sand—but I didn't even look at her.

But by bed-time, I could forgive her, and after we had undressed on the dark porch, standing with our backs to each other—Carl was already in bed—I said to her, "Do you want to read tonight?"

"Not especially," she said.

"You can read the book I got," I said.

"I don't want to read it."

"I'm almost done with it, anyway," I said. "You can go ahead and read it."

"But I don't want to read it."

"Oh, go ahead," I said. "I can finish it after you're done."

"But I don't even want to start it," she said.

"All right then," I said.

"And please turn out the light," she said. "I can't sleep with the light in my eyes."

"All right," I said.

The next morning, Carl and I ran the trot lines by ourselves; Helen stayed on the dock. She hadn't even gone swimming with us before breakfast, but had slept right up until breakfast. I rowed while Carl caught the floats and ran us down along the lines rebaiting the empty hooks and taking off the fish we had caught. As we were running the third line, we heard the sound of a motor and we saw the stranger sweep around a half turn and coast up to the dock. Helen got in the boat, and they went ripping away.

"Handsome boat," Carl said.

"Yes, I guess it is," I said.

She hadn't even told us his name.

Carl and I went hunting for crows on the island with his twenty-two rifle, but we didn't get a thing except a rain crow I shot. The crows stayed on the island nights, and at dawn they flew eastward over the trees cawing a racket, and then turned south to the mainland to hunt out cornfields. Not getting any crows made Carl mad, and my shooting the rain crow made him madder.

"What did you shoot that for?" he said.

"It's a crow, isn't it?" I said.

"Heck, you know better than that. It's a yellow-billed cuckoo. What did you shoot it for?"

"It's a rain crow," I said again. I didn't know why I had shot it. We had just been walking along and when I heard it calling, in a tone like it was pleased with itself, "Tyok, tyok, tyok," I just up and banged away at it.

"It's a rain crow but it ain't a black crow. What's the matter —you color blind or something?"

We walked over to where it had fallen and we found it was still alive. The shot had gone through its chest without killing it. Its chest pumped up and down squirting out blood with each pump, and it didn't make a sound but looked up at me with the eye in the left side of its head. I wished it had died right away.

"Get a stick and kill it," Carl said.

"You kill it," I said.

"It's not my bird," he said. "You started the job, now finish it."

I turned and began to walk back toward the river, and Carl shouted after me, "I'll be damned if I'll finish it for you."

"Hold your horses," I said. "I'm just going to look for a rock."

"The heck you are." He knew there weren't any rocks on this side of the island where the banks are cut out so high above the river.

"The heck I'm not." I broke a stick from a dead branch and went back and stood over the bird and held my breath and counted three and smashed it. Carl had started toward the boat when I had gone back to the bird. I caught up with him at the boat.

"It's bad luck to kill a rain crow," he said quietly, as though telling me a secret I hadn't heard.

"You got holes in your head," I said.

"What you so mad about?"

"I'm not mad!"

"If you weren't mad, you wouldn't shout so telling me you weren't."

"Oh, go to." I untied the line and threw it over the bow of the boat.

"You shot your luck," Carl said. "Going to rain like hell."

"Go to hell."

"Like a cow pissing off a flat rock," Carl said. He took out his makings and gave me a paper and passed me the sack of tobacco. "Trouble is, I'll be in the same rain you are."

I rolled the tobacco in the paper, wet the edge, and wiped it down. Carl struck a wooden match and held it toward me. I puffed on the cigarette. "Do you want to row or should I?"

"You can row," Carl said.

At supper, all Helen could talk about was Richard Wellman and his motorboat and her rides with him up and down the river. She was just brimming full of Richard Wellman, like low cut banks in a spring rise. His grandfather had been a contractor; no, he had not lost anything in the depression; yes, he was in love with his grandson; certainly, he was going to send Richard to college; sure, he was the one who bought Richard the boat; also, he had set up Richard's father in business; oh, it was a wonderful summer camp he was building above Andalusia—it even had an electric pump so they could have a toilet in the house. She just splashed and flooded and ripped with Richard Wellman.

I excused myself early and went down to the dock and got the double-ended Mississippi fish boat and rowed over to the island. The sun was just going down and the horizon was all fire half way up the sky so I knew it wouldn't rain the next day. But I went back into the woods and found the rain crow and buried it anyway.

By the time I got back to the boat, the river was dark and there were no lights on shore yet. I rowed for where I thought the dock should be, and when I came close to shore, I heard Carl's voice—not shouting, but talking low as though speaking to a man next to him—"Pull on your right oar a wee bit. There's a little less current tonight. Steady. That's it."

It was an awful quiet night and his voice carried as over a telephone wire. He took the bow line and tied it to a ring.

"Did you bury it?"

"Yes," I said.

"That was a good idea."

"Sky was red tonight."

"I know," he said. "Maybe burying it will keep the rain away."

"I hope so."

We went behind the garage and Carl gave me makings and we rolled cigarettes and had a long smoke.

"I think I know why you're mad," he said.

"I'm not mad," I said, this time quietly.

"Well, then, I know why you would be if you were mad," he said.

"Does it show?" I said.

"Not much," he said. "Not so's you'd notice it."

"I buried it," I said.

"Yes, you did."

"I killed it and buried it."

"I know you did."

The cigarette was sending me off the ground and then bringing me back and then sending me off again. I was inhaling.

"But don't worry," he said. "Have you noticed the river?"

"What about it?"

"Have you noticed it?" he said.

"Not especially," I said.

"Look at that maple sapling standing in the water. See the marks?"

"She's dropping, that's all."

"Yes, she's dropping, and that's enough."

He handed me more makings, and just then it came to me and I laughed so hard I blew the tobacco off the paper. The river was down six inches at the very least.

III

The next morning, Richard Wellman came down the river and offered us rides on his surf board. He had it strapped on the deck, of all places. He didn't give a tinker's dam about the finish.

Carl told him not to go below the dock, and he asked why, but Carl just said not to go below the dock or nobody there would ride. Richard said he wouldn't, so we all took rides, but Helen took the most of all. She hated to give up the board, and anybody with half an eye could see Richard had just made the offer to Carl and me to be polite. He and Helen took turns riding the board and steering the boat.

When Helen rode the board, she screamed and yelled all the time she was whipping back and forth behind the boat; and sometimes she would stand on one leg and hold on with one arm, or else she would try other tricks you might see in the movies and she would get flipped off. But she always came back for more. She was as golden brown and wild as a hawk.

After dinner, Richard came back towing one of those tin, non-sinkable rowboats behind him. He told us what we already knew—that it had air-tight compartments and so on, and then he asked us to race. We lined up his boat and our two and I said he could have first choice, but Helen jumped up—

"I want the duck boat. I want to race too, and I want the duck boat."

"Sure," Richard said. "Then I'll take my own boat."

You could tell he had not been on the river much because he preferred every kind of boat to the double-ended fishing boat, and plainly, he did not know how well balanced they were for all their size, nor how light and swift they were for all their clumsy looks, nor how little water they drew for all their depth of side, nor even how practical they were for running trot lines or setting nets or fish traps. He preferred the tin boats because their lines were more nearly like those of his motorboat, but they were not easy rowing; and his only right choice had been when he preferred the duck boat to the double-ender. And then his choice had come from its having lines like those of a speed boat.

We were to row up to the point and back, Carl giving the word go, and deciding the winner. When Carl said go, I started out slow and watched Richard over my shoulder. He was rowing fast and had got a good lead from the start, but his tin boat was awkward and he was rowing with his arms instead of his back. Being half a head taller than me wouldn't help him if he did that, so I set my back into it with long easy pulls.

Helen was leading in the duck boat, and I could tell he was letting her lead because he was sure I had the wrong boat to win by, and that he could keep ahead of me and still let her win. I was just behind him when he turned at the point. Helen was already started downstream, and she was laughing so hard she could barely row. She couldn't see how Richard was sweating at the turn nor how he chopped with his right oar, turning toward the bank.

I turned out into the stream, and current out from the point helped swing my bow around and I started down even with Richard. He saw I was getting more current than he was, and he tried to correct it but it was no use. I was using my back and he was using his arms.

Half way to the dock, I caught up with Helen, and then thinking of how much she liked to win, I dropped in just behind her. She wasn't laughing any more, but rowing hard. She reached the dock half a length ahead of me, and then we just sat there waiting for Richard.

"It was a good race," I said.

"Uh-huh."

"But he doesn't know his boats."

"He's got a motorboat," she said.

"But I beat him rowing."

"I've got eyes," she said.

"Did you want him to win?"

"It was a race. I wanted to win."

"Well, you won."

"I suppose you let me win," she said, mocking me with the tone of her voice. She looked at me for a minute with her mouth open. "Darn you. Darn you if you did."

Richard stayed to supper and met Aunt Jane and Uncle John Springer. He even started calling them Aunt Jane and Uncle John right away, and nobody seemed to mind. I felt uncomfortable enough to be sitting on tacks, and I was glad when Carl said that one of the trot lines was gone and that he and I should go look for it.

"Either she's loose or the float got busted and sank."

"If it's loose, it should be snagged somewhere downstream," I said. For floats, we used gallon glass jugs, and if one of them broke, there was usually no finding the line.

"Well, let's commence to begin to start," he said. "I'll take the fish boat and look over toward the island."

"I doubt that it would have gotten over there," I said.

"There was a south wind today," he said.

"But it wouldn't blow far dragging line."

"It might have snagged on the bar," he said. "The river's awful low on the bar."

We worked our way down the river slowly, searching the low places, Carl over by the bar and I over by the shore. We had been out about half an hour when Helen and Richard went spinning by us in his tin boat. They hailed us, and we hailed back, but I didn't pay any more attention to them, although I did notice they landed quite a ways down and went in among the maples.

But I was really surprised when a while later I looked up once and saw their boat just ahead of me. I tied on to her and took out the makings Carl had given me and had a smoke. I looked over to where Carl was working along the bar, and he waved his arm and started rowing back upstream. "It must have busted and sank," he said just loud enough to hear. "Going back up?"

"In a minute," I said, and I blew a puff of smoke for him to see.

"O-kay," he said. "I'll see you."

Just as I flipped the butt into the river, Helen came out of the maple grove walking fast, her head down. She didn't see me until she got right up to their boat, and then she sort of jumped and said, "Oh." She looked back once at the maple grove, and then she said, "Just what do you think you're doing here?" Her face was red under the sun tan.

"I just stopped for a smoke."

"Oh? Where's your cigarette?"

"I just now flipped it away."

"Yes you did."

"I can't show you the butt, but I can let you see the makings if you want to."

"You haven't got them. You're just spying around."

"Here they are."

"Well, why don't you roll me one?"

"You're awful jumpy tonight."

"Am I? I hadn't noticed."

"What's the matter?" I said.

"Nothing. Nothing's the matter."

"Where's Richard?"

"Back there," she said, waving her cigarette at the maple grove.

"Did he do anything to you?"

"Who, Richard? No, of course not."

"Well, if he did—"

"But he didn't," she said.

"You kind of like him, don't you?"

"What if I did?"

"Do you like him enough— Never mind. Here's a light. Catch it."

"What were you saying?" she said.

"Me? Oh, nothing. Do you want to ride up with me?"

"I'm waiting for Richard."

"But I can take you up as well as not."

"No," she said, "I'm waiting for Richard."

"All right." I threw her the sack of makings. "Cast me off and I'll get out of here."

She untied my line and threw it over the bow.

"See you at the house," I said.

"Rob—"

"Yes?" She hadn't called me Rob in a long time.

"Rob—you won't say anything. About this?"

"About what? About something I never saw? You got holes in your head."

As I rowed home, my back pointed upstream, I saw the sun hover on the horizon like a hawk just before it drops. The sun was just one great big red ball, but there was no redness outside of it; the sky was white all around it. Then it dropped slowly, keeping its color all inside itself, leaving the sky white around it—but not with the white of clouds.

When I reached the landing, Carl was waiting for me.

"You took a long time," he said. "What were you doing?"

"Just looking."

"See anything?"

"The sun. Just the sun, that's all," I said. "Did you see it?"

"Yes."

"Maybe not for two days," I said.

"Maybe not. Maybe not tomorrow, maybe not even the day after," he said. "But then—like a cow off a flat rock."

"Burying doesn't do any good, I guess."

"No," he said, "I guess it doesn't."

IV

A west wind came up and wakened me about midnight. It howled up the river, and then slowly began to swing up from the south, and then shifted back again, trying to collect every cloud in five states. It would be angling across the river by morning probably, and settling down for a good blow.

Helen woke up and asked what was all the noise, and when I said that it was the wind, she just rolled over muttering, "Awful lot of racket."

Even Carl was troubled in his sleep, and once or twice he said, "Got to tie up the boat. That lovely green boat's going to float away. Got to tie up the boat."

Richard came bouncing down the river late in the afternoon as the three of us were standing on the dock looking at the river. Carl and I had gone out in the morning and had taken in the trot lines and had pulled both boats up on shore, and we were surprised to see Richard out, though it looked like a lot of fun bouncing over the waves like that.

"You better get your boat out of the water," I said as he

tied up at the dock. He had been able to land downstream because the wind was so strong.

"It's a lot more fun like this," he said.

"So is jumping off a moving train," Carl said.

"Is everything all right?" Richard said to Helen.

"Sure," she said. "Why not?"

"Good. I came down to see—just to make sure. And to take you for a ride."

"She doesn't want to go for a ride in this," I said.

"Yes, I do," Helen said.

"You've got holes in your head if you go out in this." It was growing as dark as evening; I couldn't even see the trees on which we lined up the bar.

"But you like to go out in storms yourself," she said. "Remember when Mr. McCormick let you and Carl sail his boat last summer and then took it away from you because you always sailed at night or out in a storm? Well, I like it too."

"But not today," I said. "And you're not going out either—is she, Carl?"

"You listen to what he says," Carl said.

"Don't call Carl into this," she said, and she climbed down into the boat. "Hurry up and cast off, Richard." Richard gunned the motor and the boat slid away from the dock and began to pick up speed. "You're just jealous, that's all," she shouted back to us. Big drops of rain began to fall then, but we could hear her laughter even above their splash.

"Look out for the bar!" I shouted. "Stay away from the sandbar! The river's low!" But they were too far away now to hear me above the wind and the rain.

"Don't worry," Carl said, "she can line the bar."

"Oh yeah! Look!" I pointed downstream to where the darkness had hidden the trees at the bend.

"Damn! Goddamn! And all the water's rough water now. Nobody can see a bar by ripples or drift now."

The rain began to come down heavy—like a cow off a flat rock—and Helen and Richard swung downstream hugging the island bank. If praying could raise water, the river would have come up a foot just then.

"They're all right if they keep close to the island for the length of the bar," Carl said.

As they passed us on the far side of the river, I shouted again, "Stay clear of the bar!"

As though to hear me better, Helen stood up in the boat holding on to the windshield, and just then Richard whipped the boat toward the center of the river, smacking the white-capped waves, and flipped Helen out. Helen had barely hit the water when the boat struck the bar and ripped out her bottom with a sound like more thunder. Carl and I were already running to the fish boat.

I got in and set the oars while he untied her and shoved her out. I pulled straight for Helen, thinking the wind would offset the current, but there was more wind than I had expected and Carl had to correct me: "Left oar, left oar."

I braced my feet and stiffened my legs, reaching and pulling with my back. As we came near Helen, Carl shouted, "Swing her, swing her," and I pushed the right against pulling the left, the boat shivered and paused for an instant, and Carl reached out and dragged Helen into the boat.

"Go for Richard," he said while Helen's legs were still in the water. Helen choked and spat the water out of her throat.

"Richard?" she said.

"We're coming to him," Carl said.

I was too winded to talk. I glanced over my shoulder once to locate the motorboat. It was beginning to settle and I couldn't see why until I thought that the speed of the boat must have carried it past the bar and into deeper water, or else the waves had knocked it off—or maybe both.

My right oar struck the bar and Carl jumped out. The water was only at his waist when he reached the motorboat, but Richard—knocked out against the wheel—was already set-tling up to his neck. The bow of the boat was sinking first, the stern still caught on a high place on the bar. Carl lifted

Richard out of the motorboat, floated him to the bow of the rowboat, and then, ducking under him, lifted him into the rowboat.

"Get in the stern," Carl said to Helen. "We want some weight in back. Slide over, Rob."

We each took an oar and pulled for shore, Carl counting, "One . . . two . . . three . . . One . . ."

As the boat struck beach, Carl and I grabbed Richard and ran for the house. Uncle John came down the yard to help us. Aunt Jane swung the door open.

"I've already called the doctor," she said. She swung the door closed, turned toward the cot where Richard now lay, then swung around again. "What in heaven's name is Helen doing?"

I looked toward the river. Helen, in the green duck boat, was pulling for the wreck. She was already almost half way there.

"She's going to haul in the wreck," I said. "She'll pull the back end out of that boat."

I didn't stop for Carl but ran out the door and down to the double-ender. Helen had reached the wreck by the time I was launched, but I knew it would take her some time to tie on to it. I looked around once to set my course, and then didn't look again, but pulled and pulled and pulled. Then I heard the crack of parting wood and I turned just in time to see the duck boat scoot suddenly forward, Helen's legs kicking up in the air, and then begin to settle stern first. When I reached her, she was standing on the bar.

"You goddamned fool," I said.

I took both oars from the duck boat and jammed their handles first into a high part of the bar and tied the motorboat and the duck boat to them. The oar blades were chipped and broken. She must have set both blades into the sandbar to use the oars as levers.

"If they stay, they stay," I said. "If they don't, they don't. Now get in."

20

On the island, a tree fell with rush of breaking limbs ending in a sudden boom. I was too tired to row fast, but I used the wind as much as I could, and we went at a pretty good clip. At the shore, we dragged the boat up on the bank and went up to the house. The doctor's Ford V-8 stood in the driveway.

"Everything will be all right," he was saying as we opened the screen door.

V

Helen and I both woke to the sound of wings beating against the screens. It was earlier than we usually got up, but Carl was already gone. We looked around the porch to locate the sound. The sky was not even gray yet; light kind of oozed through the clouds, seeming like wet and pulpy rotten wood.

The wings fluttered again and I looked up to the ceiling. Two bats, one inside the porch and one outside, kept flying toward each other, hitting the screen, and then flying off. It was as though they were trying to kiss through the screen.

"I thought bats never hit things," I said.

"Try and catch it," Helen said.

The bat inside the porch wacked against the screen and glided off onto Helen's bed. I jerked the blanket over it and then reached under and caught it with my hand.

"Put it outside," Helen said.

"Oh, no. Bats are lovely birds. Feel how soft she is."

"Keep it away. I don't want it in my hair."

"It won't get in your hair if I hold it. Here, touch it."

She reached out one finger in a scared way as though hunting for a set mouse-trap in the dark. Then, when she touched it and felt how soft and silky was its fur, she petted it with her whole hand.

"It is lovely," she said. "But bats aren't birds. They're mammals the same as people."

"We ought to keep him," I said. "Or her, whichever it is."

"What would you feed him?" Helen said.

"I don't know, but we could find out."

"No, you better let him go."

"Why? Wouldn't you like to be able to take her out of her cage and pet her every so often? You just said she was lovely."

"No, it would die," she said.

"Do you think it would?"

"I'm sure of it. All wild things are like that. Remember that little rabbit Carl caught in his box trap last summer? We fed it everything but it wouldn't eat, and it died."

" 'Coons don't."

"But you have to keep them chained," she said. "And once they get loose, they go hiking off to the nearest river or woods."

"Yes, I guess they do."

"Wait till I get dressed and we'll put it outside."

I put the bat under a blanket and tucked the blanket edges under the mattress, and then I began to dress. I was watching Helen dress, and she watched me, and neither of us said a thing. Her breasts were shaped more like lemons than young pears. They looked soft and tender and shy like wild flowers that die quickly when you close them in your hand. But I wanted to touch them just as you always want to pick the flowers.

When we had finished dressing, we both smiled, and I felt my face go red as I saw hers go red.

"Let's put the bat out," she said.

I took the bat from under the blanket and we went outside. Neither one of us wanted to let it go. Helen kept stroking it. Its fur was lovely, soft, and dark.

Carl came toward us from the dock. "What you got there?"

"A bat," Helen said. "It was on the porch."

"So that's what it was. I got up before light this morning, and when I opened the door, I knew something came in. It brushed my shoulder, but I thought it was a bird."

"Isn't he lovely?" Helen said.

"What are you going to do with her?" Carl said.

"Let him go," Helen said.

"When?"

"Right now," I said. "I'm going to let her go right now," I threw the bat into the air. It flew around crazily for a minute, and then winged away toward the trees by the river. We watched it until it disappeared, and still we looked after it. The second bat came from around the house and shuttled back and forth, but going always toward the river and the trees. Then it too disappeared.

Finally, Helen turned and said, "The boats?"

"The motorboat's there," Carl said, "but it isn't worth a tinker's dam now."

"And the duck boat?" I asked, though somehow I had already guessed what he would say.

"Gone," he said. "That lovely green boat has floated away."

The Ascent of Corey

GEORGE BLUESTONE

MYLES WARACH, HIS EYES FORCED CLEAR IN PRETENDED understanding, was trying to appear calm as he looked over at Corey. Actually, he was wondering whether or not to believe what he had just heard. Amos Corey was sitting quietly on the sleeping porch settee in Warach's rooming house on N.W. 25th Terrace (the one marked "Tourist") as if he hadn't spoken at all. Bess, her face vacant as always, showed no signs of being in the least affected. So much had happened in so short a time that Warach was afraid he was growing confused. Less than two weeks before, Corey's wife, Hazel, had died, and Warach, with considered tact, had gone about the business of burial, settling details, respecting the tight grief that Corey must have felt. But even Corey's high loss had left Warach intact, compared to how shaken up he was after what his friend had just told him. Sitting with hands draping knees, like a mousy man who has made a decision, he had announced his plan for "putting himself to sleep" three weeks hence on his way home from Chicago.

Never had Warach been so conscious of Corey as a friend. The safety of their tenant-landlord relationship had faded through the years. And for a moment Warach wished for the distance of that lost official tie where all responsibility could be calculated in terms of rent and night lights. But the personal density impounded in the house through all those years, helped along by himself and Bess, now urged upon him the necessity for tactics. How did a friend respond to such brute, smiling facts?

"I'll take care of everything," Corey had said. "You won't have to worry," and all the time rubbing the dark wood of the settee, firmly, the way he always handled things. What had surprised Warach more than anything else, once the real shock had gone, was Amos Corey's logic.

"Please, when it's over—go to the lawyer on Flagler Street . . ." Warach, if he didn't mind, would simply become the executor of Corey's modest estate. The will, duly arranged with the lawyer downtown, would not put Warach to too much trouble. Corey after all wanted things as easy and efficient as possible. Warach was to get five of the eight thousand dollars in Corey's bank account; the bonds were to be cashed and the proceeds donated to Sister Kenny; of the remaining three thousand, one was to go to the high school library, one to his sister in Chicago whom he had not seen in twenty-five years (this the ostensible reason for his last trip), one to pay for his cremation and the care of Odin, his black Samoyan. With a feeble wink and quiet smile, Corey explained that if Warach divulged the fact of his suicide, the will was sure to be contested, and certain charlatans, appearing to register tenuous claims, would only deprive Warach of his inheritance. "Also—the pills," he said, "the pills will be hard to detect. They can't prove a thing. I've seen to that."

Not until later, much later, did Corey's cold formality seem grotesque to Warach. For the moment, in their new and queerly skewed relationship, Corey seemed to make sense.

"Why—why me? Why this money?" Warach asked, seizing the obvious detail—nothing else signified. Because, Corey explained, Warach had offered genuine warmth to Hazel and himself during twenty years of tenancy. And yes, even as Corey spoke, Warach could remember the long walks along the clean tropical boulevards, sometimes with Corey and Hazel, sometimes with Corey alone, talking endlessly, or not talking at all. And on other nights, Hazel reading aloud from

Ethan Frome and Warach listening, imagining the terrible clarity of that white Northern world. And the time all four of them, Bess having finally consented to come, walked down to the Mayfair to see "Nanook of the North." Warach remembered coming away with a rare excitement from that small movie house where, as Bess said, "they show all them foreign pictures." Remembered, too, tingling to that powdered, elemental land on the screen, and feeling the incision later when Bess, in her reedy voice, said timidly, "I don't know, it didn't have a story—I like a movie with a story . . ." To which Hazel and Corey had responded by exchanging sorrowful looks, locking hands and walking on ahead. Somehow they had never managed to go to the Mayfair again.

And now an older Corey, his pink skin the texture of ripe fruit, sat with that sad detachment of his, offering *Warach* rewards: "Who else have I got to remember? Friends disappear when you get old. More and more you sit alone twiddling your thumbs, wondering what to do next." Speaking clearly, as a man will of a definite plan, he said that old age was only an added burden to his loneliness. It might not be so bad if he had relatives who mattered, grandchildren in blue bows and starched collars who dug in his pockets on Sundays, children who wanted him around, a job that gave him joy. But selling bizarre, hand-painted neckties to the sports of Lincoln Road was not, he often said, exactly the thing to inspire a man.

"And," Corey confided in his friend, "it's too late for another woman, too late." Warach, fumbling for hope, pressed the point, but Corey clasped his hands, shaking his head. "Impossible, I know. Take my word. I've—" he began, his voice trailing off, and Warach's mind completed, "tried—I've tried," remembering that Hazel and Corey had, in their last year, changed from the hard-eyed, almost brazen rapport of their earlier days to a kind of lacey quietude, as if they were nursing the embers of a once tumultuous blaze. Warach dropped the point. After all, Corey was over sixty.

"And whatever happens," Corey said matter-of-factly, his eyes shining, "don't think I'm unhappy doing what I'm doing." Warach looked up, as if an unexpected voice had entered the room; though he had begun to speculate on the real feelings behind Corey's pink aplomb, he had not spoken, and his friend's words had the effect of an intimate touch. It was always so with Corey. There was something tactile about him. More than once Warach observed how he enjoyed the surfaces of things; the way he barely fingered the gloss-covers of dollar magazines, or twirled a pear before biting in.

"All right, but don't be surprised," Warach said, smiling grimly. "I'm going to do what I can to stop you." Corey shrugged (that impossible detachment of his) and Warach saw more clearly than ever before how Corey had lived through Hazel. He remembered how Corey used to come excitedly downstairs, his pink face glowing, one of Hazel's pictures tucked under his arm, those pastels she used to do in her spare time. They were interesting at best, tropical scenes, palm trees, stiff birds, nondescript houses of stucco, plaster, vermiculated tone, colors garish and often sentimental. And Corey would be enthusiastic not so much, it seemed, because of the picture, but because Hazel had done it. When a man is in love, Warach reflected (he had to stir the dead hearth of his mind for memories of his own youth's passion; Bess was stable and devoted as a lattice vine, but he could not say he loved her), when a man is in love, everything springs to life with intensity and precision, exciting, jangling the senses. But more than this, Corey's despair, oozing through his calm, spoke of deeper passion, telling Warach that, for Corey, Hazel had been the source of the land's illumination.

"Have you ever noticed," Corey said to Warach, "that a flower goes black in the dark?" Obviously, with Hazel's death, the light had been turned off.

Afterwards, in the room, dislocated somehow by Corey's recent visit, Bess Warach turned on her husband like some small, mincing bird and asked, "Well, what are you going to do?" The settee was still swinging where Corey, getting up to leave, had pushed back against it.

"I'll do what I—I'll do what I can. Why?"

"Nothing," Bess answered with a sigh. "But did you happen to notice? I mean the money would be enough—there's so little left on the mortgage. Poor Amos." Ignoring the dismay that must have been growing on his face, Bess seemed to give herself up to the dream, even as Warach, almost against his will, reflected: after all these years it might be nice to be free of monthly bills, ceaseless payments, balanced ledgers, to have "a little extra" for a change, to splurge the way Corey and Hazel used to. To be free of the thin, crippling tyranny of boarders' whims, to be dependent less or not at all on stray salesmen laughing raucously behind cigars; on frantic divorcees, possessed of a suffering they could never admit; or on gentle old couples who had nowhere else to go —that would be nice.

When Warach spoke again, his voice seemed to recall her. "Don't count on it, my dear," he said, "don't count on it, the man isn't dead yet!" For Bess, the dream seemed to flutter, turn to dust. Carefully, she was watching his face. "Yes," Bess said, "poor, poor Amos. He always did like to help people." For a moment there was nothing but the bleak tick tick tick of the clock in the foyer. "But Myles," Bess said, "what *are* you going to do?"

"I'll do what I can. But damn it, I wish Amos wouldn't have such a good time planning his—his—" Even as his words faltered, Warach bolted from the security of his armchair. He wanted to shout at Bess, "Of course, I'll do all I can! Of course!" But Warach didn't shout. Instead he made his way uncertainly toward the kitchen to get a drink of water.

At dinner, a blonde, overstuffed hostess, her salutations adroitly rehearsed, had offered them a glass of sauterne "with the compliments of Sherard's." Because the hostess was well

preserved and the apéritif excellent, Warach, at Corey's insistence, ordered a full bottle of wine, and then another.
Afterwards, Warach walked with his friend along the boulevards, not quite drunk enough to miss the chill that was coming in with the evening air. They felt themselves on the verge
of unseasonal autumn shivers, but not uncomfortable. A
bright mandarin sky had turned magenta, then clear marine
blue, and finally blue-black, sharpening the fuzzy outlines of
the city. Even in the darkness, the palms, the white houses,
the pastel automobiles, were visible with a clarity unusual for
that time of year. And as they walked along, Corey touched
the hard trunks of tall, lissom palms, peered curiously up at
the fronds turning green-black in the closing light, like metal
delicately hammered. Across the causeway, past the cups of
light on the thin spindles of the bridge, they came to a darkening beach. For a long time they stood on the sand, looking
out at the long page of ocean, Warach feeling acutely the
need to understand. At first he had gone through a measured
testing of Corey's armor. It seemed to him that Corey had to
be stopped from going through with it, that Corey's going
would wrench Warach's hold on all those ordered com-
promises which had become his life. Probing alternatives,
Warach had thought of going to the police, but Corey had
smiled, "I'll just tell them you're a liar." He had visions of
hiring someone to dog Corey's every move, to intrude at
some crucial point. Once he said, "Let me go with you,
Amos," hoping somehow to forestall the event. But at last
he had come to see that Corey was invulnerable. The armor,
Warach decided, could not be pierced from the outside. He
sensed the need for some psychic assault. He had, for the moment, given in to Corey, pretended alliance on Corey's terms,
playing the unreal comic game.

After a while, washed by the evening air, now thinly cool,
they began to talk again, returning as they had for a week to
the question of Corey and his trip.

"I don't know how to make you see it," Corey said sadly. "A man has to have something to look forward to. If he can't look ahead, he might as well give up. And I can't look ahead. I'm not complaining. I've had what I wanted. Look. Remember that time we went duck hunting? . . ."

Warach remembered, the Coreys' invitation up North for the hunting, and Bess refusing because she was afraid she might get one of her headaches out there in the wilderness, and wanting besides to do some work in her garden, among her beloved vegetables. And so the three of them had gone without her. Warach could remember waiting with Hazel and Corey up in that clear land, the time before dawn in the alcove by the lake, a natural blind of brush and willow, waiting in the night's frost, the twelve-gauge gun firm in his armpit, the blue-gray barrel touching the darkness; at his side, the golden retriever, patient as a wise man, pressing for warmth against him, expertly sniffing the air, and wetting his hand now and then with a damp inquisitive muzzle. From the other corner of the blind, whispered invectives against the night marked the presence of Hazel. Oh, she sang, my limbs are cold, cold, cold. Soon the morning came, a silver sheen melting across the sky and rippling with light the dark, placid surface of the water. A low, almost barren rock some fifteen yards off shore became visible with the day, but only blurred splotches of green gloss against the rock suggested the proximity of the ducks. Suddenly a lone mallard spotted the wooden decoy midway between the rock and the shore. Announcing his discovery to the others, he circled overhead in wide arcs, followed by a few of his mates. Carefully, Warach sighted his gun. Allowing a good lead on the birds, he held his aim for just an instant, then fired. A miss. Then he heard an explosion near his ear. Corey had taken his turn. Overhead a mallard broke formation and plummeted swiftly toward the lake. The sound of the shot ricocheted across the lake, and suddenly the rock seemed to be moving, floating upward in a large diffusion of ducks. Warach saw the birds fanning out across the sky, thousands of dark, curveting shafts resounding with cries, the beatings of the air, singly frail, a wild inundation in all that flapping mass. The sounds of the mallards, their abundant grace, excited him, catching his nerve ends in one clear and constant tingling. Turning, he had seen Hazel there beside Corey, her eyes careful and luminous, as if on the verge of bursting into flame. Afterwards, what Warach remembered most was how, in that enormous scattering, there had been such amazing clarity . . .

"Can I ever have that morning again?" Corey was saying. "You remember. I ask you. At least when Hazel was alive, we could always remember. But now?" He hunched his shoulders, that little shrug he used when he didn't have an answer.

"Wasn't there anything—anything besides Hazel?" Warach asked uneasily. He was thinking of himself, of the good talks they had had along the boulevards. Corey was looking out towards the water, smiling a little, saying nothing.

"Nothing?" Warach asked, and his voice seemed ridden with echoes.

"Maybe. Maybe there was. But nothing seems to matter now."

"But haven't you always wanted to take it easy? Do some of the things you never had a chance to do?"

"For instance."

"I don't know. Little things. Travel."

When Corey spoke again his voice was full of liquid sadness. "Travel?" he asked. "I decided a long time ago it's how deep you see that counts. Not how much. What else have I got to see?"

Suddenly Warach felt the pinch of failure. He was lacerated by the thought that if Corey, who had lived as Corey did, could turn his back on the time still left to him, what reason did he, Myles Warach, have for going on? The threat loomed, stark, immediate.

"Hell, Amos," said Warach frantically, "I'd be happy sitting out my days with some good whiskey at the Club. Some good whiskey and one of those deep armchairs. The kind that smells of clean leather."

Corey burst out laughing. "The Club, the *Club*, Myles? God, there's something for you! Burton Fitch working himself up over a cigar. Really something. The Club! Ha! Ha! Not the Club, Myles," Corey said, wiping his eyes.

Warach stood amazed, a little frightened by the laughter, watching Corey shake. It wasn't the best club in town, that was true. A man who saved carefully over the years could get in, and it did manage the essential forms of the B.P.O.E. That was enough. There was a certain security in belonging (Warach assumed Corey had always felt the same way) and it baffled him to see Corey degrading it. Somehow Corey's laughter made Warach feel ashamed.

"Odin, then," Warach went on, his voice weakly stubborn, "what about Odin? The dog's been faithful. You owe it to him at least."

"But I've given Odin to you," Corey said, looking straight at Warach, his voice impish and hurt again.

"Nothing," Warach said dismally, "nothing. You think nothing is better." In the silence that followed, Warach's nascent anger suddenly caught fire. "Damn it, man," he cried, "if all the lonely ones decided to end it, there wouldn't be anyone left."

Corey was looking down at the sand, forming tiny dunes with the stub of his shoe. Finally he said, "Maybe—maybe that's just as well."

"Oh hell, do you think you're the only one? Why are you so special? I've never lost a wife and I'm lonely. I never felt the way you felt about Hazel, never. I've never had my wife waiting there *with* me. I don't know why I— Look, even now you're having a good time." Warach felt his eyes moist and stinging.

"Myles, I'm sorry. What I decide is good for me. No one else. I don't mean it for anyone else, Myles. I'm sorry."

"I didn't mean that! I only loved one girl in my life. And she rode off on a train one hot morning in July and never came back. That's all there was. I never even told her how I felt. But you, you were alive for twenty-five years, Amos. That's a pretty good score. Bess is good, but I'm politely dead when I'm with her. One big thumb from head to foot, that's me. And look, a nice thick callus for a heart."

"Come on now," Corey said, wincing. "Don't underestimate yourself."

"Underestimate myself! Listen to the man! It's you I've been underestimating. Stop trying to be God—"

"God?" Corey asked as if chewing bitters.

"God," Warach repeated, his voice rising in small curls. "Stop trying to decide who should live and who shouldn't. What makes you think *you* have the right to decide?"

As if a thousand secret capsules had come apart, Warach continued to speak, feeling the evangelic passion. His words spun out, drawing Corey in. He could see Corey change, could see him turn to the goading of his voice, and for a moment he felt again the intense clarity of that morning with the ducks. For the first time, Corey seemed to break through stiff coverings to the difficult air of feeling. In Corey's moment of pause, Warach saw his power over his friend. Having stirred old moods and colors, having made him stop long enough to doubt, Warach saw that all he had to do was press forward, speak again, and the obsession for suicide would be destroyed, like a flower snapped from its stalk by a stiff, authentic wind.

"Let's go home," Warach said. In the darkness he had seen the face of his wife, had been struck by the sharp reproach that Corey was and would always be.

"No, not home. Not home," Corey said, his face almost frightened now. "Let's walk." Abruptly he turned and walked back to the road away from the beach.

Along Collins, the neon lights sketched the white hotel walls in soft pastels. The women, rustling silk and taffeta,

3 3

54932

walked briskly as to a cotillion, their tight dresses, copper and gold, shining like coins against the night. There was something suggestive about the occasional white fur, the bustles, and the swirls draping pockets in front.

"That stuff molds them like hands," said Corey with sarcasm. "Holds on till other hands take over." The men wore cardigans and their teeth showed white through faces browned by the sun. Their trousers, coverts and gabardines, did not match their jackets; grays went with sky blues, chartreuse with tans, anything with maroons. All the colors were the coolness of summer, as if someone, without overdoing it, had mixed white with darker shades. Hand-painted ties were held in place by leather clips, or trick miniature arrows and cutlasses appearing to pierce the cloth. The men seemed not to touch the women much, except in courtesy; all looked as if they wanted to. Everything appeared coated with a fine pollen-powder, like water colors well dried.

"I went to a circus once and— Well, what have we here?" Corey said. They had come to an open air carnival bustling a corner lot. Rows of gaudy lights illumined the place. Warach could see people intent on miniature golf, the electric anti-aircraft of long blue tubes, a strength-testing machine where an iron coil could be pulled far enough to ring a bell. There was a small carousel for children, and in the rear a shooting gallery. "Let's play," said Corey with a grin. Warach consented because he knew that Corey was trying to mend a crack, the most difficult thing a man can do, and he had been partly to blame.

They walked through a turnstile at the entrance. Corey led the way, browsing idly at one booth and then another. Finally they came to the shooting gallery. A man wearing a harlequin vest and marionette mustache presided over a shooting board. "Ten shots for twenty-five cents, folks. Test yer aim! Step right up! Test yer aim, Sir?" The barker was addressing Corey, who had drawn near. The shouting sounded strange to Warach because he and Corey were the only ones around.

The barker seemed to be challenging them. "Test yer aim, folks! Test yer aim!"

Corey had listlessly taken a rifle and a pocket of shells and was staring down the range at the targets. There were two rotating wheels against the back wall, a poor faded mural of the sea, several white swinging pendulums with black eyes in their bases, some stationary clubs on a lower tier, and on the tier nearest the floor, a moving line of tin ducks that spilled over the side and came up the other end to begin again. Warach saw his friend raise his rifle, slowly, professionally, aim low. The ducks. A shot whistled, echoing wildly, and was lost. A miss. Corey fired again, and Warach smelled the burned powder. Nothing happened. Then Corey was firing aimlessly, his breath coming hard, his mouth twisted a little, his face flushed, his eyes like glass. The barker stood still, a marionette put away.

"Stop it, Amos. Now stop it!" Warach was tugging at his arm, trying to break the wild ping-click ping-click of the rifle which Corey, in his frenzy, was firing indiscriminately.

Warach remembered very little of how he got Corey home, except that his friend kept sniffling to himself, quietly, as if afraid of being overheard, and that he had gotten him into bed somehow where he lay looking up at the ceiling for a long time, sitting up once for a glass of water, and saying after he finished, "Thanks, Myles, thanks. You better go." In the calmest of tones.

When he left, Warach went downstairs and sat in the dark, smoking a pipe to settle himself. Though nothing in this dangerous game seemed to make sense finally (everything looked hacked, the way it does through a bowl of cut glass), Warach felt that for all its lack of neatness, Corey's exhibition at the gallery had been a healthy thing. For the first time, Warach had scored the armor, and even though he could not gauge the end, he felt he had achieved a tentative victory over Corey.

When he slept at last, he dreamed he saw Corey drowning

somewhere, in a marsh or swamp it seemed, making shapes with his mouth as if he were crying out, though no sound could be heard, his head bobbing up and down like cork in a whirlpool. In his dream, Warach held out his hand, the fingers wide, stretching until he was almost, but not quite, touching Corey's head. And then, when he almost had him, when his muscles felt like iron spars bending, it was too late. Corey melted into the bubbles, laving the whirlpool down with him into the bowls of the water. He was gone. Warach awoke, aware that the dream had been suffused with a certain horror, with the suspicion that he might have stretched his hand a little more, distended those waxen fingers just enough to reach. That night he did not sleep again.

The following week Corey left for Chicago. Warach remained, magnifying the suspicion of his dream into an obsession. How had he failed? Warach waited, felt new fears blooming.

Burton Fitch stopped by to call on the Warachs after his trip. Wedged into the armchair given over to all Warach's guests, Burton took a cigar from a cardboard tube glossed in silver, smelled it, bit the tip on his tongue, spit, lit up, sucked in his cheeks, and finally settled back to smoke. Watching him, Warach reflected on how easy it was to dislike the fat man with the pink, fleshy hands and the sensuous face. Burton was tolerated in the Warach home because once, during the days when he first was "getting started," he had been an indifferent, timid boarder. He had moved out when times got better, but he had not forgotten them. With a kind of perverted gratitude he had made a point of coming back, not punctually, but often—for old times' sake. Having permitted it once, the Warachs had to permit it again, and now they were stuck with him. Burton was the kind of man who was good in small doses.

"By the way," Burton was saying, "I saw a friend of yours in Chicago."

"Oh? Who?"

"Your old friend, Corey."

Warach didn't like the way he said "old friend." "Yes. To see his sister," Warach suggested, as if he had heard a rumor.

"Sister? Heh, heh. Did he tell you he was going to see his sister?"

"That's what I—"

"Oh, he's a foxy one, all right. Heh, heh."

"You mean he didn't see his sister? Tell me."

"Oh, he saw his sister all right. But not for long. Had a row or something. He was staying at the same hotel I was. That's how I met him."

"How did he seem?" Warach asked cautiously.

"Sorrowful, very sorrowful. But, heh, heh—you know Amos. He makes out he's hurt or something, and then he has a high time—under protest, understand, under protest. Figures he can't enjoy himself unless he has a conscience."

"What was he doing?"

"You might say he was having a good time. Like I say, very sorrowful." Burton winked at Warach, then at Bess. It never took very long for Burton's callowness to annoy Warach. He was suddenly uncomfortable and felt frightened by it. As if on cue, Bess left the room.

"I tell you," Burton went on, "the old boy still knows how to knock off a little. He's got more needles in him than—"

"Burton, you got a dirty mouth," Warach said, not with anger, but knowingly, the way men will talk.

"Thanks, friend, thanks," Burton said, frowning a little. There was a silence during which Bess returned to the room carrying a tray with three small glasses of crème de menthe. Warach watched Burton take his, roll a little on his tongue, begin alternating the drink with the cigar.

"Okay, what happened?" Warach asked finally.

Burton looked as if someone had given in to him. "Well," he said, "there was this blonde—one of the fat and forty kind, tries to be thin and can't? I found out later everyone knew her. I saw Amos for a while that afternoon, and we talked a little, not much. That night I went into the bar, and there he was with the blonde, cooing in her ear, very serious. I said hello, but he looked embarrassed, so I took off. Probably thought I was trying to horn in or something. He was a little drunk. Looked like a school kid caught with his pants down. I still don't know if he remembered me. Anyway, an hour later the son-of-a-gun is gone, blonde and all . . . I asked a bellhop about her, casual-like. Well, mister! Heh, heh—there was a wink and some talk about a certain hotel room, a bottle of Haig and Haig, the works. Imagine, at his age. Poor Amos— Quite a—" Bess left the room. This time she didn't come back until Burton was ready to go.

Burton talked on as if Bess had gone to get him another liqueur. "I saw him for two more days, but can't say I really *talked* to him. He—Myles, are you listening?"

"I'm listening." He had been listening, conjuring up the scene to the drone of the fat man's words, resisting and doubting at first, but then, with the recognition that Fitch had no cause to downgrade Corey, giving in and believing. Fitch's story filtered through to him with a certain probing horror, for if what he saw was true of Corey, that last lonely trip assumed new dimensions. It's too late for another woman, too late, Corey had said. And Warach tried to imagine Corey sitting in that bar, his matted face lifted to the artificial light.

". . . Face was funny . . . kinda white. Maybe the light in that bar . . ." What had been revealed in that face? Had it been full of satiety, that face, Corey having mastered the blonde, demonstrating that even in the cheap affair it was not "too late" after all? Or had it been full of final, ugly defeat, an image in a cracked mirror, welcoming death with relief, accepting the only wise and blessed alternative to failure? Or had it—had it been full of smiling collusion, enjoying the fantastic gag he had slipped over on them? And would Corey, after all, come marching back some bright morning, innocent, laughing, acknowledging the joke, and over cups of hot

3 8

coffee, restore the tourist home to normal? Warach reflected on the extraordinary fact that whatever the reality had been, Corey would have achieved a kind of victory.

". . . Boy, that blonde must have been a lulu. You listen to me, Myles, the old guy can still get his piece—"

"Shut up, Fitch, damn it, shut up!" Warach burst out. Burton's eyes opened a little, but his mouth remained fixed, foolishly enjoying a joke.

When Burton left, Bess said, "I don't want that man here again." She seemed lost before Burton.

Warach, who had felt himself shivering, could barely concentrate on what she was saying. "Well, then, tell him not to come," he said sarcastically. Sometimes, even though Warach had long ago resigned himself to a kind of vegetable life with Bess, her presence clustered round him, choking.

"I can't tell him. You know I can't tell him. Why don't you tell him?" Then, each knowing the other would do nothing, Bess and Myles resigned themselves to Burton.

When Warach saw the notice two days later in a small box on the front page of the *Herald*, he was shocked only for a moment. The shock melted quickly into the feeling that comes when a telegram, long overdue, arrives with a message that has been telephoned the day before. The shock then is for the presence of the thing and not for what it says. It was a simple message:

MIAMIAN FOUND DEAD ON TRAIN FROM WEST

A man identified as Amos Corey of 585 N.W. Terrace 25 died on a Florida East Coast train coming from Chicago to Miami yesterday. A porter found him dead at 2:25 P.M. between West Palm Beach and Miami, police reported. Police attributed the death to natural causes.

Bess cried into a lace handkerchief. Warach sat in the guest chair, and, as if returning to a duty reneged in a bad moment, he tried to feel again his last days with Corey, before Fitch's disrupting ambiguities, tried to recall the angular relation, bent queerly like a view through blue rippled glass. But he couldn't, not now. All he knew was that Corey would never return.

When Bess began asking questions, he excused himself by saying he had to go out. He left quickly. But outside there was no relief. The air was thick, the sun was high, the lines of the macadam road, the traveler palms, the sleek cars passing, were fuzzy and blurred. Now all the clear logic Corey had passed off on him was gone; he felt confused; no alternative would fit. He felt his hold slipping, his thoughts moving out across the flat land, so hot and heavy and useless. The cabbage palms held the sandy earth in a net of pineapple scrub, and swamps broke the face of the land like sleepy eyes overgrown with fungus. The rivers of the land moved slowly because they had nothing to do, and the banks of the rivers threw branches low over the water, offering speckled pears for no one to eat, pausing by the water as if sated with drink but too heavy to move. A strange deadness for so much vegetation. Sometimes animals with insinuating eyes peered through the tangle of brush, and the caws of troubled birds opened brackishly against the sky. Everywhere a thin varnish of oil finished the surface of things, the fossils, the water, the air. Nothing was sure; much care was needed; for the log in the water could, in an instant, become an alligator, and the knots on the log, its small, indifferent eyes. There were coils in the sickness, ready to spring—into where? Warach returned home, his mouth not tasting of business.

In three days, Corey had become a statistic in the local hall of records. Everything went off as Corey had planned. For all practical purposes, the newspaper story held.

On a hot, bright Sunday afternoon, Warach, his wife Bess, and a few friends rode in a single black sedan to a secluded pier on the Dania beach. There, from a bronze casket, baroque and full of angels, bought with funds from the estate, the ashes of Amos Corey were scattered to a calm and waiting ocean. Someone whispered a prayer, heads were bowed, Warach wept briefly and with feeling. When he got home, he set the empty casket heavily on the mantelpiece.

"When I die," he said to his wife who was staring at the casket as if trying to divine some secret in the inscription there, "when I die, I want to be buried on a green hill under a white stone. That," he said, digging his thumb into the cornice of the fireplace, "that's something a man can understand."

The Proud Suitor

JAMES BUECHLER

ABOUT THIRTY YEARS AGO, WHEN MY FATHER AND MOTHER
were about to marry, there was a girl on our street named
Marie Pulaski. She lived downstairs in that yellow two-family
house on the corner, which they have just done over and are
letting out now in apartments to young married couples. My
mother lived next door to where we live now, so she was
just across, and down one, from Marie.

But my mother and her set were a lot wilder than Marie
ever was. Evenings in the spring and summer when people
used to sit out on their porches, and still do, for that matter,
my father would come roaring and crashing and banging up
the street in somebody else's automobile that he had managed
to get hold of, and skip up the steps, dressed all flashy, to
take my mother by her two hands and begin dragging her
down from the porch; while she swore she wouldn't go anywhere with him or even get into his car, and that it didn't
look safe. But he always managed to get her in there, even if
he had to lift her up and throw her in, while the galleries in
the porches, including Marie across the way, took it in; then
they would tear off, making all kinds of noise, with an old-
fashioned horn blaring "Ska-googah!" because I guess my
father couldn't ever borrow a fairly new automobile even in
those days.

Nothing of the kind was ever seen to happen to Marie. She

was a full woman already, being about twenty-four, with long dark hair, which as often as not she wore in braids. She would sit out in the only chair on her porch, a rocking chair, and watch the tussles between my mother and father, and anything else that might offer in the street. She used to watch such things closely enough, though they never seemed to amuse her or make her indignant, or anything else either. Her mother and father were quite old people who never showed themselves on the porch. As far as anybody could tell, Marie never came out from that house at all, except to walk up the street to go to the store for her mother.

One night in the spring of that year, as people sat out on their porches after supper, something very funny happened. No sooner had my father clattered away with my mother beside him than queer, high-pitched cries began to be heard from down at the other end of the street. Then a man in a white shirt, with necktie flying and his black trousers flashing in long, strong strides, came running straight up the middle of the road between the houses; and as he came he shouted in a frantic, bushy-black-haired way, about every fifth step: "Stop! Stop! Stop!" But upon this final cry his voice seemed to give way, he himself collapsing along with it, for he pulled up and stumbled with a short little turn over to the curb. There he dropped down, his black-trousered knees knobbing high and his bushy head down between them, sobbing and moaning for breath.

But soon it was clear he was really crying, with actual grief, blubbering out loud on the curb over there across from our house. It seems the car my father had come to fetch my mother in that night was his; and not only that but he had only bought it two days ago—not that it was really a new car. He had been drinking beer in the grill down on the far corner, where my father used to stop in on his way up our street; and when my father came in and some of my father's pals introduced him as a man who had just bought a car, my father slapped him on the back in a friendly way and said that was fine and that he thought he wouldn't mind borrowing her for the night. The young Italian—he wasn't perhaps sure of the language yet but he was glad to be making friends —smiled broadly and happily. My father asked him to point out the car. He did. And with that my father, pulling out his watch first to make sure he was on time, jumped in and drove her off. The black-haired young man's smile left him slowly as he pondered what was happening. Then after a minute he sprinted up our street shouting in that way, and only gave up when he saw that his car had already turned the next corner and he found he just couldn't yell or run any more.

The people sitting out on porches all knew my father pretty well, so they didn't have much trouble putting together what was going on. It must have been funny to them, knowing my father, to see that fellow out on the curb crying for all the world as though his car had been taken away from him, stolen, for good. But as they all sat taking it in, waiting to see what he would do, somebody said: "Don't cry."

The words were out and hanging in the street between the houses, belonging to nobody, with nobody knowing where they had come from.

"Don't cry!"

This time the people sitting just across from the man made sure of an idea they'd had but didn't quite believe at first: Marie Pulaski, watching everything closely as always, had not quite stood up but was leaning forward in her rocking chair and urging, positively ordering the young man not to cry.

But nobody, not even his mother come all the way over from old Europe, could have got through to him then. He sat on the curb and cried, and when he had got back his wind he picked himself up and walked down the street in the direction from which he had come, on the sidewalk this time, hanging his head and still crying to himself.

44

After the young man disappeared things on our street went back to what they had been before my father got there: the people sitting on their porches looking out. Marie sat on as though she hadn't done anything.

About dark, however, two men came walking up the street and one was the dark-haired young man. They stopped over on the opposite sidewalk and the other, the taller one, pointed across at the house next door to ours, where my mother lived. Probably he was explaining that if the young man would only keep in sight of this house he would be sure to see his car again before the night was over. Then the taller man went off on his own business, leaving the Italian standing there boldly with his arms at his sides, confronting my mother's house.

He stood there in his funny way until people were tired of watching him. Then, as it had been with the two words thrown out into the street a little while earlier, something happened—the man was all of a sudden gone—without people seeing just how it had come about. When after a little the street lights had quietly come on and arranged in an instant the lights and darks of our street, he was discovered in a new place: sitting with his knees up in front of him again and his feet on the top step over on Marie's stoop, still watching my mother's house.

He had bought himself a good car, my mother says. They had gone all the way to the Adirondacks with it. They didn't get back until the wee hours of the morning, when they came tinkering up the quiet street in it and stopped. But before my father could even turn off the ignition the black-haired Italian loomed up in the road just in front of the car. My mother couldn't tell where he had come from, of course, and it frightened her.

"You come down," he ordered my father.

My father tried to kid around and carry it off, but the young man wouldn't have it. My father must only get out of his car right away. It was a difficult situation for my father, with my mother up beside him. But he went around to help her get out. He didn't know if he was going to have a fight or what.

But my mother, with her boyish bob and all, had got over her fright right away and was taking it all in. And she says what she noticed most of all was that the Italian boy wouldn't on any account look at *her*. It wasn't that he didn't want to, perhaps; but he kept his face turned away as if he was ashamed to have her see him. Even after my father had told her all about it later, as a joke, she still couldn't see the young Italian, as he stepped in front of the headlights and ordered my father out, as a fool worrying that somebody had run off with his new car. His car had something more to do with him some-how—she even thought it had something to do with herself. Not that the Italian had ever laid eyes on her before. But my father had taken his car and had used it perhaps in the way it was meant to be used (my father is always using other peo-ple's things, which he says if they can't use them as well as he can they haven't any right to anyway) so that the Italian, whose car it really was, was seen to be without it in the eyes of my mother, while my father, who had never had a car of his own, had made such use of it; and as a result the young man was ashamed. She was certain he would never forgive my father. Much my father cared.

A few days later he showed himself again on our street. People might have expected he would come barging up in his own automobile, if he was going to come back at all; but no, he came on foot again, walking up the opposite sidewalk about an hour after supper. It turned out he had sold the car already, after owning it just one week. He climbed up onto Marie's porch and spent the whole evening sitting on the stoop, for there was still only the one rocking chair over there.

The young man's name appeared on wedding invitations at the end of the summer as Giuseppe Verdi Abruzzi. They were from Mr. and Mrs. Wladislaw Pulaski and requested the honor of your presence at the wedding of their daughter, Marie, to Giuseppe Verdi Abruzzi of Italy, and for some reason one of them was sent to my mother. She was surprised. My mother being what she was, she had never had anything to do with Marie, and besides she was six years younger. But Polish weddings are something even now; what must they have been thirty years ago! My mother wouldn't have refused for anything.

So, on the day of the wedding, she had my father borrow another car and drive her over to the hall that Marie's father had hired for the afternoon. She arrived a bit late. By that time the place was a regular little Poland. They were dancing and drinking, the music was going, some were singing, and there were long tables with rich heavy foods on them that she didn't know the names of. Couples came polkaing furiously by her, again and again, part of a big whirling round of people all turning on a single axis but all the time doing little epicycle whirls on their own as they came. My mother had no sooner got up to the edge than she was sucked off into it, a great big fellow with a flat Polish face simply taking her and polkaing her off, stomping, without so much as a word. But I don't think there was ever a dance my mother couldn't do, so off she went with him, having a wonderful time right from the start.

Except for one or two people from our street whom my mother recognized, the wedding guests were all relatives of Marie's. The bridegroom hadn't invited anybody. He had simply shown up for the whole thing, dressed properly, all by himself.

Not that it seemed to bother him. On the contrary, he shone. In a white coat, with his handsome head of black hair, he went about with a radiant, proud and gracious air, as was required of the most important man there. The polka my mother was doing ceased all at once. There was a minute while the musicians—a piano was up on the stage of the hall and a man had an accordion on his chest—were seen to drink from glasses on the piano. Then they began to play a waltz. A wide circle at the middle of the hall seemed to empty itself as a round, cleared bowl, with all the ladies and girls there making up the sides. Then the young Italian stepped out into the ring, smiling, and delicately began walking around its edge, nodding and smiling with approval at this girl and that one until finally he chose, turning and bringing his feet together, bowing his head slightly, though looking up at the girl from under black eyebrows with laughing eyes, offering his arms. The girl placing her own within them, he took on a serious look and began to dance.

And the way in which he danced was not at all the way they used to do it at Cain's Dance Castle or the Pine Lake Pavilion or Sherman's Rendezvous in the Adirondacks, where my mother was always going with my father. It was what my mother and her crowd would have called "ballroom dancing." Not that it was any slower than what they did to the quick, jazzy music she and my father liked; but it was a long and moving, round and full kind of dancing, a regular old-country waltz. My mother was charmed; she loved to dance. She had worked herself up forward to the edge of the circle, and so when her big Pole presented himself before her in the same formal way she accepted him at once and they swooped off together. There were only the two pairs of them, the young bridegroom and his lady and my mother and her Pole, turning and turning and turning around the floor, past the watching faces of all the young girls. Then others came sweeping out, and soon the couples were all whirling and gliding and threading among one another. But through them all gleamed unmistakably the white coat of the young Italian, dancing with confidence, never so much as grazing another, beaming and smiling and nodding to everyone in his happiness and self-assurance.

Marie danced too, with all the young men; but of course she had to wait for them to come to her, and so she didn't shine as her new husband did. And except for the first waltz, which my mother had missed, they paid very little attention to one another, busying themselves instead with all the other men or girls each perhaps might have married but had not and now forever would not.

After the waltz there was a long, noisy time when some of the people sat down at tables and ate, and Marie's old father came around to see that everybody was eating and drinking enough, and finally the musicians played another polka. Then, as they began a waltz again, all the women and girls, my mother included, crowded up in a circle; the bridegroom came around, and by some chance—perhaps he had seen how she danced with the broad-shouldered Pole when only the four of them had been on the floor—he chose my mother. And he knew who she was, not perhaps as he bowed, smiling, offering himself; but before they had turned once around the circle past all the girls he recognized her. It seems a woman can always tell how it is with a man, when all of a sudden what she does or may think of him begins to matter to him. Another couple moved onto the floor, and another; the serious air with which the bridegroom began each waltz fell away, he became very gay and lighthearted. And his gaiety didn't radiate out all around him on the dance floor as before but instead was all directed to my mother. As for her, she was only eighteen, and he couldn't have been more than twenty. The grace with which he waltzed her, the wonderful gallantry of him, the very way he held her arms and guided her, and all the strange, bold, old-fashioned tenderness toward her that he made her feel was in him—it all overcame her and made her really shy with him; though I know they considered her a "fast" girl in her own set. When the waltz was finished he didn't leave her but led her to a table and gave her some of the food and some wine to drink. Then he was off around the hall again, gracious and benevolent with everybody. But he returned to my mother and polkaed with her and stayed with her and danced the waltz that followed with her. All afternoon he continued with her, and something began to pass between them; though everything they said was just ordinary and proper to the occasion. But as he saw how my mother was feeling he looked glad, as though he would say, Ah, you do like this! And my mother responding by looking somewhat shy, as she really felt, though happy and excited, he would go on proudly, I knew it would be so!—and of course this made him, at that moment, all the more attractive to my mother. But even so it wasn't enough for him, for as they were dancing he suddenly looked at her with such pleasure and pride and confidence that he was making her happy that she understood he was going a step further; and although neither one had mentioned the first time they had "met," she knew it was about that. You see I'm not what I might have looked then! You see what I can be on my own ground!

But as they were moving around the hall so gracefully, my mother looking all around her with such pleasure, she saw my father, who had come to pick her up, standing all by himself against a far wall by the door. She felt a pang. And although, she knew, the bridegroom had seen him too, he would not relinquish her; the waltz had just begun. It wasn't that he wanted to show off in my father's face, or anything like that. He saw right away what my mother was feeling with my father there, but he saw too how attractive he still was to her, and insisting on that, he looked at her as though to appeal, But do you see it wasn't impossible?

When the waltz was over he left her and went to Marie. It was just after four o'clock. Within a few minutes bride and groom had left the reception, leaving the guests to carry on by themselves.

Riding back to her house with my father in his borrowed car, my mother felt sad. She felt glad and more at home back with my father, but still she was about as unhappy as she had ever been before in her life. It was strange, too, because she had always been lively. My father drove along, acting very glum. My mother thought about the young Italian: how he had been when she first saw him, how he had got rid of his car and made up to Marie Pulaski, and how now he was married to Marie. She knew—and of course it made her proud—that he would rather have had her, or a girl like her, than Marie. That was what the car was for. But even with the car he didn't know how to go about it; he couldn't ever really learn what a man like my father was born with. My father made a fool of him. So he sold the car and married a girl like Marie Pulaski. So it wasn't possible; he couldn't ever have taken her off in his car, and he knew she had to have a man who could. Still she felt sad, as though she had missed something. But she hadn't. How could she not have missed?

My father drove along, in a bad temper, beside her. After all, they were supposed to be engaged. During the summer they had thought they would get married. They had talked about it on the way home from dancing in the Adirondacks, at the same time the Italian was courting Marie Pulaski. But they hadn't decided when. As they rode back from the wedding together, both feeling miserable, they made up their minds once and for all. Two months later on a Saturday they were married themselves.

Marie had always stayed pretty close to home. The only time she ever surprised anybody on our street was on that one night when she leaned forward from her porch and told the young Italian that he wasn't to cry. But when he showed up to visit her afterward and spent the summer evenings sitting on her stoop and finally married her, nobody was surprised. That was the way a girl like Marie was going to be courted and married—if she was to be courted and married at all. If my father, say, had come along some night to pull her down to his car and take her out someplace—*that* would have astonished people.

After her marriage Marie lived in that same house, in the same flat even, downstairs; while her father, who owned the house, had turned out the renters upstairs and moved up there with her mother. Marie appeared outside as little as before. The following year she had a baby.

But although she had lived in it since a baby herself, the flat was wonderfully changed for Marie by her new husband. In it she would move about slowly all day, making the home, and think about him out in the city somewhere working against whatever might be out there, and wait for him at night with a deep and clumsy happiness that made him laugh at her when he came. She had no desire to go out anywhere, and it isn't any wonder people saw very little of her. Even her father and mother left them pretty much alone.

As for the Italian, he throve; he became "known" on our street, and liked—not personally, because almost nobody knew him to speak to, but they all approved of him. Those who were up early enough would see him, at six, come out of the flat wearing clean work clothes with big stiff gloves stuck jauntily in a back pocket and walk briskly, but smiling and delighted, down our street and away. He came back around five in the afternoon with his clothes all dirty but still delighted. He was so evidently happy it was impossible not to take to him. "That little Mr. Abruzzi never gets down," declared the women. "Maybe he's got a dirty job, but he never gets down."

Nobody knew just exactly what he did for a living, though it was said he "worked for the city." Some people thought he was probably a garbage man, because in our city the police and firemen are mostly Irish and the Italians are in the department of sanitation. But if he was he never collected on our street. And even so people would say: "We don't hold anything against a man because he takes out our garbage."

Marie herself didn't have any clear idea what it was her husband went off to do each morning. She only admired him in the clean work clothes she had prepared for him and supposed whatever he did out there must befit him. He, on his side, kept such things to himself and brought home the city's check twice a month.

Times changed. The country went into the depression. Marie's husband got paid less; apparently they shifted him from job to job, but they never let him go. Then my own grandfather got sick, and my father and mother, who had been living in another part of the city, moved into the house we're still in to be near him. My father lost a lot of jobs around then, but he always bounced back with another one. At that time I was a small baby. My mother was very proud of me and she used to like to wheel me up and down the street she'd grown up on to show the old ladies who used to shake their heads and ask each other what would become of her.

And looking out of her front windows on the bright October afternoons, Marie would see my mother emerge from our house across the way, cross the street with me in the carriage and then head down her own sidewalk in the sunshine—since our side is in shadow after noon. One day she bundled up her own baby, a girl named Thomasina, put her into a carriage and set out after my mother. As my mother came back along the street Marie came out with a big, old, high-wheeled black carriage and started down the steps so clumsy and self-conscious and proud of her own baby that my mother was sure the carriage would get away from her; and she left me and ran up to get Marie down with it.

Naturally they admired each other's baby. They took to airing the babies at the same time every day. They seemed to get along very well.

"What d'you keep yourself so cooped up for?" my mother asked her. Marie looked at my mother. "Cooped up?"—she wasn't cooped up; chickens are cooped up. "What d'you do with yourself?" demanded my mother. "How come we never see you in the A & P?" Marie had groceries brought to the house by a Polish grocer who knew her father. My mother

53

put a stop to that. "Why! Who d'you think you are—Rockefellers?" And on Saturday afternoon she dragged Marie down to the A & P, leaving both babies with my grandfather and grandmother next door.

They came back with two boxes of groceries on a wagon, my slight little mother pulling and larger, grim-looking Marie walking beside it. They went into our flat and my mother gave Marie our telephone and made her call up her Polish grocer. Poor Marie held the receiver out an inch or two from her ear and talked into the speaker without listening; my mother could hear the man arguing. She went and got some tea ready, but by the time she came out from the kitchen Marie had already gone in a panic over to my grandmother, retrieved her baby and taken it into her house; then she had come back out again and gathered up her groceries and retreated back within—leaving my mother's shopping and wagon out on the sidewalk.

Marie's husband came home, gay and confident in spite of bad times. Marie was very late. He came in smiling and hung around the kitchen watching her work. In her anxiety Marie bungled everything; she spilled things, she broke a dish. He watched her, smiling. She was clumsy. And slow Marie, who had never been anxious before in her life, must have hated it; she hated him for making her anxious. He saw the groceries— why were they different? Marie said nothing. He sat and wondered. Why were they different? Marie couldn't answer; her head all hot inside, her whole brain smarting, she just couldn't seem to say anything. The Italian looked at her, baffled. He thought awhile; but the only thing he could have said more, having worked through it to himself, was "No supper ready?"

If he had only said something more, or even hit her as perhaps her father might have done, he would have made Marie happy again. But he left her anxious. How she wished she'd never heard of the A & P! All night he sat around troubled and uneasy, until finally she told him she'd gone to the A & P with "lady across the street." He said nothing. But he knew my mother and father had moved in over there.

He went around troubled for a day or two. I think probably poor Marie promised herself she wouldn't ever see my mother again. But Tuesday was bright and sunny after rain all day Sunday and Monday; her husband seemed cheered up in the morning, and then in the afternoon my mother came out with the carriage and wheeled me down the street in it. Marie watched from her sunny front windows and then looked around at her flat. After two uneasy days she was glad to leave it, and in a few minutes she was out on the street pushing her baby after my mother.

At the end of the week the house was again stocked from the A & P. We aren't Rockefellers, Marie repeated to herself; she wouldn't have called her grocer for anything. Her husband noticed but he said nothing. All weekend there must have been a general uneasiness in the house. Marie told herself she would find another grocer to deliver. But what she felt seeing her husband, whose joy and pride in himself she loved, moving about uncomfortably in their own house and what she felt when he was away and she saw my mother out with me on the sunny street were two different things. And then, she was such a placid person, she resented being troubled. Once she even caught herself asking, Why should I worry? But she pushed that away as a bad thought.

They were into November. The afternoons were cold. Marie took to having tea with my mother at the end of their walk. She would sit and listen while my mother talked on, and then all at once she would gather up her child and rush back across the street to start supper. My father was a salesman at that time, and sometimes when he couldn't sell anything he just came on home and forgot about it. Then all three would have tea over here and my father, all wound up with being home where it was warm and not out trying to sell things, would tease quiet Marie and call her "honey."

Marie said "Mister" to him. "Aw, call me Jake, honey," my father would say. Marie would get flustered—my mother had to put a stop to it.

But our kitchen was so lively on these cold afternoons Marie hated always to be watching the clock and then having to pick up Thomasina and run across the street. Her flat was dark when she got there; she had a funny feeling of bringing in something that didn't belong there. One night in particular when she couldn't seem to get rid of the feeling, sure enough her husband suddenly put down the paper he was reading after supper and sniffed. He stood up and walked around on the rug with a funny, serious look on his face. He came and stood over Marie.

"You smoke?" he asked, sniffing.

Marie couldn't even seem to say no. But when he had gone back to his chair she lowered her head and smelled herself. Smoke was in her dress, on her skin, it was in her hair; she was all covered with smoke she had carried in from my mother's kitchen. She went into the baby's room and smoke was on the baby too.

Then at last one day Marie didn't make it back across the street in time, and when she came in her husband was sitting in the dark in his work clothes thinking. And another day, a Saturday, as Marie and my mother came pulling their wagon together up our street, silly and having a good time, my father came out of our house for some reason and called down to them, and Marie laughed and cried out, "Hi, Jake!" and just at that moment her own husband, the young Italian, came walking the other way home from work, much more briskly than the two of them could pull the wagon in the silly mood they were in. He looked once across at my father and then went into the house without looking at the women.

"Must be afraid of us!" giggled my mother. Marie laughed too.

Marie admired my mother, who would chatter on, and smoke, and who always seemed ready for anything. But her admiration wasn't really anything until one afternoon, bundling up her baby, she heard an automobile horn out in the street. She took her baby out onto the porch. Standing at the curb was a little black Model A Ford coupé with my mother, one elbow on the window, at the wheel.

"What's the matter with you—you deaf? Drop Tommy over at my mother's and hop in. Let's go for a ride!"

My father's company had given him a car to drive on his sales route. Marie hurried over to my grandmother with her Thomasina. "Let's try her out!" said my mother, and off they clattered down our street, the two of them in behind the windshield, my mother jaunty at the wheel with her elbow out the window, Marie sitting high on her seat in the corner, grasping the door handle.

"Don't do that, Marie—you'll fall out. Light me a cigarette, that'll give you something to do. Where'd you like to go?"

And after a while Marie, seeing that my mother could make the car behave as satisfactorily as any other car they saw and smoke a cigarette at the same time, looked eagerly out at the houses and people they passed. They drove around town. It was a gray, cold day. My mother had to throw out her cigarette and put up the window. "Come on—where shall we go?" she asked Marie. Both women were excited. They wanted somebody to see them. "Listen," said my mother, "where's your Joe today? Let's drive over and see him work —see what they do when they get out of our sight."

Ordinarily Marie wouldn't have had the faintest idea where to find her husband working; but it happened that during the week a little, older man called 'Fonzo had come to the house after supper to tell her husband something about Myron Street for the next day. It surprised her that she listened, but she made out, without thinking much about it, that they would be on Myron Street for some time.

Myron Street is just another ordinary street like our own, lined with the same two-family houses, only longer. The pair of women drove down it slowly in their little coupé without quite knowing what they were looking for. They came to a city truck with some tools and cable on it, and a yellow sign telling them that men were working, some tools on the curb, red flags here and there and some men standing around. My mother pulled over and the two women got out. It was late in the afternoon and bitter cold on Myron Street with the wind coming steadily through. The men were filthy dirty, with their backs turned to the wind. My mother was for going up and asking for Mr. Abruzzi but the men looked just so cold, in a kind of angry mood from the cold, that she didn't. Heavy manhole covers were off all along the street. Men were in the holes, down out of sight. Squatting near the first opening was a man with a hard, red face and red hands, who every now and then passed down a wooden piece three to four feet long with couplings at each end. The women went over and peeped down the hole; the interior sides seemed made of muddy stones or bricks, and down in there a man, one knee in the wet bottom, was pushing the wooden rods one at a time into a narrow tunnel just about big enough for a rat to crawl through, which seemed to run underneath the street to the next hole. The man grunted as he poked, his breath came up inside the hole and was swept away at the top, and once he picked up a hammer and swore and pounded at the rod when it stuck. He wasn't Marie's husband.

The two women walked down with the wind to the next hole and looked in, but all they saw was a little water at the bottom showing the light of day above the mouth of the hole, and the train of rods pushing out of the little tunnel and into another opposite.

Down the third hole the young Italian was out of the wind at least, lying on his back with one of his arms entirely out of sight up the tunnel to receive the rods when they came through. To get into this position he must have had to squat down in the mucky bottom, then drop onto his side in a ball with his legs tucked up and roll over on his back to extend his legs up the wet stone sides of the hole. His heavy work shoes, resting on the side of the heel, slipped around. He was feeling the same exasperated anger as the rest of the crew. He didn't mind working hard in the cold, with a chance to get it over with soon by steady work; but the sweat of morning, when work was exhilarating, freezing in its dampness at the end of the day he stood no better than anybody else. But it was his final time to go down, and as he swung himself within, the asphalt of the road barked his hand, the cold stiff skin was broken and the hand began to bleed; but he got down anyway and reached up the tunnel grappling for the rods—which would not come. He could reach in no farther. His body wriggled as he tried.

The hole rose over him, cold and wet, with a gray sky on top. Somebody was standing there looking in. It exasperated him all the more. They wanted the rods before they even got them to him. He braced and wriggled and rolled on his bad hand; but helplessly—no rods were coming.

My mother and Marie—it was they who had appeared up above and not the man to receive the rods—stood looking down at him in the hole. He was wriggling and squirming on his back. My mother says he just looked so "comical" in there his clopping big shoes rolling around the greasy sides of the hole with no place to grab!—that the two of them had to laugh, she bursting out first and Marie following after, and they stood there above the hole laughing; and at the same time they could see his effort—how hard he was trying at something and not succeeding; and they stopped. They just stood together. Then his wriggling subsided, and as he rested he looked up at them with exasperated, fatigued eyes and his mouth loosely open, breathing hard. He saw them. He stared up at them.

And they gazed down on him, in the hole. He writhed furiously a moment; he looked as though he wanted to catapult himself out of the hole at a leap. But he was really caught fast, with his arm in the little tunnel right to the armpit. As they stared at him, fascinated somehow and without knowing what to say, he writhed once more, his big shoes slipped around and a knee came down and punched his face. My mother gave one laugh, like a high bark, in the wind. The man subsided altogether. He looked away and lay still, his eyes averted.

"Hey!" called my mother brightly, finding her tongue.

Marie knelt down on the road and bent over the manhole. But he would take no notice of them. "Oh, for cripes sake!" said my mother. The man lay with an arm missing up the tunnel, his eyes open but turned away.

"Hey, you! What's the matter with you?" cried my mother angrily. Marie seemed to forget all about my mother and leaned over the hole and said into it, "Don't cry. Don't cry." But her husband only lay there, and she started to cry herself.

My mother, running out of patience with the two of them, yanked Marie up from where she was kneeling and bustled her back to the car. She took her and put her back inside her house and left her there.

When after five days Marie hadn't appeared out of doors at all, my mother went over to see what was going on. The Italian hadn't been home since they'd left him. "He can't do that!" said my mother. She called up the hospital and the city and the police department. Marie wouldn't do anything. She wouldn't come out of her house. Then one day after Christmas a detective friend of my father's called up our house and said to my mother, "Say, Belle, you know that fella you was asking for? Well, he got a passport from the Italian consul around the first of December—in New York City." "God damn him!" said my mother. "What did he have to do that for!" "I don't know," said our detective friend. "Maybe he likes this fella Mussolini."

The Prize

R. V. CASSILL

THE FIRST PRIZE IN THE CONTEST SPONSORED BY THE GOOD-
year Tire Company early in the Depression was, I remember,
an overwhelmingly large one. It was probably $25,000; at
any rate it was a sum on that scale, one large enough to
inspire a variety of religious experience among contestants,
and the scattering of lesser prizes had been conceived with
similar grandeur. Looking back from a removal of two dec-
ades and from some comprehension of the economic and
political turns of those years I am impelled to visualize the
Goodyear Co. struggling with titanic anxiety to shake free
of the chaos that threatened organizations as well as individuals, and willy-nilly I have to admire the scale of their effort.
They knew how big a battle we were in.

And I remember with a twinge that at the time of the
contest I didn't even know there was a Depression. I knew
we had moved out of the city to live near Chesterfield—
where my father was to work in his cousin's grain elevator—
for reasons that were not very happy or decent. But it seemed
to me when I weighed everything that we had been expelled
because of something ugly or shameful that my family had
done or because of some shameful inadequacy in us into
which it was best not to inquire too far. When I learned, from
eavesdropping on adult conversation, that my father had lost
$380 in a bank failure, I was ashamed of him for not having

had more on deposit. We lost our car then, too, and I was pretty sure that this need not have happened if he had had more of the installments paid on it.

There was very little talk between my parents which named the name of Depression. Since they were both faithful Republicans who supported Hoover to the end, it might well have seemed traitorous to them to use such a term—I figured then it was like not holding your breath when something very important depended on your holding it.

A big green van took our furniture to the house near Chesterfield, and the family followed in the car borrowed from my father's cousin. We arrived on a rainy evening just before dark, and there was the van backed up to the house with the moving men carrying our familiar things into its dark interior. Our rocking chairs, the fernery, and the radio were going in where they didn't belong. The thought struck me that we were moving into a house that no one lived in. That was so strange. And whatever mystery was being enacted, I didn't want it to happen. I wanted to hold my breath long enough to keep it from happening.

Through the rainy fall of our first year in Chesterfield, while I was trying to get used to the tiny school, to the over-powering skills of the farm boys who were my new class-mates, and to the big old house we now lived in, I concentrated fiercely and stupidly on the problem of our expulsion from the city and began to see it as an omen of a world committed totally to sorrow. I learned to read the most trivial disappointments as signs that the race itself was doomed.

Walking home after school between the cornfields that bordered the road I would hear the brittle noise of rain on the cornleaves and the surliness inside me would cry back to it, "Yes, that's the way things are, all right." In the dripping of the rain from the porch roof outside my window I saw a melting of even my memories of the time when things had been fun, and whatever I found disheartening or miserable I cherished.

Separating myself more than formerly from my brothers, who were two and three years older than I, I cultivated an almost erotic pursuit of tokens of decay. In this I was aided by one of the rooms on the second floor that had served all the former tenants in lieu of an attic.

Books, old magazines, a sewing machine, dress forms, and trunks of many funny sorts were piled in this room. Probably there was some sort of stipulation in the rental agreement that we were to have only "the rest" of the house, for my brothers and I had been forbidden to play in there. But if I was quiet I could slip into it from my own room without my mother's hearing me where she worked in the downstairs kitchen.

In the room a smell of paper decomposing welcomed me and alerted my senses to a kind of dream that was detailed by the thousand articles of use and the souvenirs I stirred out of the trunks. I found an old cane with a metal bust of Lincoln for its head, the metal bearing an inscription linking it to the Republican convention of 1884. One of the trunks was half full of arrowheads and stone knives, some of them bearing paper tags that indicated they had been found in the river bluffs east of town. There was a stack of tintypes in another trunk which included pictures of the depot and the dedication of the Methodist Church. (If I wanted to I could look up and see this church through the window, sitting shabbily at the edge of a cornfield, now arched over with the elms that appeared in the tintype as twigs stuck in the loam around it. As far as one could see in such views the half-luminous white of ripe corn floored the river valley. I'd heard my father say in one of his moments of optimism that this was the richest soil on earth except for the Nile valley, and I worked on this idea too, converting it so I could gloat on these riches strung senselessly under the rains and consoling my bitterness by noting how universal the waste of things was.)

A green trunk in that room yielded a box of nickel instruments which I now realize were the old-fashioned paraphernalia of a woman's douche, and which had for me then, ignorant as I was of their function, some quality of terminated ferocity, like the arrowheads piled in the trunk bottom—no longer an arsenal, but something oddly more than a mass of junk.

When my mother found out that I had been playing in the forbidden room and asked what right I had to be there, I told her I had been reading the old magazines and books—which was not entirely untrue. I didn't tell her that I had jimmied the locks on most of the trunks or that I had read batches of the old letters I found in them. Anyway, she discovered more trespasses by finding some of the arrowheads in my treasure box that I kept in one of my drawers and by noting small bits of vandalism. I had broken the head of Lincoln from the cane and for no good reason (except to mock at earthly vanity) had rubbed its nose off on the sharp edge of a lock.

She came after me with some determination then. She really insisted on an explanation of why I liked that room well enough to play there so much. "With that dirty old stuff," she said.

"Like with the arrowheads," I told her solemnly, "it would help me remember there used to be Indians right around here in the olden times."

"Ah," she said, mildly impressed and placated. "I see. With them you could sort of pretend that the Indians were still alive and more real. I see. Then I suppose you could understand your history better and the way things are by using that Republican cane."

She looked at me sharply. "Why did you break the cane then?"

"I don't know."

"You shouldn't have done that to Lincoln. He was such a great man," she said with a faraway look that seemed to suggest he should have been my father. "It was awfully wrong to break him up like that, but I'm glad if otherwise you learned anything."

My pretended agreement with her was a great fraud because her optimistic interpretation was so exactly wrong in its tendency. It had not been any sense of life in these trinkets that excited me. As they went through my hands I had exulted in them because they were evidence that so many who had been alive were dead and gone.

II

Far as she was from appreciating the content of my play in the closed room, my mother must have worried about it and found it inadequate, as she found so many things in our life at Chesterfield inadequate.

She had a bundle of grievances, and I think sometimes that what carried us through that winter and marked all of us forever with a special stamp was her refusal to admit the slipping downward that obviously accompanied our move to the little town. She had to take it but she wouldn't have it. She was going to lure me out of the old storeroom into some healthy activity whatever the cost, and for a while there was talk of getting me a subscription to the *Youth's Companion* even if that meant showing favoritism to me, since nothing comparable could be afforded "just then" for the older boys.

With the same frustrated force she approached the problem of utilities. There was no electricity in Chesterfield then and no bathroom in our house. From our arrival on she set the resources of her anguish to work on getting us a Delco light plant and plumbing, though with all her emotional heave in this direction and her heckling of my father she never worked out a practical plan by which we might expect to have them. She merely made us all hate fetching water from the pump more than we might have otherwise and made us all feel we would go stone blind from reading by a kerosene lamp.

What she couldn't hold onto with a full grasp she meant to cling to, as long as necessary, with her fingernails, and the obvious pity of this was that she could get her nails into nothing solid except us.

It was her passion's refusal to admit that things had changed which swept us into the Goodyear contest with such velocity and finally made it intolerable not to win.

Winter had come by the time the contest was announced. The evening we heard of it my brother George and I were in the kitchen helping my mother with the dishes while my father and older brother listened to the radio in the dining room.

"Hear that?" my mother cried out all at once. I thought she'd at least heard a car stopping at our front gate. But she motioned us to be still and we got most of the announcement, not quite all. She marched into the dining room and demanded that my father explain the details she had missed.

"I wasn't entirely listening," he said guiltily, sleepily. "Just enjoying what they had to say."

"Enjoying? I don't see what there is to *enjoy* when he's talking about a contest. You ought to be listening attentively, or I don't know what's the point of listening at all."

"I know," he agreed. "I'll tell you what. It sounded like someone was going to get a patch of money, all right. I did hear them say there was a first prize of twenty-five thousand dollars. Moreover there's a whole kaboodle of little prizes."

"Little?" my mother wailed indignantly. "Why . . . why . . . *Little!* I heard myself that there were thousand dollar prizes."

"I meant even smaller ones. Little dee-rigibles and things."

"A thousand dollars," my mother mourned his unconcern for this. "That's not so much it would wear our brains out figuring what to do with it. I wish you'd listen at the end of the program and be sure to get the details down on a piece of paper. No. You call me in if there's any more going to be said about it."

66

He took off his glasses and polished them slowly. "You sit down here and listen, Mother. The boys and I can finish the dishes. You're quicker at these things than I am."

"All I asked was for you to call me. Can't you even do that?" my mother demanded. "I know you're tired from your work and I wouldn't ask any more of you today."

Since he was in our big rocker and sitting as relaxed as a man can get and since it obviously wouldn't be much trouble for him to listen to the announcement, he naturally took her comment as sarcasm. So, when she'd gone back to her work, he tuned in another program.

"You hear that, Mama?" George said, wiping away like a good fellow at the dishes. "He's turned it off."

"Well," she said, "he's tired and cranky. He worked awfully hard today. You know it's always hard work at the elevator."

Then my father appeared at the kitchen door. In those days he was still wearing some of his old business suits to work and they always had grain dust in their fibers no matter how well he brushed them when he came home. The whitish dust in his clothes gave him an air of being faded like a picture from which some of the ink has been rubbed. He made a curious gesture, half in anger, half in appeasement, like a doubter crossing himself.

"You know what these darn contests are, Sally," he pleaded. "They don't mean anyone any good. They're only done to advertise the product."

"We'll talk about it later," my mother said. This was recognized by all as a threat.

"Did you personally ever know anyone who had won his postage back in a contest like that?"

"We'll not discuss it until the boys are asleep," she warned him. I think he began making up his mind to submit right then. I saw him swallow and then nod reassurance to himself that it might not be all as bad as he feared it could be.

From that first evening on, for weeks, our family had the contest like a vocation or a disease. Of course it was easy enough for my mother to find out the details of competition once she had made up our minds, and by the end of the week she and each of us boys were working on our individual lists of words that could be made from the letters comprised in the name GOODYEAR TIRE AND RUBBER COMPANY. That was the task of the contest.

You can see that the first words come easily: dog, god, ray, rite, and so on. It is when these are all put down that the game becomes tantalizing and demoralizing. Then the tongue tries nonsense syllables and combinations in the hope that some lightly hidden word will fall out to be added to the list. And that makes quite a noise in the house.

Once at supper I began mumbling to myself and my father, driven beyond exasperation, slammed down his waterglass and howled, "Groggy wayorv, boogly, boogly, woogly, arf." Then he glared around the table with the tears of the rejected squeezing angrily out of the corners of his eyes.

"Not at the table," my mother cautioned me. She turned to my father. "I don't know why you're so set against what the boys are ambitious enough to try to do. I should think you might better want to help them."

"I won't. Great Jesus, I won't," he said helplessly. "What in His name would I be helping them to do? Lose their minds and jabber like apes?"

"They've been working with our dictionary, and I don't know that *that's* bad for their education," my mother said. "The contest gives them something to look forward to." She satisfied herself with such explanations, and for my part I was thinking self-righteously that my father, in his outburst, had used *f*'s and *v*'s which, of course, were not permissible under the laws of the game.

According to my mother's first, rather easy-going plan, each of us was to work exclusively on his own list and even keep it partly secret from the others so there would be a sort of intra-family contest as well as the larger one. We worked from the dictionary by turns. It seemed to me sometimes when

I was blundering unsystematically through it, dreaming by lamplight, that each of us might win a prize that suited his own intelligence and deserts. My mother would probably get one of the thousand dollar prizes. Dave and George might or might not get something. Maybe one of them would get a fifty dollar prize, since they were older than I. For myself, I thought and felt that I should win one of the chrome-plated models of the dirigible *Akron*, the lowest prize offered. I think probably a hundred of these models were being given away. I remember telling my mother that I didn't think I was good enough to win more than a model, but that this suited me because I would rather have it than money anyhow. Altogether I managed to make this model into an image of what I was worth and of what the world would pay me for being what I was.

"You have to work hard if that's the prize you want," my mother warned. "Don't forget there'll be people from all over the country trying to win, just like you are."

When the deadline for submitting entries was approaching, my mother decided that we needed a larger dictionary to work from and that we should borrow one from the school. The question of who should borrow it became major. One of us boys should ask our teacher, she thought, but we all balked at this as being too embarrassing. The other boys got away with this argument, but I was caught—perhaps because I had done more excited talking about the contest than they.

"There's nothing wicked about borrowing a dictionary," my mother bullied me. "We're not doing something dishonest. We're working as hard as we know how to earn something, and if more people would do that I expect our country would be better off. Just explain to your teacher . . ."

This is odd, but maybe if I had believed that we were in the contest for the sake of competition I wouldn't have minded explaining to my teacher why I wanted the dictionary. Caught as I was in the dream of certainly winning a thousand dollars and a dirigible, I couldn't face it. It seemed to me like putting on airs to go to my teacher and admit the glory my family was headed for.

So my mother finally borrowed it. I remember her coming in through the snowy yard, a little after I had come home from school, with the big dictionary wrapped in a shawl to protect it from the mist in the air. Her face before she saw me was set with a harsh intensity, as of someone who has refused humiliation by sheer refusal to recognize it. Seeing me, she smiled and said, "Look. I borrowed it from your teacher after you'd left. She was good about lending it. Now you see that she would have lent it to you if you'd only asked her. Don't you see?"

"But what's she going to think of us?" After all, it was I who had to go to school the next day and possibly face my teacher's amusement, envy, or scorn.

"I didn't tell her what we were using it for," my mother said with a sly grimace that she meant to be comforting. "I fibbed to her, so don't you worry."

When I thought this over I announced that I didn't want to do the contest any more. My mother flung her arms around me and pressed my face very hard against her side. "Of course you do," she said. "We've worked so doggone hard this far that I'm convinced we're going to win. Maybe not the grand prize, but something. There's no reason why you can't win that dirigible if you want it. Don't you see that yet?" She frightened me with her determination, and even that was a lesser thing than the sheer giant onrush of the contest, beginning to reveal its true scope.

In the last week before the deadline—and this must have been in late January, at about the time of the thaws when the three of us boys would have liked to be playing outside—my mother bore down on us all. Some one of us had to be at the dictionary all the time. There wasn't any more talk of the contest's being educational or fun. It was work and we had to work hard enough to win. We combined our lists now, at least to the extent that our inefficient systems permitted. We had begun without much system at all and, except for my mother's, our penmanship was terrible. So, whether a word discovered in the dictionary at this late date or on someone else's list could legitimately be added to ours was a matter none of us could be quite sure of. Certainly each of us had duplications in his list, and none of us ever had quite the same total as any of the others though we tried to balance them for a while. Very late my mother tried to get us to alphabetize our lists, but this only got us in more tangles.

On the last afternoon Dave went to the post office immediately after school with his list and George's—that was a nervous precaution, since they had to be postmarked that day and some act of God might demolish the post office or block the road to it if we waited until too late.

On the other two lists at my mother's insistence we were adding all kinds of the nonsense combinations which earlier had been only a means of helping us find pure words. Some of these, she said, we might have missed in the dictionary, and it was the responsibility of the judges to decide if they were eligible or not. "*Reay*," she said. "That could be a girl's name. Put it down, anyway. *Burrec*. That sounds like a kind of donkey, I guess. *Yarg*. I don't see why that shouldn't be a word if there's a word *yard*. One doesn't sound like it meant any more than the other one, does it?"

She had the clock sitting on the table where we worked—the post office closed at six—and I knew that now nothing but time running out would stop her. My father came into this intensity and stood behind us, watching us without saying anything. Pretty soon my mother spoke over her shoulder to him. "If you're not going to help, go somewhere else. Go start the fire in the kitchen. I'll get supper as soon as we're finished."

"I won't," he said; and then after a long deliberation, "God damn the Goodyear Tire and Rubber Corporation."

"Company," I said.

"I suppose you mean God damn me," my mother said.

"I don't," he said. "I mean . . ."

"Shoo. Go on. I can't think while you're staring at me."

He went into the bedroom and after some banging of dresser drawers returned to throw an envelope and two ten dollar bills on the list of words she was working on. "There," he said in a tone that was dignified only by its slightness. "There's some money and my insurance policy. I'm leaving."

"Ha," my mother said.

"You've turned the boys against me and driven them half crazy with this contest. I warned you not to do it."

"Then leave," my mother said. "*Dooger.*"

After he was gone she kept muttering more and more absurd combinations of syllables. Her face flamed, and I could see a vein in her temple bulge with her effort, but she was not writing down any more of her inventions.

She looked up at George long enough to say, "Follow him and see where he goes." Then she glanced hard at the clock and told me to get my coat and rubbers and be ready to run for the post office. "We can't be late," she said. "You can run part of the way or go Scout's pace. You know how to do that."

With an attempt to cheer me, she said, "You and I have more words than the others now."

But, giving a last look at the physical ugliness of my list, I said I wished there were time to copy at least this afternoon's work.

"Maybe if they can't quite make out some of them that will be a good thing," she said craftily. Her imagination apparently had strained to cover every accident of incompetence, weakness, taste, or unfairness on the part of the unknown judges, and it seemed to me that she had intended that each of our lists be somehow corrupt to fit the imagined corruptness of the major human types.

As I was going out with the big manila envelopes containing our two lists, George arrived back to report that my father had started west across the cornfield, had cut back within about a quarter of a mile, climbed the fence into the road, and was right now hiding inside a culvert about two hundred yards from the house.

"Ha," my mother said. Her voice crackled with unhappy triumph. "I supposed he wouldn't go far. He'll get hungry after a little while and come in. Now *run*," she commanded me. "Be sure you make it to the post office."

The culvert where my father was hiding was an obstacle in the road now. I could hardly bring myself to walk over him like that, but I knew I had to hurry. The road was wet. Now at sundown it was beginning to freeze and I could feel the delicate ice crunch under every step with a beautiful sound and sensation of touch. The rosy light over the cornfield, reflected in a thousand puddles islanded in the loam, seemed to me too strongly and unhappily beautiful for me to stand, and it occurred to me that I might die right then, being so divided by feelings I had never encountered before, wakening to my first realization that living was something that one must choose against hardship to do.

At the culvert I left the road, knelt in the water of the ditch bottom and looked in at my father. He was sitting right in the middle of the concrete tube. In the dim light I could only see his silhouette and the glitter of reflected light in his eyes. I am sure he saw me, but neither of us spoke.

Then I ran for the post office. I think I ran all the way, because I got there in plenty of time to put the envelopes in the letter box. Walking home afterward I felt how my knees were wet from where I had knelt in the ditch.

III

Of course none of us won anything from the Goodyear Co. In about a month the winners of prizes over a thousand dollars were announced. First prize went to someone who had over three times as many words in his list as there had been in the largest of ours.

"Three times," my mother said. "That's a lie. That can't be. They must have used foreign words like French and German, Spanish and all. And they *said* that was against the rules."

My father commented, "Maybe one of you will win a littler prize. They're going to announce more next week." After the bad day of the mailing of the lists he had relaxed, had been permitted to relax, and by this time was even displaying a mild hope that something might come from all that bother.

But then the last of the cash prizes was announced and there was nothing left to wait for except the names of the winners of the model dirigibles.

"If the others didn't get any money I'm not going to win the dirigible," I said to my father, answering one of his soft optimisms aggressively.

"You don't know," he said. "I wouldn't wonder that your list would be just right for a smaller prize. You know, it might be like having the right tool for the right job."

"Yes, the right tool," my mother said. "We should have had a typewriter. I can understand that now that it's too late. Even if they didn't specify that you had to use a typewriter."

"You told me that my words they couldn't read might be a good thing," I said.

"Well, on that . . ." Her lips worked carefully while she made up her mind how to answer me. "Yes, that may be so. Don't give up hope."

From this last posture she established against defeat and from my own premonitory sense of loss I began to develop the notion that they were all demanding that I win, and I added the strain of what I considered their expectations to my own. Partly for them, partly for myself I strained all the tricks of emotional force—on the order of holding my breath, crossing my fingers, figuratively—to affect what the announcer was going to say when he came to read the last list of winners. I accepted in a subterranean agreement, that I owed it to the family to win, for if I won that would help make up for my father's hiding in the culvert, my mother's fibbing to the teacher, and our general humiliation in prostrating ourselves before a big company that had so far ignored us.

Each name on that list of winners should have been mine and none was. I wanted to howl when the reading was over, and yet I felt that, having lost, I didn't even have the right to do that. For the first time it came to me with undeniable force that beyond our mere failure to win we had lost something that had been put at stake.

After the trial of listening my father sighed tranquilly and said it appeared to him that these last prizes had been awarded on a geographical basis. "Did you notice how there was hardly ever more than two from any state except New York? You heard how this gentleman up in Red Oak got one. Well sir, that's enough for this part of the world, they likely figured. You can't tell me these contests aren't rigged some way. Naturally you didn't have much of a chance when they did things like that," he told me.

He put out his hand to rumple my hair or pat my cheek, but I flung myself beyond his reach, behaving spitefully to cover my sense of worthlessness.

"There, there, feller," he said. "There, there now."

"I worked hard," I screeched. "I had as good a list as anybody's."

"Sure you did. I'd lay money you had a better one than some of those as got the money."

I said, "I'm going to kill someone for this."

His head jerked as though I had burned him. Then his eyes searched beyond me for my mother and he seemed to be crawling humbly and with awkward slowness to some complicity with her. I saw this happen, but I chose then not to understand it. I thought I understood how every man's hand was against me. From then on.

"Everything comes to he who waits," my father said.

"You'll see that, because that's the way things are. You remember when we came here we had such a hard job getting along without electricity and didn't think we'd ever have any?"

He paused for me to answer and I wouldn't.

"Now they're putting a line in," he said in a hearty tone, as though I might care about *that*. "They're going to bring the wire down from Parsons to Chesterfield and we'll have it out here, too. Then we can get us an electric radio and a lot of things, maybe. They were unloading poles on the other side of Chesterfield today."

"Somebody else got my dirigible," I whined.

"It would only be a little tin thing. You couldn't have any play out of it. Your mother and I thought that when the roads dry up we'd get you boys a bicycle. Wouldn't you rather have that?"

I set up an awful racket, protesting that I didn't want a bicycle or anything else but the dirigible. To which my father replied that I only wanted what I couldn't have and if that was the way of it he couldn't help me. I believed this dictum, if nothing else he said. I heard it wailing through my dreams that night like a sentence of wrath to come. Maybe on purpose I dreamed toward morning that all my family was dead. My father was dead in the culvert where he had hidden, and I was kicking up wet grass from the ditch to cover him in.

At school time I pretended to be sick so I could stay home. As a matter of fact I sulked with such ugliness that my mother suggested on her own part that I should go play in the store room, where I had not been for some months. I considered her recommendation and even walked upstairs to glance in at my former retreat. The dead room would not receive me, and the chilly smell of it really nauseated me. Losing the contest had even cut me off from that.

Everything was so senseless I might as well go do it like the rest until I was dead. I would just be too smart to hope for anything again, that was all.

But they tricked me back from that state too. I came from school one evening about a month later to find my model of the dirigible *Akron* on the dining room table. There was a mass of wrapping paper broken back from around it and some excelsior that smelled like newly sawed lumber.

It was a very shiny model, though somewhat smaller and harsher looking than I had imagined it would be. It said GOODYEAR TIRE AND RUBBER CO. on the side.

"What's it for?" I yelled to my mother as she came in from the kitchen to see how I was going to receive it. "Did one of us win after all?"

She smiled her best. "Sure," she said. "Isn't it a pretty thing, now? I guess this proves that if you do your level best and really want something you'll get it, doesn't it?"

I might have accepted the moral of her comment without argument, for moral significances seemed to me at that point lighter than air, but the practical accounting worried me. "How come they didn't read our name on the radio if we won?"

"We didn't *exactly* win," my mother said. "Your father and I thought that you'd worked so hard that you *were* a winner and deserved a prize. We wrote to that man in Red Oak and bought it from him."

"Oh," I said. Why did they do that to me on top of all the rest. I couldn't stand it and I said, "Thanks a lot."

Just before suppertime my brother Dave caught me outside in the yard and said, "All right you big jackass, you got your dee-ridge-able. Aren't you proud of it?"

"You leave me alone."

"I'm not going to leave you alone. They had to pay fifteen bucks for it and now maybe we can't have a bicycle this summer."

"I never asked them to do it."

"Oh no," he said. "Oh no, you didn't. Just whining like a pup that you didn't get anything in this contest. Did any of the rest of us get anything?"

"I didn't want them to buy it. I didn't know they'd be such big fools."

"I don't know," he said despairingly. "I guess they were because you're such a big fool. Listen, if you don't make them think that you're real glad to get it I'll kill you."

It was not—or not exactly—his threat that weighed on me. When he left me I had nothing to face except—as on the evening of my father's flight—the width of sundown and spring air, empty but nonetheless resonant with things learned and half-learned, again multiplying by its beauty and silence the real threat of death if I turned away from my family and their organized ways of stinging me. I could see then that I would have to keep pretending the dirigible was fine, and I have never learned what else I could have said.

A Spot in History

JAMES B. HALL

BECAUSE THERE COULD BE NO JUMP TODAY AND BECAUSE
Carney had stood withdrawn in the middle of his ropes and
canvas and produced the keys from the secret pocket of the
trousers, and because the buckskin pike outside Wilmington
exploded from the dark tree tunnel and opened out again into
the purple of back country towards the low hills and river,
and because their house was the kind where gravel tracks end
abruptly inside a barn yard, he tracked the boy.

You will come to the end of gravel tracks, the deputy
had said. And here, past the cattle's tongue-swept block of
salt, and up the flagstone walk with the iron handrails on
each side leading to the back stoop, the door. Behind him the
monkey cage. Not a cage, but an exerciser built of odd lengths
of pipe upward and extended until the whole jungle was
passages to walk through, grasping first one pipe then pulling
along to another. The pipe collected for quarters and dimes
from every junk yard in the county, wired together sometimes, but now crazy and rusting against the sky. One piece of
bed quilt stuffed in a windowpane fell out, so he knocked
again and louder to bring down the roof of the house upon
the inside footsteps.

Even before the father opened the back door he knew
the kitchen: split wood and the metallic smell of nutmeg.
Past the vacant wood box and into the front room where all

blinds except one were down, and in the diagonal of that light the man had been rocking alone. Now the father sat down again, heavily, and rocked in his grinding country way. Nor heard the flight of starlings alight and yammer and fly away again from the pine trees outside: that tied-up bundle of clothes in the front seat of the sheriff's car beside the deputy . . . yesterday.

". . . From that carnival," the father said, "I presume."

"Condolences, yes." He knew this was good because Carney would be pleased. This was Building For the Future, this was getting Public Relations.

"And was there, I presume?"

"Oh, I'm always there. But yesterday I was watching with the others. I'm only a mechanic, you might say."

Before the father could lead up to the details—those things more than the deputy would say since elections were yet two years away—the woman called. From behind which of the seven paneled, black-oak living room doors that opened off his room, he could not tell for the cry was the wife when the motordrome rider went over the top of his track and the brace cable across the top of the pit cut through a new six-ply tire and snipped his head off, then the wife had cried out and fainted except not this loud.

The farmer led the way through one of the dark oak doors and down a corridor into her own wing of the farmhouse. At first he could not see her nor the effects. But her wicker chair squeaked; she was in the darkest corner of her parlor, bundled in the smell of mould.

There was no canopy over the chair now, but she was up-reared in the darkness. The wicker squealed when she twisted the big muscles in her shoulders but her legs remained without motion, blanketed in the darkness.

"Oh, *you* saw him. I can *tell*," she said. "Oh, blood of that boy be forever on your head. Amen."

The farmer did not ignore her but he hesitated, then stood aside.

Her voice spread out across the room between them like some purple foot-thick layer of consuming noise.

". . . The first *fruit* of my *toil! Comfort of my age,* (pause) *and* the sole survivor of *my own* family. A noble line, Sirs (she rocked).

". . . Remembering everything: all the Kings of England, in their order. *Bonaparte's Retreat,* and all the choruses. And most of *Hiawatha:* Oh, by the shores of Gitchaguma!"

"A fine boy," the mechanic said, "but . . ."

The farmer stepped forward into the dead air between them towards the watch pocket, where the check was, in the corner.

She smashed his toes with the root end of her sassafras cane. The father stepped back nimbly. He had been watching that stick. The mechanic thought, He's going to kill her, now, but the farmer stepped back just beyond the end of that sassafras root and watched patiently.

She pointed the stick as a hunter might point a shotgun into a brush pile. She nodded along the stick towards the mechanic. He walked on tiptoe towards the corner of the room as though the stretched-out trousers and the jacket might twitch. The boy's check in the watch pocket felt like warm folded money in his hand.

In his own front room the father rocked again in his stifling air. The mechanic saw the farmer clearly, now that the last ray of light was going. He saw the boy's other things would remain in the attic upstairs: the half-kept baby book with the curious, full-blown angel pictures on the paper cover; the clipping of the newspaper which said about the baptism; the three Tom Swift books (and *The Airship,* and *The Searchlight,* and *The Giant Cannon*); the one scuffed-out baby shoe; and yet, underneath all those attic feather beds the boy's grandfather's flint lock rifle, black and rusted and forgotten. But still loaded. He saw the farmer would sell out and move to town, there to sit out his time on a bench in front of some grocery store that gave credit to country people. But now he was only shut-mouthed and alone.

The scream and rattle-wing of the starlings in the pine tree made almost night fall. Outside, the monkey cage was reared against the sundown. He could imagine the boy leading the woman through the maze of pipes, trying to help her get the use of her legs again, since she had not walked since the birth of the boy, but no: not even a strap attached to each leg would bring the feet forward except at a drag, while she held on to the pipes.

The barnyard was behind and he drove back through the tunnel of the trees towards their fairgrounds. Carney's Packard was a big dog running the highway, belly low and growling at the slabs of concrete.

Inside the fairgrounds and inside the race track the braced ladders of the high diver platform seemed to spear the moon. He sensed but could not yet see the humped trailers and the curved humped tents anchored by ropes and by the Model-T Ford axles sledged into the hardpan. He squirmed on the automobile seat for a minute so that the eyes could begin to see in all this darkness. He heard a foraging breeze make each brace and guy wire creak as though—secretly and all through the night—this carnival was growing, reaching out slowly, capturing more and more of this wet undefended grass. Across the race track in the regular fairgrounds he heard the hysteria of a small refrigerator motor, racing as though to cool all of that August night.

There was the smell of dew on the greasy rags near the motordrome where the riders of motorcycles chased each other inside the wooden silo ten times each day. At the far end of the area was the jumper's cannon towards the sky; the net was low in the darkness in front of the grandstand. He labored to put up that net but from one hundred and eighty feet in the air Consolo always said it looked like a bull's eye. No bigger. Consolo, the jumper when the show ran like some fatal clockwork, when offers came in to take the show all over the world, when the audience never stomped or called, More! More! By listening under the sputter of the mantles of a gasoline lantern he knew Consolo had come from the high trapeze, a catcher in Italy. The whole family had been with a show for years, then Consolo dropped his brother over the middle ring in Milan and after that he left the family act and came to America to Ringlings. Finally Carney got him. Consolo always worked in a white helmet and when the talker stopped Consolo climbed the ladder to the cannon, to hesitate, to look. He would stare at the crowd and he would pull them down inside with him. Then the pulled lanyard and he would be above the trees and rising. At the top of his jump he could jack knife, and fall into that spread-out net. Everybody thought that day he was faking, but when they carried him to his trailer and said get up now, he did not move. Above the net, just as he bounced once into the air, after he landed, he died. Then Carney telephoned ahead to this Wilmington to insert the ad.

One mauve light bulb where Carney kept the other blue suit, where he made deals with county commissioners, where he withdrew to lie down at night; parked around this one mauve light the parts truck and the power plant and the cook shack. All that canvas bulged forward regularly to breathe. Inside the hot innermost room of Carney's trailer he saw the upended orange crate and the bottle of beer and the cot. Carney raised from the pillow and scooted back over the cot until he was resting his back against the bulkhead of the trailer. The undershirt was the color of the hardpan dust that had blown across all those summer fairgrounds. From under the pillow his teeth: Carney plopped them in his mouth, like eating a doughnut.

The mechanic laid the Packard keys on the orange crate beside the bottle of beer; inside the breast pocket of his tan mechanic's shirt he could feel the warmth of the boy's folded-up check.

"I wasn't out in your car with any girl, you know. I been out making you some money."

Carney only let his eyes drop wider open. The arms were rolls of white unbaked dough, but the hands and the wrists and the neck were like hardpan. The dark wrists and hands dropped to the floor of the trailer, and the cot began to shake. Then Carney rolled his head and face forward out of the shadows of the corner of the truck. There were two big fish-bowl tears, from his laughter. The cot sagged and the uneasy trailer yawed. Oh Jesus! Jesus—awhoo! Awhooo! Then he stopped.

"You're smart, sonny," he said across the orange crate. "You are intelligent!" (Ohhh Awhoooop!—the split-throat nicker of an old stallion.)

"No! No! Sonny," and then Carney was in control of his wobbling body.

"Well," the mechanic said. "I thought you would be glad to buy it back for fifty."

"Twenty years. That's what the sheriff told me, if it's endorsed by forgery. Because when I saw you leave I just picked up at-ere telephone to ask The Law. Yop."

"But you would have paid out $100 to his parents."

"Yop, *if* it was ever found—not burned or buried with his clothes—and *if* they asked, and *if* it was a real check and not just a carney check see? No, all of Greater Shows is right in that black safe. And I'm Mr. Cash. That little old black safe don't need to be opened tonight for you."

He turned to go out of the trailer, ashamed and feeling like one of the briar-hopper hicks that tromped each day into the grandstand or tromped ten times a day up the motor-drome ramp. After all the years of talking like Carney and acting like Carney, and almost thinking like Carney himself ("I'm sorry, I made a mistake") and forgetting gradually his old home, the farmhouse outside Cincinnati. Carney let him get to the door.

—Hold on! It's just that you try so hard sometimes. Now

8 4

stand here beside this cot, Sonny Boy—I say—and answer up:

—You put out your forty dollars and a big story for a check that was only paper but looked all right, forty dollars?

—That's right, Carney.

—Here is your forty dollars, forty dollars (takes this in plain view).

—Hold on! You used my Packard automobile. Hand over twenty dollars car rent, I say, twenty dollars.

—That's right, Carney.

—Insurance and for gas: twenty dollars more, I say, now you give me.

—That's surely right, Carney (hands over in plain view).

—Hold on! You were working overtime. So I give you back twenty dollars for you to go *out* there. AND twenty dollars more to return from the country (passes the last twenty, in plain view).

—Hold on! . . . I say, hold on!

"Oh Jesus, we ought to be in Vaudeville: Carney and Stupid: or, The Big Exchange."

Now in the middle of the nets and canvas he was even, except for the time on the road, but that time he knew was all Carney's anyway. Except that he was a hick, now, after all these years of forgetting. Carney had tossed him back his forty dollars for being a joke, just to show that Carney was like a father to him. Except now he did not want to be a mechanic any more. He wondered exactly about that black safe in the corner, in the shadows. But he still liked Carney and he still wanted to be kidded a little once in a while, as long as it was all right.

"Sit down, my boy," Carney said, "now we got a deal. You are in it. Everyone is in it."

Carney leaned back on the bulkhead of the truck, relaxed now. His belly curved outward and upward like a side of a tent.

"The show business. Now you wouldn't get this but that high diver is *passé*. The bucking Ford is out, too."

The mechanic sat down on the orange crate and listened.

"So I sell out. Everything. I cut everyone's wages (except yours, Sonny). I buy up lots of scrap machine guns and tanks and we will mock-up a portable pillbox. At night we will sell them a battle: Ypres, or Stalingrad, or Berlin. (Around New York City we can even mock-up a Buchenwald.) While the flame throwers warm up the Greys slip out of the pillbox. Then a frontal assault with the Blues firing everything. We blow up the pillbox, but *they* don't know all the Greys are out, but will hope so. Then our commentator says neither the Ins nor the Outs were hurt. Now you wouldn't get that, Son, but *that's* show business.

"And Herbert, you lead the Blues. You carry the satchel charge. You'll give them a full-fledged battle, for one dollar."

Carney lay back on the cot and placed the big cigar delicately between his dry lips. In the heat of the summer night it was a long time ago when he joined Carney, just outside Cincinnati. It was in a country filling station where his father had put him to work when his father left town again. Carney had walked into that filling station and had asked to have a quick Packard wash. Now during the winters he watched all the equipment while Carney went to Miami to play the horses. Now he was someone Carney could pat on the shoulder if the business was good. And though he acted like Carney and though he wore black glasses even at dawn, he was not comfortable with the jumper's cannon because he would not jump, and yet it seemed the thing he should do. Perhaps he couldn't bear to find out if Carney would quickly fire him, if he ever got hurt. Or perhaps it was the thought of a crowd . . .

And yet the day before yesterday was noon and county fair, when the band music of sunshine made the Ferris wheel turn white-spoke and seat rocking above treetops. Noon, and the merry-go-round turns faster to calliope for the carved horses are riderless and all the children are eating from a family basket and white napkins under the maple trees. And

8 6

on the track at noon the bay horse pulls a yellow sulky plop-plop-plop half around the track and then back, warming up. And at noon, the fair is chromium and bright windshields in the sun and the high diver tests his brace wires and the turn-buckles and sights his ladders for alignment, for he will climb slowly by band music to the platform and will sight down at the shallow tank framed in the triangle of light formed by the edge of the platform and his heels. He will sight stead-ily through that small triangle. When the drums roll he will hold his breath. Then tip the head back slowly. The shoulders overbalance into space. And down.

The mechanic was beside the cannon when he saw the boy coming through the glitter of driven steel stakes and the reflection of the sun on strings of light bulbs. The me-chanic did not look up from the windlass crank for he was drawing back the acutator spring. Nor did he take off the black glasses, but he knew who was standing beside the wind-lass crank listening to the *creak, creak, creak.*

"You the crew chief?"

"Yop. And I'll bet you got a message from Garcia."

The boy was really twenty-three. His farm shoes were cov-ered with the dust of a gravel-track road. His necktie was the Christmas four-in-hand, pre-tied at some factory, and the mechanic knew it fastened around the neck with elastic and a black hook.

". . . I have already signed my release."

So he explained again to the boy exactly how to stand on the two sponge-rubber pads inside the barrel. He would call the break . . . "and don't relax the knees—"

"Don't you think the place to begin is jumper, sort of at the bottom? Build a better mousetrap my mother says."

He did not take off the dark glasses but he paused and looked as sharply as he could into the boy's red face. He realized and rejected that he had also thought—when he left the filling station—that *he'd* be a partner someday.

". . . So I'm going to jump. He says show him I'm a real live wire and bring 'em in and produce."

He saw the wispy wet red hair fall below the rim of Consolo's old helmet. Carney had tossed this goof Consolo's old white jacket. The sleeves were too long but Carney said you will have to wear it anyway.

"I'm going to do it. I knew it when mother read the ad. It's in the blood."

He wondered if this one would really jump. He had seen these country boys before: they came walking down the road, maybe limping from the time they were first sent out to work with a scythe when they cut themselves badly on the foot, but they came to join up as though there were nothing left now among the gravel tracks and cattle salt in the sand-briar hills that always stretch out towards the rivers from such a place as Wilmington.

"So I've got to jump," the boy kept saying. "I'm tired of sleeping in the loft and reading my correspondence lessons on steam fitting. And I'm tired of being badgered about making a man of myself."

He stared at the country boy through his dark glasses but now he could feel neither one way nor the other. By the noise he knew this was a Friday crowd. They were stamping the grandstand to pieces with their big shoes. They were people just off work from up-the-alley garages and from the gun factory and from the County Highway Department. And, of course, the farmers. They were laughing at the bucking Ford. Then the high diver, and this jump.

The boy was concealed behind the cannon. He stepped out, erect when the talker called his last act of the day and of the season in Wilmington. When they saw him step out they laughed just a little. Because of the ad they knew he was not the regular jumper and besides he kept hauling at the chin strap of the helmet. The lower part of the costume was plainly overalls. They thought he must be a local boy but none of them had seen him before; he had simply read the ad and had come out of some of the last of the back country, to get ahead. Or perhaps there was someone who said he was from beyond Villar's Chapel, and that they knew his Daddy. Then the band played "On the Mall."

"Hold your knees stiff. I won't trip it until you are ready." This with the lips averted from the crowd. He saw the sweat was running from under the white helmet. He saw the boy look up the long slender ladder as though the rim of the sheet-metal cannon was one mile away.

When the crowd saw the boy put the first foot on that ladder they settled down. They had not expected this one to take even that first step. He climbed rapidly, almost at a run. Quickly he threw one leg over the rim of the gun—slid down, out of sight.

The amplifier made a faint hum from the trees where the loud speakers were concealed:

. . . And now, he is in position—

The white helmet popped up over the rim. "I want to see the net. I can't see my net from inside."

He climbed up the ladder towards the helmet. The boy was holding on to the rim, his knuckles on the edge like a row of small white eggs.

"What's the trouble? Didn't we set it up to suit you?"

"Lower it. I want it lowered. I'll give them a real show."

"Consolo used this setting. You will land pretty close."

"Lower it. Or I won't jump."

Carney was below on the ground, looking up. "What's the matter? That guy yellow?"

"No, I'm not," said the helmet. "Lower it down."

"OK," said Carney. "Give 'im a couple of notches."

The mechanic climbed back down the ladder and turned the set wheel on the quadrant. He lowered the aim perhaps one inch.

. . . And now the management has approved that aim. Imagine yourself, my friends, inside that gun.

8 9

The helmet popped up again over the edge.

The crowd laughed and booed. The timing was all wrong. Carney would really be sore now. But he couldn't fire the guy either.

"I can't see my net. I want it away down. Or I won't jump."

"Fellow, you better go along with . . ."

"Like he says," Carney called up to the rim, "he's the jumper. You ain't. *You* could have that job you know."

The mechanic climbed back down. The helmet disappeared. The voice from inside the gun kept calling, More! More! until the cannon was aimed flat at the net. The crowd stopped yelling and stomping. Some thought the guy was yellow. Some wished now they had not come at all. Then all of them were very quiet like children. Noiseless, now, except for the *plop-plop-plop* of the bay horse warming up on the race track, and the small refrigerator motor in the fair grounds still running.

Inside the cannon the echoes, *In the blood. The blood.* Inside there was the perfect hoop of daylight at the muzzle and the flat rope net set squarely in front of the eyes.

Carney fifty yards away on the steps of his trailer, standing in the sun. Carney nodded. "Yes."

He pulled the lanyard. Hard. The helmet hit the ground in front of the net. The white jacket disappeared into the wires and the glittering metal stakes. The whole net was a cloud of dust. That was all he could see because of the legs of the policeman running.

That had been Friday and the next day he had borrowed the Packard to drive through that dark tunnel of trees toward the back country where he'd found the fierce woman and the old man who—though he never knew it—was already broken by the depression, and the depression before that. Now he sat on the orange crate in Carney's trailer listening, watching Carney reach under the cot for another bottle of beer, seeing him drink half and seeing him pass over the last of the warm beer to his own receiving hand. This was the end of the season. Soon they would strike the canvas, then he and Carney would wait alone for another spring, in some other county. Then there would be the Blues and the Greys and the satchel charge. Just at dawn there was a knock on the door.

Carney rolled quickly out of the cot with that lithe movement that an old bareback rider never loses, even in flesh. He put on his black glasses and walked to the front of his trailer.

"Who in the hell are you?" Carney said, as though he had run into a tax collector.

Outside in front of the trailer this kid was wearing silk coveralls, with white patches of parachute silk stitched all over the legs and shoulders. This kid was short and blocky like Consolo except he was blond and not sullen. He couldn't stand still. He kept hopping round like a little boxer warming up. He carried a staff made out of a piece of old airplane tubing. Inside his bundle, fastened on the end of the tubing, you knew there was another pair of tight-rolled blue-silk coveralls.

"Saw your ad," he laughed. "You should know I won't jump for cash. Only on percentage. I got an angle."

"You don't say," Carney said. "Say, where did you come from?"

"I'm from the Big City, man. I just rolled off a freight train and hit a-running."

The kid did two back flips and then dusted off his hands. Then the kid reached down at the sides of his coveralls and pulled up folds of cloth that were sewn into the seam. He stretched his hands above his head. The web of cloth was reinforced with metal ribbing. They were outstretched, taut, white canvas wings.

"Y'see, I drift right over their heads and then break into the net. It's fancy."

"Nope," Carney said and the mechanic was glad. "I got other plans. This jumping is finished."

"Suit yourself," the kid said and he picked up his staff made out of old airplane tubing. "See you in the money. At the Garden. Ha!"

Carney hesitated only a second. Then Carney ran off after him. He called the kid back. This kid was the type. He would pull them all in. Carney put his hand on the kid's shoulder as they walked along . . . very friendly, patting him (*pat, pat, pat*).

The kid broke for the cannon and began to crank the windlass. He did not have to be shown. Carney trotted across the area to the grandstand like a young stallion. No one else was awake. Carney was a one-man private audience. Already he was gaping at the cannon. His neck was red as any country hick's. He was waiting to see his new little jumper.

Therefore the mechanic went back into Carney's room and stole the car keys out of the secret pocket of the other trousers. He sneaked the Packard around behind the trailer. That little black safe wasn't so heavy as he had always thought. It fitted very nice into the trunk of Carney's own automobile. He drove, with no dust, out of the quarter stretch and out of the fair grounds.

Now someplace down the buckskin pike take the drill and a tire tool and open up that safe. Reach inside and feel that slick greasy money, the season's take that no horse in Miami will ever get. Then drive and drive and drive: spend all that money at the towns along the way, driving always south. For behind, there is only that expense of innocence and ahead there is sunlight and the great winking hotels where salt waves lick all night at the white, slumbering beach.

And he thinks: they will catch me. Perhaps in the Poinsettia Grille, in Georgia. But Carney is a goner, so are the motor-drome riders and the high diver, and especially that new blond jumper from the big city who would change everything. That big door will slam.

Yet pictures will be in every paper, and even perhaps in the books on history. And what else does a man want?

A Season of Mists

CARL HARTMAN

SOMEHOW A MOUSE HAS FOUND ITS WAY INSIDE THE GUITAR and now it is busy running around in there, in the dark, scratching at the thin wood and bumping up against braces and struts; it starts, stops, starts again; it must learn the way before it can run smoothly round the curving sides. The guitar is lying flat on the sofa and is a big, beautiful one; it is dustless, gleaming, its dark finish polished to a great deep richness so it shines there like an exhibit against the dull old cushions. The mouse has been inside for some time now, making his frantic little noises.

This is Hy's guitar and he would not like to have a mouse in it; it cost over four hundred dollars (not counting the case), and no mouse belongs in such an instrument. An instrument like that is more than a possession, and must be guarded carefully. But Hy himself is fast asleep in his easy chair across the room, and has not yet heard the sounds of the mouse.

He is an old man, a Negro, a musician. On the wall behind him hangs a framed photograph of himself seated and holding this guitar of the sofa; he is playing the guitar but looking outward, smiling, and the picture seems to make the guitar bigger even than it is so that he is all angles sticking out from behind it. The photograph is a commercial one and bears the printed legend: Hy Walters plays a *Beldin*, the World's Finest Instrument.

Too well printed ever to fade, that picture has been hanging for more than twenty years against this flower-papered apartment wall. Beneath it, in sleep, Hy's face is not smiling but is nevertheless the face of the picture. There is the same careful regularity of features, a little lined now but still as remarkably neat as if he had somehow been allowed to select and arrange them himself, to suit some plan of his own making. All about him there is an idea of almost painful neatness, and even in sleep, relaxed, his body slumped any-which-way in the chair and his hands dangling long and bony over the chair-arms, there is nothing in his awkwardness to deny the idea of neatness. His clothes were good clothes and are clean, pressed, cared for well enough to have changed shape along with him; his shoes have a barbershop shine, his hair is newly trimmed, his hands are scrubbed and the fingernails are carefully manicured—all the personal attentions given to extreme, as if learned and disciplined out of some half-ridiculous but serious vanity once designed to guard against the threat of a sudden return to vague times of Memphis back streets and ignorant parentage. Yet these things are not mere manner or front, they are stronger than that. They have a curious insistence which seems present even in the picture, to be undeniable and demanding attention even there where they exist almost defiantly, undimmed in the glare of photographer's lights or by twenty-odd years behind glass; and now even sleep does not change them.

But the sounds of the mouse have been part of a long dream already forgotten and have finally wakened him. He stirs in the chair, listening. The mouse has learned its way around the obstructions and its flight has become very rapid. Its noises come out of the soundbox amplified into the sounds of many mice fighting or playing in a nearby room, boldly it seems to Hy, flaunting their boldness like a threat.

He gets up slowly, unfolding himself cautiously against the sharp pain any sudden movement now brings but standing at last with an old-man kind of proud tightness that makes him seem taller than he really is. He is ready, waiting; but for a little while he does not move. There is a feeling in the room just then, something with which motion is out of place; summer is coming; sleepiness and the real warmth of afternoon sunlight have begun a calmness that strangely might almost make this room seem free, to be part of the outside and the real bigness of things, where a man belongs. He has after all come a long way to this room, this comfortable if lonesome apartment, this particular moment of awakening. He has made a mark in the world, and if the world has forgotten, that is no one's fault; it is only that he has outlived his part in it. And in this moment contentment itself seems almost possible, even fixed this way between the stiffness of apartment house walls: the three friendless floors below and the six above and all the inflexible patterns will soften somehow, will bend and permit it.

But the mouse is running furiously. Ugly and insulting, its noises recall a need for action, for some token response. Hy does move; takes a step forward, toward the sofa; then stops again to listen and watch the sunlight catch on the six guitar strings, this light too coming to him amplified, silver flashes reflected in a rhythm almost regular as the shifting weight of the mouse rocks the guitar gently from side to side. He is curious because the rhythm of the flashes seems not quite to fit the rhythm of the sounds; the sounds come steadily but the flashes pulse a little unevenly, with a briefest hesitation just before each alternate beat like the sweep of a lighthouse beam viewed from far away.

Then suddenly he is fully awake and angry and he shouts at the mouse:

"Get out of my guitar! You goddamn mouse!"

He uses his voice well, neatly as his clothes, and the sound-box will have amplified it going in. The sounds of the mouse stop instantly.

"You got no right in there," Hy says to it. "No right whatsoever."

He goes to the guitar, picks it up, shakes it; the mouse thumps around inside but will not fall out through either of the F-holes. Hy shakes harder; he is infuriated and can picture the mouse making droppings in there, dirtying the clean wood, perhaps spoiling the tone of the guitar. But he calms himself and sits down with the guitar across his knees, to think of the proper thing to do.

"Now if it was a round-hole guitar," he says, "then I could take off the strings and shake you out easy."

It's foolishness like this that a man shouldn't have to deal with. The mouse is scratching again, and someone is knocking on the door.

"Come in," Hy says.

It is Jonah Scott, who used to play bass and once played in a band with Hy. Jonah has immense hands, fingers that could go around a bass neck twice. But he played the bass like a machine, like a bass-playing machine that didn't have any real feeling in it anywhere, so it is just as well he has almost quit.

"I'm a son of a bitch, Hy," Jonah says. "What the hell you doing?"

That is what he always says.

"Nothing," Hy says.

"That is sure one beautiful box," Jonah says. "I reckon that's about the finest box ever made. Why you got it upside down that way there?"

"Well," Hy says, "a mouse got in it."

Jonah laughs. He is always laughing at things not funny.

"Cheese," Jonah says. "Put some cheese around and the mouse will come out to get it. Use to have all kinds mice in my fiddle all the time down at the old Roxy, you ever play there? Full of mice, the old Roxy, place gone now, burned down. I ever tell you how I played there once with Jimmie when he had that big band? I tell you, Hy, now that Jimmie—"

"I know," Hy says. "I know all those stories pretty well."

"Well," Jonah says.

Now his feelings are hurt and he will say exactly what Hy does not want him to say. There is something in Jonah that makes him mean, a mean old man.

"Whyn't you sell that there box anyhow, Hy?" Jonah says. "What you need it for these days now?"

Of course Hy will not answer this; it is a question nobody ought to ask. It's true enough that anything he plays now could be played on any old cheap guitar, any piece of junk like the one he started with, and it is true also that he needs the money. But how could a man just turn around and sell something like this, an instrument built to his order (and he went to the factory and watched them make it, finish it and line it and then alter it this little way and that, all for him, to be just like he had always thought a guitar really should be to get the most out of it), something he has been halfway over the world with—how can a man think about a thing like that? When his wife Ellie Senior died and he needed money for a good funeral, then he had tried to think about it; but in the end the whole idea had just seemed too big to get hold of. It was true even then that his fingers were getting stiff and he was about through as far as the better spots went and he knew it and everybody knew it; but instead of selling the guitar he had borrowed money from their daughter Ellie Junior, a disgraceful thing for a man to do. But Ellie Junior had just laughed when he said that and had not been angry with him at all.

"Listen," Jonah is saying. "This afternoon now is the time we got to go down to the union and see if they got anything for us. It's better to go down there than to just call them up."

"You go," Hy says. "They never got anything for me these days."

"You want too much," Jonah says. "You're too particular, you got to realize things just ain't what they used to be."

The only way to get rid of Jonah is to go with him. But for Hy it will be a waste of time. It always is, week after week.

They ride downtown on the streetcar, swaying together on the last, straight seat, Jonah's cracked old shoes beating some kind of awkward time on the dirty floor.

"In the old days," Jonah says, "we could ride in a taxi if we wanted."

Next he will talk about how the union ought to have a pension system. He goes on and on like that, forever.

At the proper street they get off and enter a large building. They rise in an elevator to the eighth floor, where a green neon sign says A.F. of M. In a cold marble hall men are seated behind grilled windows, as in a bank.

"Scott and Walters," Jonah says at the first window. "What you got for us?"

"Hello there," the man says.

He is bald and white and he smiles like a friend at Hy. He is looking through lists, studying cards in a file.

Hy is suddenly very tired, aching all over from the streetcar ride, so he sits down on a bench by the wall.

"Well," the man says, "there might be something this week. Not much for guitar men though."

Which is only what Hy expects and just as well at that. The last affair he played, about a year ago, he doesn't like to think about. It was with an old friend, a bandleader who had just come through town and asked for Hy; he wanted Hy to play "Miserlou" and "Swingin' Down the Lane" and "Tea for Two" and had expected to hear Hy play those songs the way he used to but Hy couldn't even imitate the things he had been famous for not so long ago. His fingers remembered exactly what they were supposed to do but he couldn't make them move right at all; once that night he had got his hand clamped around the neck of the guitar in a big six-string chord and his hand had tightened up some way so he couldn't get it loose for a while and he sat there like a fool for six or eight bars not able to play anything except that wrong chord. The musicians had all been nice about everything and that was somehow worse than if they had been mad at him.

But neither will he take Jonah's kind of job, where it doesn't matter what you play.

"I got to have some work," Jonah says. "What the hell we pay dues for?"

"I'm looking," the man says. "Keep your pants on."

"Thanks anyhow," Hy says to the man; and to Jonah he says: "I got to go do some things right away."

And he ducks out of the door before Jonah can say much.

The elevator takes him smoothly down to the street.

He could cry in the stillness, waiting for the streetcar; but if there is no use in hope there is none in bitterness either. It is hard to force a choice between impotence and frustration, to translate a headful of memories into action; still, this day like any other, this coming night and some unknown number of future days and nights, all alike, must be focused on something; a man must live somewhere.

So when he gets home he will eat his supper and put on his tux and put the guitar in its case and start out. On the first-floor landing, just as always, Mrs. Parman will be waiting for him, leaning against the railing with her arms folded over her chest, and just as always she will say to him:

"Well, Mr. Walters, off to work now?"

And just as always he will say:

"Evening, Mrs. Parman, anything for money you know!"

Then a small laugh, old as the joke. She is the janitor's wife and means nothing to him except that she is always there to see him go. He is not even certain whether she knows the truth of the matter: that he will walk slowly twice around the block, carrying the guitar to a job which does not exist and then returning by the back stairs to sit in his apartment with the lights off, playing the radio softly until it is time to go to bed.

It is a foolish deceit, of course, and he hardly even fools himself.

Now he climbs on the streetcar and sits alone, jouncing patiently a hundred and thirty-two blocks through the twilight, back to his own street.

He has eaten his supper and washed the dishes and put on his tux and is tying his maroon bow tie when there is a knock on the door; and when he opens it he finds Ellie Junior and a strange white woman standing in the hallway.

"Hi," Ellie says. "This is Mrs. Krause."

"How do you do," Hy says and they all come in and sit down. He looks at Ellie and is glad to see her. She is a fine girl and she is twenty-two years old and really beautiful, lovely in a way Ellie Senior never was, perhaps because she did not come up from Memphis where she worked in a laundry once, so many years ago; and if she lacks some of the calmness her mother had, well, she has a livelier kind of dignity he is not sure he does not like better. Things will be different with her; she knows how to wear good clothes and she has a fine job singing with a downtown band and soon she will be more famous than he ever was, what with the radio and everything.

"You look fine, Ellie," he says and they are smiling at each other.

She is kind too in the way she gives him money, just putting it in the bank so he can almost forget he hasn't made it himself. Times change fast, all right; first she is a baby cutting teeth, a child, and then she is a grown woman and sometimes now he hears her singing on the radio at night in a way he doesn't much like, doesn't quite understand, though it seems to be the thing these days. But Ellie is serious about her music and there is nothing cheap about her and she will do all right at whatever she does.

"Well," Ellie says. "What's new?"

"I've got a mouse in my guitar," Hy says and Ellie laughs and it seems to him that perhaps there is something funny about it after all.

"It ran around and scratched at things," he says, "but now it doesn't any more and I'm afraid it may be dead in there. I'm pretty worried about it."

"Dear me," Mrs. Krause says. "They do get into everything, don't they?"

Hy picks the guitar up, holding it with professional carelessness by its neck.

"My what a *lovely* instrument!" Mrs. Krause says.

"It's almost as old as I am," Ellie says, "but I believe it's in better condition."

Hy shakes the guitar so they can hear that the mouse is still inside. When he stops shaking, the mouse scratches again and runs a little.

"Still alive," Hy says.

"Perhaps it will come out," Ellie says. "It can't be very happy in there."

"You might try some cheese," Mrs. Krause says. "It might come out to eat some cheese."

"That's a good suggestion," Hy says.

"Mrs. Krause works at the hospital over on Bond Street," Ellie says. "She has charge of recreation for the whole hospital."

"Is that right?" Hy says, looking at Mrs. Krause.

She is a big woman with a quick smile, friendly looking.

"It's an awful big hospital," Ellie says.

"Yes," Hy says.

"Mrs. Krause is looking for somebody to teach people over there how to play the guitar and maybe the piano a little," Ellie says quickly.

"Patients that are convalescing," Mrs. Krause says. "They get well faster if they have something to do, you know, and we thought it would be a good idea to get somebody to teach them to play a few instruments, musical instruments, and then when they all sing together, you know how folks do, they can accompany themselves. Miss Walters was kind enough to suggest that you might be able to help us out."

"It was just a suggestion," Ellie says.

"No," Hy says.

"Oh, please do!" Mrs. Krause says. "Of course it wouldn't pay much at first and we'd have to see how it worked out, but then we'd be so happy to have a man like you, a musician with real experience I mean, and we have a little money to spend for instruments because you might not want just any-body to play your own guitar, would you? But at first—"

"No," Hy says. "No, not ever."

He must have startled them somehow because they are both looking at him like he was crazy; but Ellie Junior won't look at him in the eyes. Ellie Senior never would do a thing like this to him. *She* died right there in the bedroom, from some disease he cannot even remember the name of; she lay right there under that comforter she made herself before they were married and that she washed regularly every four months since so it is all faded and thin now, lying there right this minute on the bed. Ellie Junior will never wash anybody's old comforter a couple of hundred times and then just die under it like that; what does she know about it all? She and that woman don't know what it is to have to look through your mind over and over for some memory fresh enough to be worth thinking about again. And if they just feel sorry for him the hell with them, they don't understand anything about it.

"It wouldn't be worth putting on my hat and coat to go do a thing like that," he says carefully to Mrs. Krause.

"Now Mr. Walters," Mrs. Krause says, jumping up and talking right into his face. "Everybody has to do some things in this world they don't want to do and I can't see why . . . well, it just seemed to me that lots of aged persons, you know, persons that—"

Hy is about to shout at her but Ellie has her hand on his arm and is telling him something.

"I brought you a present, Poppa," she says. "That's really why we came. It's a record I found yesterday."

Then she has it going on the machine and Hy is smiling and hugging Ellie.

"By God," he says, "listen to that."

It is an old record but in good shape and he is playing on it with a band a million people used to know just by its theme-song or the way it sounded, and the record is out of print now and he had forgotten all about it. The band is dated but there is a long guitar solo with the band quiet in the background and the guitar cuts through big and clear as it is supposed to. Hy has not thought of this solo for years but now he remembers what he is going to play before the record plays it.

"By God," he says again when it is over. "Why, they told me I was crazy to play a guitar in those days. Can you imagine that?"

The record is his, to keep and play whenever he wants to. Ellie is smiling at him from the sofa and she has one hand resting on the side of the guitar. He cannot understand why he never thought to look for a copy of the record himself.

"Banjos were the thing in those days," he says to Mrs. Krause. "They told me I was crazy to play a guitar in those days. But what banjo would do anything like that for you? I can still remember making this old record. Why, that was right after I got this guitar the Beldin people made for me like I told them, and the next day after that, no, it was the next week, that picture there was taken of me to put in some magazine. We made this record late at night in a studio in New York and there was a big fat man, see, that cut the records and he has a dial, see, a round dial with a needle in it to tell him how loud the sound is going into the machine and he sits up on a big high stool and waves at you while you play, to play softer or louder, you know. I never paid him much mind but I guess he done a pretty good job at that. That night we made this one record over six times to get it right and I didn't get home until past daylight, either."

"That's a hard kind of life," Mrs. Krause says.

Then Ellie is kissing him goodnight, she has to go to work, and telling him not to worry about anything and Mrs. Krause is shaking hands with him but not saying anything and then they are gone.

To sit by the machine and hear himself like someone else playing and to see that he is good makes a kind of feeling that almost embarrasses him. But the solo is really fine, anybody could tell that. There is a long run that starts up high with harmonics at the thirteenth fret and goes down in triplets incredibly fast, almost blended together but each note played so cleanly that it will stand out by itself if you listen for it. Some stand out more than others and these accents make a kind of pattern like that of the tune but different in a strange and exciting way and Hy is actually trembling to think that he did this, he made this thing which seems to have some meaning; and at the end of the run, just before the band comes back in, there is right there forever on the record a sound someone in the band makes, a kind of sigh, a sound of respect for what has happened. Hy can remember as if it were yesterday that sound as it was there in the studio, though the person who made it, the face and name, is gone.

There is something about that sound, that scene, that he should have understood better while it was really happening; and with it there are others. All those days vanished: the thousands, millions of notes played in those years and all left somewhere behind; the hundreds of miles ridden in buses and cars and trains with other men from town to town and city to city, the cities and towns themselves identified only by their railroad stations or bus terminals, known only through a second-rate hotel and a bar and the place of work; and drinks drunk in countless rooms and on endless similar bandstands with forgotten people now dead or gone away some-where, numberless faces pressing in and all confused now with fragments of strange melodies never heard before and never played since: everything is there, cut mysteriously into the grooves of a black disc like this one so long ago by a perspiring fat man whose name was never known but who has now become so terribly important. The taste and feel and smell, the warmth and the coldness of it all is right here on this flat piece of shellac in his living room.

And he can see now that all his life, through all the noise and confusion of all the jobs and all his working toward one thing or another, through all of that the one thing he really wanted (more than he has wanted not just to be a Negro or not just to be Hy Walters or even not just to be a man) was to make something beautiful, something more than you could call by any of the names he knew; and he has done so; it is here, proof is here in his possession and at any hour of the day or night, in any weather or mood, he can send it flooding out from the cloth-covered speaker.

There is a difference between having a notion of your achievement stuck in your head along with a lot of other things, and having it out where you can see what it is.

He goes to bed still smiling, first carefully closing the cover of the record player, with the record still inside.

He wakes before dawn, in the complete silence of the house.

At once he thinks of the record and remembers every-thing about it. It is as if he has been thinking about it all this time, instead of just sleeping.

It is there, of course, and safe. Perhaps he will spend the afternoon having some extra copies made from this one; then if one should get broken there will always be another.

This idea delights him and he turns on the light and gets up and puts on his bathrobe.

But along with the pleasant feeling there is another that has been pushing up through his mind, and by the time he has the bathrobe on it is there looking at him.

It's quite simple: some day, somewhere in the world, someone will put the needle down on the last copy of that record and nothing will come out but scratches. The music will be gone; all that smooth run that is worth a lifetime of work and care will be one grinding roar, a noise some child might make with a toy. The music is his and he is strong because no one else can ever play it quite the same way; but that is also its weakness.

Well, he has known that all along; and now in the living room he has suddenly to fight to keep from laughing out loud.

He has opened the top of the record player and is looking at the record. There it is; and suddenly Hy is full of hate, not for the record and not for himself, not at anything special but only because he or anybody else should need this proof not just of the value of his life but of the simple fact that his life has been lived at all. It is an old anger but he knows now what it means and what he must do.

He takes the record from the player and breaks it neatly in half against the side of the table and drops each half into the trashbasket.

He pulls one end of the sofa away from the wall and then has the guitar by its neck, holding it like an axe and swinging it up and then down hard so that its body smashes and splinters and breaks into pieces against the back of the sofa. The strings make a wild twang as the guitar hits, but the sound of that strange open chord, the top E just a little flat, is lost immediately in the sounds of breaking as the guitar's back snaps. He lets go of the neck. It has snapped too and is dangling there like a broken toy from the strings.

The mouse is not dead at all but lands running, noiseless on the carpet, gone quickly out of sight.

The room has changed now and until he becomes used to

what has happened he cannot stand to be in it. Therefore he gets his coat and hat and puts on his shoes and socks and trousers and goes down the dark hall and down the stairs and out into the street. Morning has barely begun; through the gauzy light the pavements and parked cars and the houses and their steps and windows and front doors and doorbells and numbers and mailboxes are growing quickly from shapes to things, and he is looking at them all.

When it is time to go back he will do so, and he will eat breakfast and then get the pliers, the side-cutters, out of the guitar case, and with them he will cut the six silver strings through their middles where they are hanging, E-B-G-D-A-E, draped over the sofa back. At the instant of each wire's parting the teeth of the pliers will meet with a tiny click he will feel along with pain through the bones of his hand. There will be six neat cuts to sever the neck from the body, and then he will gather up the pieces and carry them to the incinerator and drop them in, perhaps waiting just a moment to hear them hit bottom four floors below.

Summer: Sun and Shade

DAVID CLAY JENKINS

I REMEMBER MR. BREWSTER FOR THE WAY HE KEPT TAKING his handkerchief out of one of the back pockets of his trousers and wiping his brow with it. His face would contort in a grimace at the heat of the Alabama summer day, he would wipe the sweat-drenched handkerchief across his forehead, and the little beads of perspiration would disappear for a moment and then reëmerge in exactly the same places as before. He was a rather stout man who in hot weather was usually dressed in baggy striped seersucker trousers and a white shirt, open at the collar, with its sleeves cut off unevenly above his elbows. Early in the summer, his neck and arms had that virgin whiteness that usually characterizes the skin of indoor workers. In cool weather, he wore his collar buttoned up and a necktie and coat, but in summer he had to do everything he could to keep cool as he walked from door to door with his breadbasket on his arm, selling his wife's homemade bread.

In Alabama, when the sun really begins its blast, the grass withers on the front lawns and the yards become baked clay. The tall, dry, spiky Johnson grass in the vacant lots rustles when a torrid wind happens to blow, and it is as treacherous to walk through as it would be to walk barefoot through broken glass. When school closed, in May, I looked forward to vacation, but by July the summer, for a nine- or ten-year-old, became little more than monotony, loneliness, and heat.

For relief from the heat, at least, I would ride around on my bicycle. I would cruise about on the level stretches of road or up and down the easier slopes. There was one hill, which we called the Big Hill, that was entirely too much to ride up in ninety-five-degrees-in-the-shade weather. Approaching it down the Little Hill, I would coast, exerting as little energy as possible, and then, at the foot of the Big Hill, give four or five hard shoves on the pedals before I got off. And then I would see Mr. Brewster with his breadbasket on his arm and his handkerchief in his hand, standing in the shade of a big, languishing cottonwood halfway up the steep slope, wiping his brow. Then he would put his handkerchief back in his pocket and heave a sigh, almost audible from where I watched, before he trudged the rest of the way up the hill with the slow, faltering strides that were characteristic of him. They were not sure steps, but they were determined ones, and he assisted his legs by leaning into the slope and pushing down on his thighs, first with one hand and then with the other, until he reached the level ground at the top of the hill.

When he had walked out of sight, I would turn back and pedal away to some flat stretch of road where there were trees. Sometimes I would get off my bike and lie down in the shade. Our mongrel shepherd dog liked to dig out a hole in the ground and lie in it. I learned, by trying it, that this was a good idea, and though I was usually found out afterward, the new-turned earth was a solution to the heat and worth the scolding I knew I would get.

Every weekday morning at about eleven, Mr. Brewster came around to our house with the bread. It never struck me as odd that a breadman should wear pince-nez. I remember how Mr. Brewster's hung on a black ribbon around his neck and how they would fall off his nose while he was talking to my mother in the shade of our long front porch. I would be sitting in the swing that hung on chains from the ceiling across one end of the porch, and I would sit there watching them and listening to their conversation. Mr. Brewster was a chatty man. Because of the way he talked, I put him in a different class from the friendly milkman, who came at six o'clock in the morning. The milkman would give me rides in his electric wagon if I was up early enough, and let me have pieces of the spongy white ice around the milk bottles. Mr. Brewster spoke more like my father than the milkman did, and he had a certain bearing about him, a dignity, that I did not associate with the other callers—the grocery boys, and the good-natured Negroes who came on the garbage trucks, making a great clatter and commotion, with their guttural yells of "Way-hi-hup!" as the men on the ground heaved our trash cans up to the one who stood on top of the heap of garbage in the truck. Mr. Brewster was out of their class, and not so much a friend of mine as the others were. I watched him more with curiosity than with any real interest or liking. He was respectable, and seemed to me to belong to that world of my mother's that I hardly understood—a wireless world of gossip with the neighbors, emotional radio programs advertising soaps in the mornings, long telephone conversations in the afternoon, and visits with Mrs. Pyron, the new next-door neighbor, who would come in with a bit of pudding or ice cream she didn't want to have to put back into the icebox, and stay on for an hour's conversation.

One hot Saturday, Mr. Brewster came up on the porch where I sat swinging backward and forward in the swing. Our dog lay as flat on the cool tile floor as he could get; he never barked at callers in the summer. In cool weather, he did, but in summer the dog just lay on the porch in a mess of his own shed hairs, hugging the cool tile and panting.

"Hello, there, Robert," Mr. Brewster said cheerily. "How are you today, young man? Is your mother in?" He could see her behind the screen door, sitting in the living room, in the breeze of an electric fan, eating ice cream and talking with Mrs. Pyron.

"It was just more than I could bear," my mother was saying. "So I told Norman that if he didn't use more discretion in the groceries he sent us, and if there was any more lettuce like that last head, he could just look for me to be stepping into the car and driving down to that new supermarket."

"It's really *so* much easier," Mrs. Pyron said.

"But of course there's that long drive, and it's just so hot I can hardly move these days," my mother said.

"You'd think we'd all just *burn* out," Mrs. Pyron said, scraping her plate.

"This is the smoothest cream I've ever tasted," my mother said. "It's so much better than what you get at the store. Is this the recipe you brought from Albertville?"

"I made it from Creamola. Just thought I'd try it, I've heard so much about it on the radio."

"Law, the things they have on the radio nowadays!" my mother said. "But it does help to hear about something new like this. It was so nice of you to bring it."

Mr. Brewster was polite; he had waited on the porch all this time. Finally, he said to me, "Would you mind calling her, young man?"

"The recipe said it would be smoother and richer if you added the white of one egg," Mrs. Pyron went on, "but I just added two yolks and—"

"Mother!" I called.

"I never did hold with following directions to the T myself," my mother said. "Virginia says that it just amazes her the way I add a pinch of this and—"

"Motherr-rr!"

"*Just a minute!*" Mother said, annoyed at my interruption. "And a pinch of that, and it all comes out all right. Virginia says it's just amazing. Whenever she tries, it all comes out a *horrible* mess."

I could hear, on the porch, the rocking of the swing and the panting of the dog, while the sounds of the fan and the conversation in the living room droned on. Mr. Brewster took the handkerchief from his back trouser pocket and put down the wicker basket that had hung on his arm. It sat there on the floor, and the loaves of his wife's homemade bread, still warm from the oven and neatly wrapped in tissue paper, wafted their yeasty odor across to me on the hot, heavy air. He held the handkerchief by two corners and waved it delicately backward and forward in the breeze, and then he folded it neatly into a square and with one stroke wiped the beaded perspiration from his brow. The beads popped out again at once, looking rather like the moisture on a cool pitcher of water.

"As far as I'm concerned," my mother said to Mrs. Pyron, "you can just throw half these recipe books right out of the window, for all the good—"

"*Motherr-rr!*" I called, louder this time.

"What is it now?" she answered, at last. "Can't you find some way to amuse yourself without pestering me?"

"It's Mr. Brewster with the bread," I said.

"Oh, it's *you*, Mr. Brewster," my mother said, coming to the door. "Will you ever forgive me for keeping you so long out there in the heat? I didn't think it was you. These children nowadays—they can't seem to amuse themselves unless it's going to Wild West pictures or spending money some way. *You* know how it is."

"Oh, yes, yes," he agreed knowingly. The handkerchief was back in his pocket, the breadbasket on his arm again. "These loaves are fresh from the oven, Mrs. Black—as good and tasty as homemade bread *can* be. I won't be by tomorrow, since it's Sunday. Would you like to have two loaves, or only one?"

"Why, two of course, Mr. Brewster," my mother said. "Now, you come in here in the cool a moment and rest a bit. Mrs. Pyron and I are only talking. We had some ice cream, and it's just the letter for a day like this. We haven't got any more, but I'll bet a glass of good, cold ice water would suit you. You look just *burnt* out, Mr. Brewster."

"Well, it's a temptation, I'll admit," he said. The draft of

112

the electric fan in the living room caught one of the rayon curtains and it billowed against the screen, reminding me of a face pressed against a windowpane.

I saw the knees of Mr. Brewster's seersucker trousers sag for an instant, and then they straightened and he went in through the screen door. It closed with a bang of the catch that held it tight and kept out the flies that buzzed spasmodically against the outside of the screen or flung themselves down helplessly on the tiles.

"Why, Mr. Brewster, you've gone dead pale!" I heard my mother say.

"Oh, it's nothing, really," he said. "This weather is just getting me down a little." I couldn't see him now, but I could hear the faltering scrape of a chair and could imagine my mother's stoop of concern as she stared at Mr. Brewster and saw how strange he looked.

"Now, you just sit here in front of the fan and I'll be back in a minute with that ice water," she said. The heavy fan groaned and vibrated as she shifted its direction and turned it up to full speed before going into the kitchen. Now it stirred the curtains at more frequent intervals.

"Whew! This climate's not for me!" Mr. Brewster said to Mrs. Pyron. And I knew from memory what would follow, he had said it so many times to my mother. "Now, you take the woods around Bangor, Maine," he said, "or a little lake island in Denmark this time of year. Cool breezes at night, just warm enough to be pleasant in the day, then cool again at three or four o'clock. A man can sleep in a climate like that, with night breezes cool enough for a blanket."

I heard my mother come back with the ice water. There was a silence while Mr. Brewster took a deep drink. "There, that's better," he said. "Nothing nicer than a cool glass of ice water on a day like this."

"You've been in all those places, Mr. Brewster?" Mrs. Pyron asked.

"He's been in those and more," my mother said, "with

Madame Brewster." The *coup de grâce*.

"Oh, yes, Mrs. Brewster and I have seen a bit of the world in our time," Mr. Brewster agreed. "And we hope to see more. There's nothing like travel for a liberal education, I say. Now, you take these young snips graduating every day, almost, from college. And they think they are *educated*. My advice to them is to get out and see the world. Why, when I was in Germany in 1924, I learned more in two days than I'd learned in all my four years at college put together. I learned that money is a funny thing. It comes and it goes. Gold is the shakiest commodity on the market."

I sat on the porch listening, but not very attentively. I can't be sure now why this story of adventure and travel should have interested my mother so much and yet have left me as unmoved as the usual Sunday-school lesson. Perhaps it was because Mr. Brewster struck me as being so much less romantic than the milkman, the Negroes on the garbage truck, and the delivery boys, riding their bikes no-hands. But to my mother Mr. Brewster was a thirsty traveller from far-off places, adding a vivid moment of actual adventure and color to her radio-soap-opera world. Like most children, I had a throbbing world of my own alive in my imagination. How weak and watered the breadman showed up there!

Mr. Brewster had been a chemist for one of the leading manufacturing firms in town, and during his spare hours had done some research of his own in his laboratory at the factory. There, as luck would have it, he had found a new way to improve the gasoline used in automobiles. He had sold the secret of his process to one of the big oil companies and in a few months' time had become rich. As a young man, he had always wanted to travel and see the world. So with his new wealth he had seen America first, as a not so young man, and then he had gone to Europe. There he had met and married his wife, in a little Alsatian village, and they had travelled farther. During the European inflation, they had bought a new Mercedes. There seemed to be no end to their money; the more they spent, the more there was. Once, in Germany, when they went out shopping, they had changed three hundred dollars into marks and had had to hire a boy to follow after them with the money in a little cart.

And that was the story, as far as Mr. Brewster would tell it. "Bang it comes! Bang it goes!" was all he would say about what happened next. The rest was a familiar story in our neighborhood. The two had come back to live with Mr. Brewster's mother shortly before their child was born. Mr. Brewster had thought it would be good to stay at home for a while; it would be a rest—and a change, too—to be back in the fold. And then it had happened—bang it goes! From the first, Mr. Brewster had kept his money in a small neighborhood bank; the manager and the president were friends of his, and they had seen him through all the exchanges and letters of credit for his foreign travels. Then, in the boom, these friends of Mr. Brewster's had speculated with their depositors' money, had been caught at it and put in jail. The bank had collapsed; there was nothing left in Mr. Brewster's account. He had gone back to his company and asked for his old job, but they had told him he was no longer young enough, in fact, it had been made plain that they considered him an old man. He had set up a small laboratory at home and had puttered about there, hoping to make another lucky discovery, but nothing had come of it. The only thing he tried that seemed to bring in any money was the bread route. His Alsatian wife knew how to make good bread. The profits were small, but they helped out, and Mr. Brewster could still work in the laboratory at night.

The electric fan rattled on, the dog panted, and a single fly ticked and buzzed against the screen door.

"Well, I'd better be getting along," Mr. Brewster said, and his chair scraped.

"Mrs. Pyron, I want you to try some of this bread," my

mother said. "You never got *Continental* bread like this in Albertville."

"I don't know, now," Mrs. Pyron said. "Mr. Pyron likes his bread in a sealed wrapper, and already sliced."

"But it's as delicious as cake," my mother said.

"Well . . ." Mrs. Pyron's voice sounded uncertain.

"You might try it for a week or two," my mother said. "And then if you didn't like it—"

"Well, I'll try it for a week, then," Mrs. Pyron said.

"Now, I don't want you to feel *obliged*," Mr. Brewster said, obviously embarrassed.

"I *don't*," Mrs. Pyron said. "You know it *must* be good bread if *I* buy it."

"Of course it's good," my mother said, dismissing the bread. "You take a deep breath of this cool air before you go out in that blazing sun, Mr. Brewster. Are you sure you're all right—no more of those dizzy spells?"

"I'm quite all right, Mrs. Black, quite all right," he said.

"Well, we want you to stop in again," my mother said. "I enjoy talking with you so much. Be careful on those steps, now."

Mr. Brewster came out onto the porch, and a hundred flies shied from the tile floor to a safe distance from his feet; the dog opened his eyes, shuffled, slobbered, then whined and closed his eyes again. On the steps, Mr. Brewster turned to speak to my mother in the doorway. "Don't worry about me, Mrs. Black," he said. "I know my way around by now. I'm *down*, like so many of us, but I'm not *out*." He laughed, and she laughed, and Mrs. Pyron came out with the fresh loaf in her hands, and the two women watched while this shining man, the traveller, the world citizen, plodded away along the scorching pavement and turned the corner to go down the little hill.

I don't know what made me follow Mr. Brewster that day —curiosity, boredom, or foresight—but I circled along slowly behind him on my bicycle through the heat waves rising from the street. He made a few calls at the bottom of the Little Hill. Then I got off and watched him as he began the climb up the Big Hill, pushing down with his hands first on one thigh and then on the other, the basket swinging on his arm. I plotted his every movement as he approached the cottonwood halfway up the slope. He stopped, put the basket down on the sidewalk, took out the handkerchief, carefully unfolded it. Then, suddenly, his knees buckled, and his body keeled over, and the handkerchief floated leisurely down to the grass. The way he just lay there on the ground startled me.

I pedalled my bicycle up the Big Hill as far as I could, and then walked to where he lay. I remember that his face was redder than usual, and I remember how his open eyes stared at me, and how the eternal beads of perspiration stood on his forehead. I spoke his name, and when he did not answer, I remember, I tugged at his seersucker trousers before I went back to the house for help.

When they covered his face later and took him away, both my mother and Mrs. Pyron wept, but I now recall with wonder that it meant no more to me at that moment than if a beetle had rolled on its back and died.

The Bell of Charity

CALVIN KENTFIELD

EARLY IN THE MORNING, MY MOTHER HEARD THE NEWS. Someone phoned her—I don't know who—and she did not get up from her chair after she had hung up. She found a number in the telephone book and asked the operator for it. "Hello, *hel*lo," she said. "Is this Mrs. Pearly? Say, this is Mrs. Garrett. . . . Yes. . . . Yes."

I could see her from the kitchen table, where I was having breakfast, and I knew she was talking to someone who was not an intimate friend, for her voice had the same quality it had when she spoke in company and raised her coffee cup with her little finger sticking out. "Weren't you a friend of Mrs. Kite's, old Mrs. Fred Kite? . . . Yes, well I thought so. . . . Yes, well she died. . . . I thought probably you hadn't, I just heard a minute ago. . . . Yes, last night in Graham Hospital. . . . Well, you know she's been so awful sick, poor old soul. . . . Well, I knew she used to come up to your house when she came here to see me. She'd always say she was going on to Mrs. Liedermeyer's house or to Mrs. Pearly's. . . . Yes, I knew she did, and I thought you'd like to know. Of course it'll be in the paper but . . . Well, that preacher, I suppose. He seemed to see a lot of her while she was sick. . . . Fred?" Fred was Mrs. Kite's son. "Well, yes, he is. He got married, you know. . . . Yes, I certainly was, too. He

118

lives in St. Louis—you knew that—him and his wife, so I don't suppose he'll be up here until tomorrow. . . . Well, you know, I think she must have told that preacher all the details when she felt herself failing, because he seemed to know just who to call, and all. . . . Why, he's that major or captain or something, down there at the Salvation Army. . . . Yes, I *did think* about that, and I just believe *I* will. Somebody certainly should. . . . No, no. Why, *no*, I'll be *glad* to. All right then, Mrs. Pearly. . . . Yes. . . . Yes. . . . I'll put you down for fifty cents. . . . That's quite all right. I knew you'd like to know, Mrs. Pearly. Good-by."

My mother put down the receiver, brushed a white strand of hair away from her ear, and took the receiver up again. "Four seven nine W," she said, and turned and called to me, "There's more coffee on the stove, Ira." Then, while she waited for her party to answer, she took a piece of paper and a pencil from a shelf under the telephone and began to make a list. "Hello, *Minnie?*" she said. "Ya *up? . . .* Ya *did?* My land, what were you doing up so *early? . . .* Well, it is cooler then. You aren't *washing? . . .* Well you just better take it easy. You're just not able to do that kind of thing any more. . . . Say, you know old Mrs. Kite died. . . . Last night at the Graham. . . . Yes, well poor old soul, she's better off. She was all alone, you know. . . . Well he certainly *did*, and went off to St. Louis. Can you *ima*gine any woman marrying him? Ugh! . . . Say, would you like to give a little something for flowers? I said I'd do it. . . . Well, I *know* I'm not, but poor old soul. I don't suppose there'll be very many. . . . Well I'm certainly *not* going to tire myself out. Just a few of the people she used to come see. . . . I'll put you down then. . . . No, no, Minnie. I certainly won't. I'm not *able* to, any more. I'll just make a few calls, and I can get the flowers from Alma, next door. . . . Well, *pretty* good. This heat, you know. . . . Oh, yes, I take it easy, and I follow my diet, and I don't overstrain myself. Well, I just *can't*. Now, just like the other day, when I was hanging up the clothes, reaching up, you know, I just got so *dizzy*, and cold sweat came out on my face and I felt so *hot*. I came right in and laid down like the doctor told me, and after a little while—well, it was several hours—I was all right. Oh, I still *have* them. . . . Yes, I know. That sure is right. Say, Minnie, talking of washing, don't you just miss Roy? . . . Yes, I sure do. Poor old Roy, he was *so* good, and *such* a help." Roy Virgil had been everyone's handyman for as long as I could remember. "Well, Minnie, I tell you, I just don't know what we would've done without him," my mother said. "And clean, he'd clean up the tubs so nice and leave the basement so clean. I really couldn't afford him, but he was such a help, and, well, I just wasn't able. Whenever I think of Mrs. Kite, I think of him. . . . Yes, well you know they were all of them around down there at the Salvation Army, and Roy's children and Fred were so thick, you know. She was awful good to that boy, poor old soul, her troubles are over now. . . . Say, you remember before Roy died, he gave those goats of his to Don Karmaier for his house out there on the River Road? . . . Well you know for the longest time they just kept that slope trimmed down so *clean*. You know, Minnie, I believe those goats've died. I was by there not so long ago, and Don was out there himself with a lawn mower. I just believe those goats've died. . . . Yes, well I will, Minnie. . . . Now you just be careful and don't you go lifting that heavy basket around. . . . Yes. Good-by. . . . Well, I don't know. I expect it'll be the Potts's Funeral Home, but I haven't heard. She was a pensioner, you know. . . . Oh, yes, the state'll pay. . . . Oh, yes, they've got a *nice* lot, thank the Lord. She had to sign her house over to Fred when she took her pension, but they let her keep that. . . . Why, it's there on the corner, down the slope there by Ed Tatters'. . . . Why, *yes*, I'm sure. You know where that big black stone is, and the Ryan vault? . . . Well, it's just in back of that. There's a peony bush there, and a faucet. It's awful close to the road, but shoot! Old Fred, her husband's buried there. They say she had that violin and that Chinaman's hat of his buried with him, but I don't know. Old Fred didn't have much sense. Well, he was a little, well, goofy, you remember. That's how young Fred got like he is, but he had enough sense to buy a lot to be buried in and keep them out of potter's field. . . . My, yes, it certainly *is*, it certainly is a blessing. Poor old soul. . . . Yes. Well, good-by."

My mother hung up, and added several names to her list and looked up some numbers in the telephone book. I was watching her over the rim of my coffee cup. She called another number, and when she got her party, I could tell by the way she talked that it was a friend of Mrs. Kite's but not one of her own. The next lady she called was a very old friend, and they started talking about me.

"Yes, that was him you saw," my mother said. "He's home. . . . Oh, why, he came in just a couple of nights ago, Tuesday I believe it was. . . . No, he never told me he was coming but, well, I had a feeling he might. He never said, but the last letter I got was kinda, well, I had a feeling. . . . Oh, he's been working on a boat or something of that kind. He could tell you more about it than I could. . . . Well I suppose it's what he wants to do, though I don't think he's very satisfied. . . . Oh, no, no! He mentioned something about it when he was here at Christmastime, and I just laughed. I told him I couldn't imagine what woman would want to marry him. Course he don't tell me much. He's the closest young'un I ever saw. I don't know *how* he got that way. . . . Oh, yes, don't you remember I told you he was here at Christmas, just for a couple of days? But aside from that, it's been seven years since he was home. Yes, sir, seven years. He couldn't even come home when his Daddy passed away, he was out on the ocean somewhere."

I knew she was saying all of that for me to hear. I watched her, and I saw her eyes cloud up when the vastness of the ocean, which she had never seen, entered her mind.

"Say Mabel," she resumed. "You know poor old Mrs. Kite died. . . . Oh? Who *told* you?"

She talked for a few minutes more, then hung up and began calling still other people she had listed. I poured myself another cup of coffee and stopped listening, preferring to recall the woman who had died, whom I had known only as a faithful pilgrim, one who loved to come and visit and stay all day.

For years, Mrs. Kite had lived at the foot of our hill, and visiting us had been easy, but some time—I couldn't remember when—she had moved with her family to a house a little way out of town, on the edge of the Mississippi bluff. Thereafter, the pilgrimage back to Billy Goat Hill to see her old friends —one or maybe two at a time—had become an arduous one. She was fat and her legs were swollen, but down the bluff she would come, nevertheless, crossing Soap Creek, which was the city limits, and coming the back way to our edge of town. Through the wailing aspen woods where the carcasses of old cars lay rusting among the trees she passed, through the wild rocks of the Hollow, unheeding of the creepers that tangled the lonely path there, and of the brambles that picked at her brown lisle stockings, and the black snakes and blue racers that dwelt in the grass. She looked both ways when she reached the abandoned Wabash tracks, then crossed, and went on past the row of shacks that squatted along the right of way, ignoring the churlish dogs that bayed and yapped and reared at her from the bitter ends of their chains. On she went to the foot of Billy Goat Hill.

My older brother and I often saw her coming, for in the summer we lived long, dramatic other lives in the Hollow and the auto graveyard. Likely as not, we would run ahead, keeping—like Arabs—to the concealments we knew, to warn our mother. But if our Arabian, or other, existence compelled us to stay where we were, we would crouch in the hot ribs of some old Plymouth, or under a certain stony ledge, drawing our mantles about us and giggling and shushing each other until she passed by.

After each step up Billy Goat Hill, she rested. Viewed from our house, she appeared over the hill's crest hat first, like a ship coming over the horizon. Her face followed her hat; her goitered neck, her shoulders, bosom, waist came after; and then her mammoth satchel bag appeared, hanging from her wrist to only a few inches above the bulging insteps of her shoes. Emerging thus—in a sense, Anadyomene—she gave warning of her coming.

Once, the summer that I was eight, my mother and I, through a portiere of sweet-potato vines, watched her from our sun porch as she gained level ground and turned in to the house on the corner. "There she goes in Mrs. Birch's. Thank the Lord!" my mother exclaimed. We continued to watch for a minute or two. "She's rang four times now," my mother said, "and Mrs. Birch don't answer, and I *know* she's home. She's hiding from that poor old thing, you just bet your bottom dollar."

Mrs. Kite stepped off Mrs. Birch's porch and turned toward our end of the street. "Here she comes!" my mother said, and hurried to the telephone. I don't know whom she called, but I heard her say, "I just thought you'd like to know."

I hid in the dining room, by the window, where I could see the street but couldn't be seen from the front door. I watched Mrs. Kite labor toward us over the broken bricks of our neighbors' unimproved sidewalks, looking ahead and a little heavenward, with a broad, faithful smile upon her ugly face, oblivious, apparently, of the commotion she was causing or of the intricate betrayals of her progress. "She's in front of Alma's!" I called to my mother, who quickly said good-by, and called another number.

"She's coming up the steps!" I called, and I heard my mother say, "I just thought you'd like to know. I was going to town this afternoon, but of course I can't now."

The doorbell rang.

"Well, good-by, she's here." My mother passed me on the way to the front door, and I heard her exclaim there, "*Well!* Mrs. *Kite!* This *is* a surprise!" and I heard the screen door slam.

My mother called me to the sun porch, and I saw our visitor's face beam even more brightly than it had on her way to us, she was so glad to see us and be welcomed. "Surprise!" she said. She brought with her, besides her satchel, a strong smell of sweat and washrags.

"You remember little Ira," my mother said, indicating me.

"Uh-*huh*, uh-*huh*," said Mrs. Kite, like the courting frog in the ballad.

"This is the *baby*," my mother pursued. "Sit down, why don't you?"

"This is the baby," said Mrs. Kite, as if she were telling my mother who I was. "Sit down, uh-*huh*! Whew!" She sank into a wicker rocker and immediately began to rock, while one warted hand probed her bag and withdrew a little lawn handkerchief to wipe her brow. "It's hot and my kid a-fishin'," she said. She was referring to Fred.

"Yes, isn't it hot, though?" my mother said. "Think of the poor gardens."

"Think of the poor gardens," said Mrs. Kite.

I slipped away. I had planned to go to town with my mother, and I was furious. I came back an hour later and hung around in the doorway between the dining room and the sun porch. As if nothing at all had been said while I was gone, my mother asked, "Why don't you take off your hat, Mrs. Kite?"

"Yes, uh-*huh*," said Mrs. Kite. "Why don't I take off my old black hat?"

She did so, revealing another tight hat, of hair, and I was convinced, then, that she had a second head in her bag.

Beyond the screen, the murmurs of the afternoon receded, and my mother nodded in the middle of a sentence. Finally she said, "I'm sorry, Mrs. Kite, but I've just *got* to take a nap. Now don't let me sleep very long."

"Don't let her sleep very long," said Mrs. Kite.

"Wake me up in thirty minutes."

I turned and ran as fast as I could upstairs, grabbed an alarm clock, and ran back. My mother had left her seat, and I saw her go into the living room. She sank down upon the davenport and almost instantly began to snore. I went to the sun porch and slipped into the Morris chair she had vacated. On the wide arm, I placed the clock, training its bold face on Mrs. Kite. "I've got a little boy," she said to me, and I told her she wasn't telling me anything, because I knew it.

That was all either of us said. The curtain of airy plants outside the windows let in an emerald, aqueous light. The clock ticked. Mrs. Kite rocked and rocked, and picked her nose, and smiled from ear to ear. Her goiter gave her a frog's throat. She watched me and the clock with drowsy, wide-set eyes. Finally her mouth relaxed and dropped open, and her long, grooved tongue rolled out and rested upon her lower lip.

Now my mother, at the telephone, said good-by to the last person on her list, and heaved herself out of her chair. I was still at the kitchen table. "You remember old Mrs. Kite, don't you?" she asked. I nodded, and she said that she had died. I remarked that I had already heard the news, and she said, "I'm going to run over to Alma's and tell her, and see about some flowers."

Alma lived next door, across a wide yard, the back half of which was neatly planted with flowers. In the yard were an arbor and a small greenhouse. Alma and her husband had a modest florist's business and made enough, according to my mother, to keep them in Phoenix in the winters.

In the evening, my mother often sat on a chair outside her back door and said how nice it was to have such a pretty view to look at. There were some other chairs on the grass there, and a table. That evening, my sister, who is older than I, and married, and lives on the other side of town, came to my mother's house for supper. Her husband had gone to a stag fish fry. She brought a chicken, and my mother made potato salad, and spread a cloth on the outside table. After supper, when the three of us were drinking our coffee and looking at Alma's flowers, my Aunt Shug, who lives across the street, came over to return a clothesline she had borrowed. She said she had to go right back home, but she agreed to sit down for just a minute. She sat on a green wood-and-iron bench my mother had talked the cemetery custodian out of. "Say, Nin, have you heard when old Mrs. Kite's funeral's going to be?" she asked my mother.

"Why, yes, it was on the door at Potts's, and it was in the paper tonight," my mother answered. "I believe, if I remember right, it was to be tomorrow afternoon."

"They've got her there now, I suppose," Shug said. "Poor old soul, she never missed a funeral."

"No sir, she didn't. She and Mrs. Virgil, Roy's wife. You remember Roy, don't you, Son? He used to come help me with the washing, but I've got a big, strong boy to do it for me now."

"They came to Tom's funeral an hour ahead of time, and sat down and stayed all through, and were the last to leave," Shug said.

"I'm not exactly a boy," I said dryly, "being twenty-seven and a half years of age."

"And that Mrs. O'Blenness came with them," Shug went on. "And I heard she went to another funeral afterward, and then she went home that night and died of a heart attact."

"Well Esther Virgil was already at Potts's this afternoon, long before I ever got there," my mother said.

"You mean to say, Nin, you've been down to see her so soon?" asked Shug. "I wouldn't think they could have her out yet."

"Oh, yes, and she looked nice. You know, Charley Potts is really *very* good." My mother went on to describe what Mrs. Kite had looked like, lying in her coffin, and the dress she had been wearing, and who all had been there. It was all fresh in her mind because she and I had just returned, only a short time before supper, from the funeral home. I had driven her down but had refused at first to go in with her. However, after she had gone on alone, I had changed my mind and followed her.

As I approached the front door, I noticed to one side of it a small black bulletin board, which said, in white plastic removable letters, "MRS MARY KITE 2:30 SAT," and on the glass of the door itself was another sign, saying "FRIGIDAIRE CONDITIONED FOR YOUR COMFORT," and still another—a card—bidding me "WALK IN." I did so, passing quickly into the parlor where lay Mrs. Kite's remains.

Besides my mother, in the cool room, there were, among the living, Roy Virgil's widow, Esther, and her daughter, Esther Roy, and Son Virgil, and Fred Kite. Little Mrs. Virgil, as always at wakes and funerals, was sitting back in her chair with her hands folded in her lap, enjoying herself. She was wearing a hair net and a house dress—a faded print of cherry clusters—and she smiled grandly at me, showing the bright-orange gums of her false teeth, though I could tell she didn't remember me.

Beside her, beneath a potted palm, was Son, about thirty-five, sitting with his legs stretched out in front of him and one arm thrown over the back of his chair, causing his Hawaiian shirt to gap and expose his navel.

Esther Roy, who was nearly six feet tall, limbed like an oak, and pregnant, stood beside my mother at the casket. They were peering in, and Esther Roy was clutching a tiny handkerchief in one hand and with the extended forefinger of the other was pointing out various aspects of the corpse as if she were trying to sell it.

"Don't she look nice, though?" my mother said.

"Yes," said Esther Roy. "They did a beautiful job on her."

My mother, turning from the casket, saw me. She came over and put her arm through mine. She introduced me to Mrs. Virgil, who said wasn't it just grand to have me back, and to Esther Roy, who said exactly the same thing, and to Son, who welcomed me with an enormous grin. Then she turned to Fred Kite, who was sitting near Mrs. Virgil. "Hello, Fred," she said. "You got here sooner than we expected."

Fred looked at her but did not speak.

"Do you remember my baby boy?" she asked.

Fred looked me up and down and said, "I never would've knowed ya."

I never would have known him, either. He was prosperously fat, his clothes were new, and fitted him—though the collar of his shirt was dirty—and he sat straight in his chair with his arms crossed over his chest, clearly detached from the whole affair.

"Well, you won't have to worry about her any more," my mother said, her eyes beginning to cloud.

Fred looked away.

My mother stepped up to the visitors' register to sign our names, and I stepped up to the casket. Esther Roy stepped up beside me. "They did a beautiful job on her," she said.

They certainly had. She looked calm and peaceful, as she was supposed to look—entirely different from the way she had looked at Christmas. I had forgotten I had seen her then, briefly, in the falling snow. I turned to ask my mother if she was ready, but she was waiting, and everyone rose to smile us out—everyone but Fred.

"So Fred got here, then?" Shug asked.

"Oh yes, he's here," my mother said. "But, you know, there wasn't but one dinky bunch of flowers, and the church sent those."

"You remember when Mrs. Kite used to come and sit, and bring Fred with her?" my sister asked.

"She just loved to sit on that porch of ours," my mother said.

"And repeat everything you said to her," said Shug, laughing. "Yes, yes, uh-huh, uh-huh." And Fred—you remember how she used to bring him along when he was little?"

"Uh-huh, uh-huh," my sister mimicked. "Little! He wasn't so little." She cocked her head and pursed her lips and rubbed the uplifted side of her face with her fingers. "Well, you know," she said, drawing out the long syllable of the verb, "I kinda think Fred used to be kinda sweet on me."

"Well, I *know* old Fred liked me," my mother broke in, "because I've heard him say to Daddy many a time—"

"He'd come with his mother and sit," my sister said. "You know, just sit, like that, and *look* at me, and *look*."

Shug laughed and said, "Why, yes," and my sister gave a low, shuddering witch's laugh.

"Many a time," my mother said, "old Fred—oh, he'd say it to *me*, too—you know he used to come up here and visit Daddy, they were old pals, you know, him and Daddy, and he'd say—"

"Oh, yes," my sister said.

"He'd help him sometimes in the yard, or Daddy'd give him little things to do, but I've heard old Fred say a dozen times if I heard him once, 'Burrell,' he'd say"—she raised her arm and held it there, with her forefinger pointing straight out, as if she were a statue with sword drawn—"'if I'd've seen that girl first, *you'd* never got a chance at her!'"

She dropped her arm, and Shug roared, "Just think, Nin, you could've married Fred Kite, and all your life you could've been serenated with 'The Devil's Dream.' That was the only piece he could ever play. Remember when they lived by the cooper shop at the foot of the hill, how he used to come up the alley just *covered* with dirt, like he'd spent the night in a coal shed? With that hat on? Like a tramp, except, of course, he *did* work. With his toes sticking out and scratching on that fiddle 'The Devil's Dream'? My *land*, such a cat's meow!"

"You remember old Fred Kite, don't you, Son?" my mother asked.

"No, I don't think I do," I said. "I remember young Fred coming up through the alley, though, all the time."

"He sure did," my sister said. "And he'd just *look* at me, and *look*."

"When Burrell died, you should've married him, Nin," Shug said. "He would've played 'The Devil's Dream' at your wedding."

"Oh, he was dead and gone by then," my mother said.

"Mo-ther," my sister said with a slant to her voice, cocking her head again, "if you'd've married Fred Kite, would I be me?" She laughed immoderately. "I mean, who would *I* be?"

Shug roared again, "You missed your chance, Nin, to marry a musician."

"You know, in the paper tonight," my mother said, lowering her voice, "it mentioned they had a first little girl that died at birth."

"Now that I come to think of it," Shug said, "I *remember* she had a first baby."

"Well you know when that little thing was born, it had hoofs, just like a little cow or something, or a little goat," my mother said.

"Oh, Mother!" my sister exclaimed. "That's not true."

"That's what they say. It had just sorta little hoof-feets."

There was a long hiatus in the talk, filled in with private thoughts. The sun was departing and the air was beginning to cool. The sky flared up over Shug's house, across the street, as if her shingle roof, her Indian cigar trees, and all the inflammable earth to the westward were afire. Next door, Alma was gathering flowers. Behind her, like an enormous grasshopper's eye, the mansard panes of her little greenhouse flashed back the last rays of the sun.

"I've just got to go," said Shug, not moving.

"She must have been a hundred and thirteen, wasn't she?" I asked.

"Why *no-o-o*," my mother said.

"She wasn't much older than I am," Shug said.

"How old are you?" I asked, smiling.

"That's none of *your* affair, young man," she said. "Say, how long are you going to stay with us?"

I was about to say I didn't know for sure, that I didn't know anything for sure, but my mother spoke up ahead of me. "Oh, he's going to be here for a *little* while, anyway," she said.

I could not remember having discussed it. To change the subject, I asked what age Mrs. Kite was, since she wasn't a hundred and thirteen.

"Well now, let's see," my mother said, figuring.

"It was in the paper, wasn't it?" my sister asked. "It must've been."

"Well, now, we can figure it out," said my mother. "Esther Virgil, Roy's wife, was two years younger than Roy, and Roy and you went to school together, didn't you, Shug? Well, I'm two years younger than you are, and you're sixty-six—"

"And proud of it," said Shug, placing her palms on her knees and bending forward as though she really meant to get up and go. The ball of clothesline was still in her lap.

"So Esther Virgil must be the same age," my mother concluded.

I said, "That makes you and Esther Virgil both sixty-four, but how old was Mrs. Kite?"

"Well," my mother said, "Esther Virgil had Son at the same time Mrs. Kite had Fred. They're only a couple of months apart. Of course, there's her daughter, Esther Roy, but she's older."

"Say, Nin," Shug said, settling back, "what's that boy's real name?"

"Roy, like his daddy," my mother answered, "but everybody has always called him Son. My, but he certainly is good to her. Esther Roy, you know, is married, but Son takes *such* good care of his mother. She's such a little thing, you know, and he just *works* for her, and *carries*, and goes *here* and *there* and *everywhere*. Of course, they all work down there at the Salvation Army. They live over there in that little house Roy used to have. And Son keeps it up *so* nice."

"They're not quite right, either, are they?" I asked.

"No, but he certainly is good to her," my mother said.

"I've *got* to go," said Shug. "I haven't even done my supper dishes yet."

"Well neither have we," my mother told her. "Do like we do, and don't worry about it. You know, Minnie and me have got it all figured out that Esther Virgil is related to Mamie Eisenhower."

"Leave it to Minnie," my sister said.

"Well you know Douds up the river there—that little place above Bonaparte—well, Douds was named by some of Esther Virgil's family. Esther was a Doud before she married Roy, and Mamie Eisenhower's family were Doudses from around up in there someplace, oh, way years ago . . ."

I stepped into the house and filled my coffee cup from the percolator, and called out, asking if anyone else wanted another cup. My sister said she did, and my aunt said no, she had to go home. She was still there when I returned, however, but the color had gone from the sky above her house, and the long, gradual darkening had begun. Soon, I knew, we would all fade—my mother in her garden chair, my sister and my aunt on the graveyard bench, myself astraddle a kitchen chair with my arms crossed on the high back and my chin resting on my arms. Our faces, hands, and clothes would gradually fade, the darkest first, until only Shug's and my mother's two white heads of hair would remain suspended. After they were gone, there would only be our voices.

But it was not yet dark enough for that, nor was it dark enough for lightning bugs, though the mosquitoes materialized the instant twilight began. My mother slapped at her plump arms and her already bitten legs as she finished her private grafting of Esther Virgil to Mamie Eisenhower's family tree, ending—by some circumlocution I did not follow, because I was thinking again of Mrs. Kite in the falling snow—with how good Son Virgil was to his mother.

"Well, young Fred was always good to poor old Mrs. Kite," Shug said.

"Well yes, he was," my mother agreed, with some qualification in her tone, "up until the time he got married. I haven't talked to her since then, nor seen her even—alive, I mean. I don't know how she took it, and now we'll never know."

"Come to think of it," Shug said, "I haven't seen her, either."

"I have," I said, but nobody heard me, because my sister asked at the same time what was the matter with her, that she died.

"Well she had a goiter," my mother said, "but that wasn't what killed her, if you ask me."

"Say, Nin, weren't you just surprised when you seen Fred at the funeral parlor?" asked Shug.

"No, I wasn't, not a bit, because I already knew he was here," my mother answered. "Mrs. Pearly called me today—you know Mrs. Pearly, down there on the corner by the cemetery, Mrs. Kite always went down there whenever she came, she was the last one on the line. I don't think *she's* seen her, either. Mrs. Kite kinda stopped coming when Fred ran off. We used to call Mrs. Pearly the Last Ditch, but she don't know that. Well, she said she'd seen Fred coming up from the depot from that afternoon train, and he was all dressed up—"

"In Louie's suit!" my sister cried, and began to giggle.

"Yes. And his wife wasn't with him," my mother finished.

"Oh, she *never* comes with him," said Shug. "Whenever he comes up here, instead of coming with him, she takes a trip someplace else. That's what I hear."

133

"You know, Brother," my sister said, "Fred got married in Cousin Louie's suit."

"*What* suit?" I asked.

"Well," my mother said, "*we think* he did. Nobody from here was at the wedding, but it was the only suit he had."

"And I was told—" Shug began.

"Well it was his *courting* suit, anyway," my sister said.

"But *what* suit?" I asked again.

"After Louie died," my mother said, "May was going to throw his clothes away, but I saw that suit and I said, 'May, don't throw that suit away, I think I can sell it for you.' It was a *good* serge suit, cost over sixty dollars, so May says, 'All right, Nin, I'll take five dollars for it.' So I just gets busy and calls up Mrs. Kite, and I says, 'Mrs. Kite, I've got a suit here I think will just fit Fred,' and I told her about it and all, and told her she could have it for six dollars. I figured if it was worth five, it was worth six. She said she'd sure like to see it, so I took it down to her and she bought it. And it was his courting suit, though the poor old soul had no idea then he was going to go off and get married."

"What happened to the extra dollar?" my sister asked, before I got the chance. "I hadn't heard about that."

"I gave it to May, but, oh, she wouldn't take it for the world," my mother said. "She made me keep it. Well, I did the work and the running around and all, and I'm not really as well as I used to be. It was worth a dollar."

"Did he have a clean shirt on when he come from the train?" asked Shug. "You know, they tell me she won't wash for him and she won't let him spend his money for a laundry to do it."

"His mother certainly never treated him like that, she always kept him so clean," said my mother.

"Well you know, Nin, he got her through an ad."

"Not exactly an ad, Shug—one of those love lost-and-found offices."

"Agencies," Shug corrected her. "It's the same thing."

"It's the same thing," my mother agreed. "He had several on the string. All last fall, he took train trips to Des Moines and Peoria and St. Louis. Looking them over, I guess. Ugh! And his poor old mother sitting home alone. And you should've seen him! I seen him two or three times last fall, when the leaves were dropping. Oh, I'd get so *lonesome* I'd think I couldn't *stand* it, and I'd get in the car and go down to the depot and watch the train come in, just to see who was coming and going. Every time I'd hear it blowing down by the bridge and I'd think, oh, maybe one of my boys is on that train, and oh, the river down there would look so sad and winter coming. Going and coming just makes me almost cry."

"And the time one of them came, you wasn't there," said Shug.

"And the time one of them come, I wasn't there, yes sir. But I used to see Fred going courting. Oh, you should've *seen* him! In Louie's suit. It fit him just real nice, and a checkered flannel shirt with a necktie hanging down, and *white* shoes, and if he wasn't spiffed up I'll tell you. His hair he had pasted down on his head with enough grease to slide me down the hill, and *he* was going *courting*. Same outfit every time."

"What was that song old Grandma Garrett used to sing?" my sister asked. "About the frog and Miss Mousie's den?"

"I used to sing that to you kids," said my mother. She started to sing:

"Froggy would a-wooin' go, uh-huh, uh-huh,
Froggy would a-wooin' go, uh-huh, uh-huh,
Froggy would a-wooin' go,
Whether his mama would let him or no,
Uh-huh, uh-huh."

My sister clapped her hands to her cheeks and moaned and almost had a fit, saying, "Imagine, imagine, imagine answering an ad and having *that* step off the train to meet you!"

My mother said, "One time, you know, the stationmaster

come over to me after the train had gone, and he said, 'Mrs. Garrett, I've just said the worst thing. I said to Fred Kite, I said, "Why, Fred, you almost look like a human being," and you know Mrs. Garrett, I didn't mean a *thing* by it, but I was so *surprised*.'"

"Which woman did the poor guy take?" I asked, though I already knew.

"He must've taken the one in St. Louis, because he got on the southbound train last time he went, just after Thanksgiving," my mother said. "The stationmaster asked him where he was going, and he said he was going to get married, and he hasn't been back since—that is, until today. Poor old soul had to die to get him back."

"I just can't get over it, what a shock it would be," my sister went on. "I just wonder what the woman looks like."

"Like *him*," said Shug. "Don't you know she'd *have* to?"

Fred Kite was not clear in my memory of the past, as his mother was. I could remember him tagging along behind her sometimes when she came visiting, but his face escaped me. Too many faces had intervened, I suppose, too many things had happened. I had knocked around a lot, here and there, and been disappointed, though I had never said so, and had come home, not certain what I wanted to do or where I wanted to be. I was certain I didn't want to stay, but I had never said so. I had kept pretty much to the house, except to go out for cigarettes or to the library, and except for the trip to the funeral home. I had seen Fred there, and, as I have said, I never would have known him.

I remembered him as a baggy figure tramping the alleys as his father had done, crushing the cinders and gravel of all the back ways. His clothes were clean but were hand-me-downs from bigger men. The coats were so long in the sleeves they hung over his hands as he walked, always with his arms dangling slightly in front of him. My father once cruelly and accurately referred to Fred and his mother as monkey and organ-grinder, saying Fred would dance to her tune, but then he was sorry he had said it.

I remember one summer when Fred was adolescent and he came with his mother to our house. My sister was nearly grown then, but my brother and I were small and my father was alive. They came at dinnertime, almost on the stroke of noon, taking seats in the kitchen to watch us eat. Mrs. Kite gave us her amphibian smile. Fred stared.

My mother, whose gift it was to do so, made conversation. Everything she said Mrs. Kite repeated. Everything Mrs. Kite repeated, Fred repeated. My brother and sister began to laugh, but I didn't. I was the sober one. We had always been told to be polite to Mrs. Kite. In spite of himself, my father had to laugh, and when I saw him shaking at the head of the table, I laughed, too.

My mother tried to cover up for us by blaming our laughter on something the poodle dog, whose name was Cutie, had done. "Here, now, you stop that!" my mother said, wagging her finger at the dog, which was begging around the table for bologna skins.

"Here, now, you stop that!" Mrs. Kite said with great pleasure.

"You stop that!" said Fred.

My mother began to giggle, trying to keep her face straight, saying "Kids! Kids! Stop that!"

Mrs. Kite, joining in the gaiety and grinning even wider, shook her head and wagged a finger in a mock scold, saying, "Kids! Kids! Stop that!"

And Fred, bewildered and disturbed, beat his knees with his fists and shouted, "*Kids, kids, kids, kids, kids!*"

I think he knew what was going on.

My mother, there in the twilight, was saying she didn't think Mrs. Kite knew what Fred was up to when he took those trips. When she came to a pause, I asked her if she remembered the time I had just been thinking of.

"*I* remember that," my sister said.

"My, yes!" my mother said. "So do I. Poor old soul, *she* didn't know what we were laughing at."

Dark had nearly come. A chance breeze, like a cat's-paw at sea, passed softly through the locust trees and over the short grass, displacing a few strands of ghostly hair, intruding upon the tenants of Alma's garden. Alma herself had long since gone into her house, and she had a bright light in her kitchen window.

Shug stood up to go home, but before she took a step, she said in the low, dusky voice of scandal, "I'll tell you *this* now. Mrs. Liedermeyer told me his mother *thought* they were, but they *weren't* married."

In her hand she still held the ball of clothesline she had meant to return. Without a word, as if I were still the little boy who did the errands, she handed it to me. For a moment, I held it in both hands like a crystal ball, then I rose and carried it into the house. I did not turn on a light, for I knew my way in the dark. I paused, and looked down at the ball that rested like a head in my palm. It was too dark to see the face of it now, but last winter, I was certain, I had seen it.

I had gone to town, and snow was falling. I had been surprised to see Mrs. Kite, who, according to my mother, never solicited for the Salvation Army, in an Army booth. She wore the Army's bonnet on her head, and her tunic was open at the collar, revealing a muffler wound around her goitered neck. I was walking by, but I stopped to make sure it was really she. I was about to speak when she looked at me. She didn't know me. She gave me the same wild, unseeing look she was giving the shoppers and the falling snow. There was a snarl on her lips, and shaggy mittens on her hands, and one mitten held a bell the army of charity had given her. She clutched the bell as if it were a creature she had killed, and with deliberate downward jerks of rage, she shook it.

I put away the clothesline and rejoined the others, who had

neither moved nor spoken. As if my return were a signal, my mother said, "Poor old soul, she *never* knew."

The light went out in Alma's kitchen.

"Sitting down there on that porch, all alone, and not well, year in, year out. I know what it is, all alone in that house." My mother's voice was on the verge of breaking, but there was yet a touch of outrage in it when she added, "I suppose he'll sell it first thing, now that she's gone."

Shug said, "Oh but Nin, you don't have to worry, now that Ira's back."

A screen door slammed.

I hastened to explain that I did not mean to stay.

Before another word could be said, Alma appeared in the twilight, bearing above her head a huge bouquet as though it were a torch to light her path. She walked carefully across the grass, minding her feet. When she was before us, she held out the flowers for us to see and, in the closing darkness, touched each kind and named it. "Glads," she said, "and lilies, and babies' breath."

I could tell by my mother's voice she was trying not to cry when she said, though she could barely see them, how beautiful they were.

The Wedding Shoes

KIM YONG IK

BUT I CAME AGAIN AND AGAIN TO WATCH THE SILK BROCADE shoes set on a stool before the old man at the market. My previous decision not to come any more made me stand longer each time on the market corner. Each day I returned, one more pair of wedding shoes was missing; yet I had never seen anyone stop even to look. Those buyers must have come like my memory of a wedding day that was not meant to be sad but was sad. Now on his wooden stool there remained only five pairs. They seemed to contain the whole emptiness of the refugee-crowded market. I would have emptied my money bag for a single pair before they all went away, yet I was still afraid I might buy sorrow instead of wedding shoes.

Between the late-autumn vegetable mongers and a fortune-teller who talked to lonely, superstitious faces, sat the shoemaker. On the day I first had discovered the old man in the market, I had been looking for new rice, the round full kernels, when suddenly I saw him. I went closer but stopped as soon as I recognized him, the shoemaker who had lived one fence behind my home before I came to Pusan. It was obvious he had fled from the war area, perhaps with the shoes on his back. My mind shrank immediately, and bitterness poured out. I repeated aloud the old, spiteful words, "Even a three-village fire does not hurt one when he imagines the burning of three-year-old bedbugs that gnawed him."

How often my fists had closed tight, holding bitterness and sadness when I thought about that shoemaker—that mouth that had refused my proposal for his daughter in marriage and had even bragged about his trade and insulted the butcher's trade of my family. I might have nodded to the shoemaker's wife. Not to the old shoemaker. Never!

That day, when I had gone over to his house to open the marriage talk, remained closer to me than yesterday. It always cast a clear shadow before me as if I watched a mirrored picture in the river. No matter where I went, that picture walked ahead. It was the day after an unexpected storm. The air was clear and rich, leaving dreamy blue distance between the four hills and the sky. The thatched roofs of the village glistened young and smooth, for the farmers had re-covered the wrinkled faces of their roofs with golden rice straw. Early, before the noisy sparrows that nested under our eaves could have flown to the harvest field, my father had left for the Pusan market to buy a beef cow. That morning, several farmers had come to our home saying they would need ribs of beef, veal, head parts of cow for their children's wedding days. I had heard their lighthearted voices rolling on loud as if they were talking to someone across the fields. Each praised the match and home chosen for his son or daughter, mentioning every pleasing thing that might have come from the lips of the matchmaker.

"Grasshopper mating time follows ours, you know," an old farmer said. "The new rice and the pleasant chilliness pull two together under the one quilt. The wedding food will not spoil. The whole valley will come to the banquet, and then over the autumn, moonlit hills, they will go home singing, using their full-rounded stomachs as drums to tap on, blessing our brides and bridegrooms."

They talked on till wine-time when the sun was half way between the hills and the sky. Then, leaving, they noticed the large pumpkins on the shoemaker's roof beyond our fence and spoke in praise: "Those are so heavy the roof may fall in." Having had no new coating of straw for several years, the roof looked gray-dark and too flimsy to support the pumpkins.

One farmer said to another, "When we were as young as green pepper days, we thought we could not marry without the shoemaker's silk brocade shoes. Don't you think our children are smarter than we were? They laugh at such expensive customs and tell us to buy beef instead."

My home was quiet again. My mother said, "I wish they had not talked so loud." And, it was true, as often as the farmers came to our house and told of the ripening marriage talks for their children, just so often the shoemaker came home drunk at night and kept half the village awake. I could see why he had grown bitter and hurt, for few visited him to place orders for shoes. I could remember in my own green pepper days, or even just several autumns ago, the farmers would go first to place their orders for wedding shoes. It was to the shoemaker they told everything the matchmakers had said, forgetting to leave until their tobacco ran out. Only afterward would they call over the fence to tell us how much beef they wanted. Later, the village women would go to the shoemaker's to ask who had ordered wedding shoes and about all the other things he had heard. For the shoemaker knew the inside and the outside of everything as his work concerned village social life.

My mother would draw out a long sigh, an envious sigh, as she awaited customers, and say, "The shoemaker's threshold is being worn out by the people's feet." But that was long ago. Each year fewer farmers visited even over the fence. Instead, they came to our house to tell of the marriages and to buy beef.

I do not know what made me decide that day to go courting. Perhaps it was the pleasantly chilly autumn wind through the red, dusky maple; perhaps it was the color of the sky; perhaps it was the echoes of my heart to others' marriage talks; perhaps every thread of that colorful day might have moved my long-timid feet toward that house.

It was so near that a village woman might point a stranger to my house by saying, "If you fell on the shoemaker's yard, your nose would hit the butcher's house." Whenever I thought about proposing, however, the shoemaker's house receded many hills beyond. So my mind had crossed many hills, many a year, but finally that afternoon it had reached close to its destination.

I did not expect the shoemaker's daughter to be at home, for I knew she had gone to work in the kitchen of a relative. The shoemaker was out, too, but his wife was taking stems off red peppers and she greeted me at the porch. At first, I thought, I must talk of something else on the way to my heart. But I felt my throat grow narrow and the words would not come out. Her hollow cheek as it faced the autumn sun held the sadness I had seen there whenever money lenders stood at her gateway. At last, I had to say that I did not come for the money they owed us; then there was nothing else I could say.

After what seemed an eternity of embarrassment, I blurted out, "I want to marry your daughter!" I could not look at her. I heard her saying that she would consult her husband. Then I looked, stealthily. Her face clearly showed a pleased acceptance. I don't remember what else she said. When I left, I felt I had left my eyes behind watching every expression on the happy face of the shoemaker's wife.

At home, when I told my mother about my visit, she said confidently, "The shoemaker will be so glad to welcome a prospective son-in-law that the next time you visit him he may put both his legs into one leg of his wide trousers."

That night I could not sleep. I went in and out of my room many times to see whether the shoemaker had returned. Amid the fallen leaves in the frosting yard and the crickets, I waited

143

for his footfalls that would presage the brightest moment of my life.

The stars glistened so close to the hills that the flying kites might be able to reach them, I thought. I could think of nothing that might prevent my marriage. If two cousins had been as friendly as the shoemaker's home and ours had been, they would have been called "closest cousins." The gourds that grew on the dividing fence were always shared without a quarrel. My father had been selling the shoemaker ox hides ever since I could remember. Of late, as he was very proud, his wife would come to us asking that we sell her hides and promising to pay the following month. We knew they could not pay, but we would let her have a piece large enough for two pairs of shoes. So now, whenever his material ran out, the shoemaker would come home late at night, singing a happy song in the saddest of tones, and with his bitter, drunken remarks awake the neighbors. His wife, by chance meeting my parents on the road, would hasten to bring up some startling piece of gossip, then hurry away. We knew she was trying to divert our minds, so we never mentioned money.

The shoemaker had always liked me. When I was no higher than the fence, he would make room for his daughter and me to sit in a corner of his workroom, putting aside his small adz, chisel and nails. I was fascinated as I watched him stud the round silver nails in the hide-bottoms, paste bright colored silk on the upturned sides, then put brocade of a matching color on the nose of the shoes. He once said to me, "When you grow up to marry, I'll make the most beautiful wedding shoes for you, for your bride and for the matchmaker."

Again one day, he looked long at my face, then glanced at his daughter, and called my name. "Sang Do, you have a clean, handsome face. Your matchmaker won't wear out her shoes, going to your future bride's home so often to ripen the marriage talk. But—the bride's parents want a matchmaker to talk for them. The silvery tongue pleases them, you know."

His eyes were lowered toward the shoes, but his mouth, slightly smiling, faced toward me. I felt the magic of his twisted mouth—the mouth that always opened to talk about brides, bridegrooms, their parents and the go-between women. In those days he had made a living by making at least three pairs of shoes each month, one each for the bridal couple and one for the matchmaker.

His daughter and I later went to school together across two hills. He let her wear silk brocade shoes, even to school. Often she did not want to wear them, for she was the only girl who did, and she could not run so fast as the other girls.

With his bamboo pipe in his mouth, holding out a pair of shoes toward me, he asked, "Sang Do, don't you think the sky blue silk and red brocade are beautiful? Don't you like my daughter more if she wears these shoes?"

I nodded to him, with honesty. I did not see any advantage in being born a girl except for one thing—to wear silk brocade shoes.

The village women talked about the Buddha mole between her eyebrows, the dimples in her cheek that would attract boys, but as far as I was concerned, I never thought about her face. I loved her shoes that others did not have. With them, to prevent chafing, she wore white muslin socks, and on the narrow path to the school, I often walked a step behind, watching the line between the white socks and the canoe-shaped shoes. The line always gave me the feeling that I was taking the sweetest nap. When on days after rain the water rippled across the lower path, I would cross, carrying her on my back, using all my strength not to fall. She would cling to my back like a green frog, and how I loved those shoes dangling on either side of my waist.

As I advanced in the elementary grades, I seldom watched the shoemaker any longer. The outdoors interested me more and, besides, he talked very little about weddings now. His mouth remained glued tight even when I asked whose shoes he was making. Somehow that twisted mouth looked unbear-

145

ably bitter and unapproachable. I was surprised one day when it unfastened abruptly. "Nowadays," he said, "it is more like grasshopper mating. Hasty marriages without putting on wedding shoes. It's worker's shoes, Western shoes, rubber shoes. I would rather have my daughter wear silk brocade shoes for one day than rubber shoes for a hundred days."

I then realized he was making shoes without orders for them. My eyes stared at the insteps, then I forgot what I was looking at. The unfinished shoe seemed to float away as it became larger until it looked like an ownerless boat on an uncharted sea. I could not understand why the farmers did not covet such a beautiful thing. As I watched the blood vessel swell in the shoemaker's neck, he continued, "They think they can buy three pairs of rubber shoes with the money they would pay for one of mine. But I would not trade one of mine for a hundred of theirs."

Young though I was, I knew he was growing poor. In autumn he did not even patch his roof, where it might leak the next summer. When his daughter came to buy beef with too little money, how much I would wish that my father might give her a generous amount! He always did.

When in late summer the alarm of a coming typhoon startled us, the wife and daughter came to our house for over-night, bringing with them a carefully wrapped bundle of silk brocade shoes. They feared their roof might blow off.

I did not realize, though, how hopeless the situation was until one spring day when his daughter told me that she would quit school and become a kitchen maid. I begged her to reconsider, promising that I would steal beef from my house to give to her if she would not leave; but that did not prevent her going. She stayed at the Tile-Roofed House earning her three meals a day.

On my way home from school, I would walk by the house, but I could not go inside. I would stand on my toes and stretch my neck trying to see her through the space between the end of the house and the sorghum hedge. I was not tall enough, especially when the hard rains washed the road down as deep as a creek. Only when she came out could I get a glimpse of her, of her full skirt, her brocade shoes. How beautiful they were—the shoes which stayed longer in the air than they did on the ground. I felt as if the Tile-Roofed House were taking away my wedding shoes.

All that spring, while the green frogs sang in the rice field, I went every day to see the moving shoes. Soon, however, the double-chinned farmer of the house found me peeping into his yard and he planted a cherry tree to fill the space where I had stood. Word got around as quickly as the light of the kerosene lamps came on after sunset in the village houses, and every man smiled at me without saying a word. Vehemently, the shoemaker said to me, "Sang Do, I won't lower the price. I'll let her wear them even in the other's kitchen. Then when she marries, I'll let her take all the shoes with her."

The wedding day he mentioned seemed remote, far beyond many mountains. I thought with despair how many straw shoes I would have to wear out to reach my wedding day. The shoemaker raised my chin with his stubby thumb and, looking into my eyes hopefully, said, "Perhaps next autumn some wedding homes will buy shoes. Then she will be able to return."

Since that spring, the cherry tree had borne ripe round fruit five times. Still she did not come back, but worked on in another's kitchen. And now, on this night after I had made my marriage talk, I decided that before the snow came I would take a big hide of ox to the shoemaker for him to make the most beautiful shoes for his daughter. On the wedding day, my family would spread the white homespun linen for the shoes to walk on, as some do in a marriage between one-fence neighbors, instead of hiring sedan chairs.

The autumn night had deepened with the stillness, and I had walked I do not know how many times around the freezing yard, before I heard the hoarse, drunken voice of the shoemaker. He was putting his own words to a popular tune: "A farmer greeted me; it is a fine autumn day; how are your pumpkins growing, shoemaker?"

Soon a light brightened the square paper window, and a shadow moved across it. The shoemaker's wife has gotten up, I thought, to meet her husband. I shivered a bit. I went out and leaned over the fence, pressing my chest against it to hear the wedding talk she would surely bring to him. At last I heard quarreling voices. The paper window was flung open as if by a wind, and the angry words flew out. "I won't give my daughter to a butcher's home."

I could not trust my ears to believe until I heard further. "Because I owe money to you butchers, did you think you could get my daughter so easily as a widower takes a servant girl? Butchers would not know that there is a matchmaker. She is the daughter of the finest silk brocade shoemaker within ten mountains."

The words came to me like round flower bowls falling one on another. His wife said something frantically, but her voice was drowned out by his cracking tones. "The flattering that comes under the tongue to get more pieces of beef has made the butcher's mind big. I am the wedding shoemaker!"

The next thing I remember is my mother standing beside me gripping my wrist and gasping, "What are you trying to do?" I found myself trembling at the gateway holding a butcher knife in my hand.

My mother snatched the knife away from me. I did not expect such strength from her. The tone of her voice was surprisingly severe. "You should not scratch others even with your fingernail. What would the people think of us butchers?"

Something clawed my insides and flattened my chest and stomach. I bit my own arm to forget that deep agony. Then I knew it was a pain that neither tomorrow nor the next day could ease. I slapped the earth and cried.

For many days I stayed in my room and avoided the sunshine as might an unmarried girl who was pregnant. When the sun was as low as the hill, I would walk up the nearest rise and bury my face in the golden foxtails and wonder how I was not crushed by such a mountain of sorrow.

Many people crossed the hill. Old women's feet looked heavier than others, some in soiled gray oxhide shoes. The sight of the shapeless shoes sickened me. I did not notice at first that they had once been silk brocade ones. They moved as heavily as my heart.

The autumn crossed the hills and went farther. Not even in the brightest field, nor on the four hills, could I see autumn. One day when no one would be surprised if snow came, I saw the matchmaker go into the shoemaker's house. My heart was past sinking lower. One thing, however, I feared: I could not endure to see the shoemaker's wife come to buy beef for her daughter's wedding and perhaps ask for a piece of hide for the shoes.

My mother knew all the anxiety of my soul, and my father knew half. He arranged to send me to Pusan to the butcher market where I was to work with my uncle. My parents hoped that outside the valley I would become calm and change my directions with the wind, and tried to tell me that there were girls everywhere. My father did not say these things to me directly, but when I left for Pusan—a short winter's day walking distance—he said with provocative vagueness: "Chase the spring wind with city girls. Then your mind won't be fixed on one girl."

Spring did come to Pusan, with soft, peppery winds from the Japan Sea. It blew the skirts of the city girls in every direction—but I did not chase the spring wind with city girls. Somehow my mind was always chasing wedding shoes, the beautiful ones my childhood had dreamed of when I had watched in the shoemaker's workroom. Strangely, I did not picture the future bride, who now belonged to the past. She and her shoes never faced me. I was always behind her, watching the backs of the silk brocade shoes and white muslin socks with the canoe-shaped line around her feet. Whenever my mind followed, they crossed hill after hill as if destined to move away from me. The shoes that contained my happiness never faced toward me.

I could not stop chasing the wedding shoes until one day the war came into Pusan. My parents fled from their valley home and came to the city to live with me. People poured into the city; with no invitation, they were guests of no house, but guests of the dusty street—road guests, they called themselves. As they could not, of course, feed their oxen, they sold them to the butchers for a dog's price. The paper money of inflation piled up in my pockets like leaves, without adding to my joy. It did not even occur to me that I was thinking about the brocade shoes no longer.

Summer passed, leaving no memory behind. I did not notice autumn until it too had almost gone. Somewhere within me, the fleeting shadow of southward birds moved over the cropped fields. I wandered in the market, vaguely looking for new rice. Then it was that suddenly my eyes fell on the wooden stool with the silk brocade shoes upon it. The nose of the shoes faced me, watching. I do not know why I went closer—only to fill my mind again with anger and bitterness. My impulse was to take all the shoes and fill them with money to show my wealth, but four or five steps before the stool I stopped. So many wrinkles had gathered in the face of the shoemaker that his twisted mouth looked like a tallowless wick. That mouth wouldn't open any more to brag. I stayed to see who would buy his shoes. No one even looked at them, except the market hangers-on who ask the price of everything. One of them shouted: "Charging sky-high price for behind-the-time shoes! Old man, you are asleep, scratching another's leg instead of your own itching one."

He remained sitting with unbending back, unmindful of their taunts. The front of his stomach looked as if it touched his back.

As his piles of shoes began slowly to diminish, I came again and again to look. The sharp feeling against him was receding farther and farther as his wares dwindled. Instead, sadness rose in me and rose again. As the days grew cold, the twisted mouth opened to draw out coughs without white breath. I wondered what would become of him when all his shoes were sold. In my mind, the coughing mouth would blur into one that had once been opened with smiles over his own wedding talks in his own warm workroom. How light the wedding shoes looked, I would think.

Then I would grow aware of the noises of the market and walk with the crowd: every kind of shoes—straw shoes, rubber shoes, hobnailed shoes, all looked so heavy. It may be that the weight is determined by the wearers. There was nothing, nothing left in this land, not even the one day of joy, the joy that would fill the mouth of the wedding shoes.

Sometimes I hoped he would recognize me. Then I would have a chance to ask him what had become of his wife and daughter. He did not notice me, however. At least, there never was a sign of recognition in his unblinking eyes, and I could not speak first. I did want to possess a pair of his shoes before all went to strangers. But I was afraid I might buy wedding shoes that were not wedding shoes. I watched his merchandise with the intensity of one who sees a night road ahead just before the moon hides behind the black clouds.

When I saw only three pairs left, I did not come any more. It was unbearable to watch the shoes whose brocaded noses faced me and know they would soon turn away.

The first snow came early. The footmarks on the road touched me as if the silk brocaded shoes had gone that way, the finest silk getting wet. Then I realized that the snow could actually be wetting the silk. I hurried back to the market, hoping the shoemaker had not brought his shoes this afternoon and, at the same time, hoping he had. I could hear my heart beat as I came near the market corner. Two pairs on the stool under a black umbrella faced me. I was glad, holding a joy in my two fists as tight as possible.

I did not see the shoemaker. Someone else was there—a yellow blanket over her drooping shoulders and her dark hair fluffed with snow. She was holding the umbrella over the shoes rather than over herself. Was she the wife of the shoemaker? At first I was not sure, she had so greatly changed; but later I knew her. The snow was falling slantwise. I wished she would wrap the shoes and take them home.

A man wearing a Western style coat and wide Korean trousers stopped and looked through his eyeglasses as he spoke to the old woman. As he was fishing in his pocket, I walked up, taking all the money I could hold in my hand, and putting it down in front of her. I said, "Here—let me buy the shoes."

The man was perhaps one who ran an antique shop or sold souvenirs, and he gave me an unhappy look. His anger might have been visible had it not been for the fluffs of snow that misted his glasses. He left, talking to himself.

She dropped the yellow blanket and pulled her head back as if my money were counterfeit and I was trying to deceive an old woman. Her gray eyes were tired, sorrowfully indifferent, like the wintry road that could not hold more shadows. I hastened to say, "I am Sang Do. Where is your husband?"

For a moment she looked at me absently, then her lips quivered violently and showed her toothless gums. I heard her crying without voice, a hoarse sound like the winter wind. I knew then a hopeless thing had happened, for I had seen the same manner of crying from old women who had lost their dear ones. I picked up the umbrella she had dropped and held it over the shoes. The flakes of snow fell at the line of the shoes. The old woman took each shoe reverently, wiped the snow from it, then placed it on a newspaper with one over the other and wrapped them carefully.

"He did not want to sell them to strangers," she said, "at rubber-shoe prices. But I chased him out from the refugee quarters every morning. He would lower the price on just one pair for two or three days. Then I nagged him again to sell. When only two pairs were left, he was stubborn as a child. He would come out to the market but always came back with two pairs—until—the cold, the empty stomach. . . ."

She did not finish her words. I did not know whether it was the snow or something else that ran down her cheeks. Then with sudden ease, she resumed. "He died in front of the silk brocade shoes. I know that was all he wanted."

She looked for a moment at the paper money I had put down on the stool before her, then handed the wrapped parcel to me as she added, "With this money, I can give him a decent burial."

My hands did not move to take the parcel. I felt as if I would be taking it from the shoemaker's hand that still held it as tightly as a sleeping child holds a willow whistle. I shook my head and said, "Keep the shoes for your daughter."

For a moment I wondered whether her daughter had married or not, then I realized it no longer mattered. She was now the owner of the silk brocade shoes. I just wished she might be alive somewhere to receive them. I folded the yellow blanket, pushed the money inside, and put it over the bundle of shoes. When I had placed them in the arms of the old woman, she held them all close for a moment, then walked out bending her head slightly as if carrying a baby.

"My daughter," she said, "is dead. She was killed last summer in the bombardment."

Ah, but I already knew. I had already felt this death in my heart. Opening the umbrella, I followed her a few steps behind, stretching my arm forward to shelter her. Someone behind us shouted, "There is a good place. Someone is moving out, leaving a wooden stool!"

Outside the market, the wind blew up snow. I brought the umbrella back to a half-open position so that the wind would not take it away, and followed, hoping she would not fall with the silk brocade shoes.

A Nest of Gentlefolk

ROBIE MACAULEY

THERE WAS A MAN OUTSIDE WHO SAID HE KNEW WHERE THE
fellow was hiding, but he had to wait until we could find
Oscar's pipe. It turned out that the pipe was in a desk drawer
just where Oscar had left it; the tension relaxed and everybody turned back to what he had been doing. "Let him in,"
Oscar said.

Oscar stood by the window putting some tobacco into the
bowl of the pipe and the two of them stared at each other
for a minute. The old German was thick in body and limb;
he might have been built, not born, he was so riveted, so
bolted, so bound, so ribbed, so keglike. You thought so until
you saw his face, which was a tender raw color and delicately
insane.

There was a long pinched nose, absolutely classic lips, fine
white hair and for eyes two blueberries that slid around in
their sockets of cream.

In whatever side street or second story we set up our
office, the CIC sign hung out like a welcome to the whole
European underworld of fantasy: a Salvation Army, a pawn-
broker's, a confessional, a zoo, a second-hand dealer in fables.
Those White Russian colonels, those Albanian slave laborers,
Mongolian deserters from the German army, Dutch Com-
munists, French spies, German anti-Nazis who had lived like

ghosts for six years—all came through our door to deposit unbelievable specimens, bones, queer fish, curios. But we examined them all, assayed them all. Now and then, stuck to the bottom of some huge ugly fake Chinese-vase of a story, we would find a genuine rare coin of truth and these were what kept us going, our margin of profit.

All this was quite unknown to Oscar, although he was the officer-in-charge. He smoked his pipe whenever he could find it, ate his dinner and filed reports with the G-2. He was a kind of proprietor who could not tell you what he bought and sold.

But I could see all of that change the moment he stared across his desk at the old German. I could see the sudden spark of imagination from freak to freak, for Oscar simply had never met one of his own kind before.

Oscar wore his air of junior-officer efficiency like some absurd garnish of camouflage; underneath it he was tallow, a fat gray candle without a wick. This strangeness the G-2 colonel (a nasty schoolmistress of a man) could not fail to notice and daily he would jab and jab Oscar with his sarcasm or, sometimes, thump him with fury when things went wrong. When Oscar returned from these meetings and sat at his desk his face looked like the face of a circus clown (the one that always gets hit) who has just stripped off the grease-paint smile and the cherry nose and sees his own naked misery in the mirror.

"Tell me about it," said Oscar to the old man, although he knew only three words of German himself. The man began in a sludgy whisper that belonged more to the trunk than the head, *"Herr Hauptmann, Ich wollte . . ."* Larry Stein, who was sitting at one of the desks, began translating without even turning around.

I had been on such chases and I knew the story before it began. There was a castle on the hilltop, rather inaccessible; the mysterious comings and goings. There was the man with the moustache seen in the garden, the servant who got drunk in the Wirtshaus and said this and that, the people on the road who looked like SS men, the plane that came over one night just after the surrender, seemed to land and then to disappear.

None of us quite realized what was happening. John Short was sitting on the field safe cleaning his fingernails and reading a copy of *Stars and Stripes* spread out on the floor in front of him. Gillespie was leaning out of the window; Larry stared at the wall and translated; I tried to finish a letter to my aunt in Muskegon who sends me lidlike peanut-butter cookies. All was tranquil. But Oscar and the German stared at each other in a frenzy.

They had been kicking aside some trash in the attic and —suddenly! Yes! They were holding it up to the light. It *was* the philosopher's stone! "Men!" Oscar shouted in a choked voice. "Get ready to move!"

He had jerked up the field telephone and wrung its lever; he was calling, "Get me Thimbleful—you, Stein, get a jeep out right away. Gillespie, the M-3's. No, no, *this* is Thimbleful CIC, what I want is Thimbleful G-2—Mac, the maps, some rations . . ."

As it turned out finally there was something wrong with the line and Oscar never got through. We had all been tramping aimlessly about, in and out of doors, up and down stairs, waiting for the moment when Oscar reached the colonel. Then after the flash of blue fire, the sudden electrocution, we would have applied artificial respiration, offered him a drink and said, "Well, after all, there *could* have been something in it."

But the colonel couldn't be reached, so here we were out in the courtyard beside the jeep—Stein, Gillespie, the German and I—loading in boxes of K-rations, field glasses, two M-3 submachine guns. Then Oscar appeared in the doorway; he was carrying a pair of handcuffs.

He turned around and yelled back to John Short inside, "Listen, Johnnie. Get through to him as soon as you can. Tell

him the whole story and say that I'll send back the co-ordi-
nates as soon as possible. Tell him to stand by; we may need
some help." Full of such spirits, Oscar came banging down
the steps and sprang into the jeep. The rest of us were quiet.
It was as if three teetotaling Baptist deacons suddenly found
themselves in a taxi with a wallowing drunk.

We were living in one end of a big sour-yellow building
that somehow had the appearance of an immense stalled
trolley car on which a black roof had been clapped. The
yard was sleepy and dusty with sunlight; at the other end
of it the German women were hanging up their wash. For
three weeks the world had not believed in this bogey, this
desperate runner, this wild refugee who now and then took
hiding in the haunted house of a mind like Oscar's.

Larry drove and Oscar sat next to him. In the back seat
I was crowded between Gillespie and the old man, who
stared and worked his lips. We switched around the corner
of the gateway and joggled down the street towards the
end of town. We passed the Postamt, the Friseur, the
Drogerie, through whose wavy greenish fishbowl windows
people peered out at us. Three old women stood like stalks
planted in the middle of the sidewalk staring at the carful,
wondering why the old fellow was being carted off like that.
A dangerous Nazi, probably, and no one had ever known!

"Little do they realize!" Gillespie whispered to me. I knew
he loved this now that we had started because he got his
greatest pleasure out of watching elaborate fireworks displays of folly that somebody else must pay for.

Oscar's face was raging calm; he studied the green map
in its glassine case. A horse and wagon backed up to let us
by, some kids sitting in the gutter shrieked at us, windows
flashed in the sun, we ran into a big puddle of shadow and
then passed through the gnawed stone arch at the town gate
and headed due south.

The landscape we were now driving through was robbed
from a copy of Grimm or Andersen; it was pure kindergarten

legend. Under that childhood-blue sky, on that road winding among meadows green as first innocence, in those Hansel-and-Gretel woods, it was possible to believe in chasing dragons. In Bavaria.

But, on the other hand, the whole country had the atmosphere of a Potëmkin village. The world had been carefully faked for our coming; the streams were colored a deeper blue, the grass and trees dyed a greener green, the buildings sprayed with artificial sunlight to give just the right antique effect, the papier-mâché hills covered with cardboard terraces, the people put into peasant costumes. A mile behind this quaint countryside was a dreary landscape where bodies of dead Jews were stacked in camps, ruined munitions factories sprawled beside greasy rivers and sullen people in ragged overcoats walked in the rain. Or that's how it seemed.

The old man looked bewitched as he sat beside me; the wind caught his hair and made it a blaze of white fire around his pink skull as he turned his sensitive face from side to side.

Larry Stein drove fast and I could see him turn toward Oscar every now and then. He was an Iroquois right out of *Leatherstocking Tales* with a profile like a chipped-flint arrowhead and a savage pragmatism. In big cities he was the world's best woodsman and guide; he had hunted and fished that wilderness alone since one day in 1936 in Berlin when he came home from school and heard that his father had been dragged off. He was trying to get Oscar to stop at another CIC detachment to pick up some help. He was describing a fortress high as Gibraltar and packed with SS men.

Oscar finally gave in. I knew Stein was hoping that someone, preferably a major, would point out what a wild-hare chase this was. So we turned where the sign said *Calliope CIC*, dipped through a hollow, passed a village with a chow line in the square, dodged round a Signal Corps truck stalled in the road, saw the village straggle, thicken again like a meandering sentence and come to a stop with a tall house like an exclamation point. On the door was written *Calliope CIC* in chalk. The huge black arrows pointing down to the cellar windows were still unerased but somebody had tried, with thin blue paint, to change the street sign from *Hermann Göring Strasse* to *George Patton Strasse*, but the point of the joke was lost in dribbles. I went inside with Oscar.

Dust on the windows, flies, wall maps, field desks, empty bottles, pfc. "Where's the C.O.?" Oscar asked. The man was dissecting a Luger on the table and he waved at a door without unsquinting his eyes from the scattered steel bowels and vertebrae in front of him. Thumps, crashes from the other room. A paper skidded out of a desk, somersaulted, hid under a chair. A crossdraft of dust in the sunshine.

When we opened the door onto a big schoolroom, four were tossing a medicine ball around and about six of them were playing football in the middle of the floor. "Captain! Captain Berry!" Oscar shouted, but a lieutenant was carrying the ball, an old knit cap stuffed with rags, and nobody paid any attention. In a minute they were all spilled on the floor, laughing and yelling.

In time Oscar was able to make the captain listen to him. The captain sat on a table (holding the ball so the game wouldn't go on without him), brushed off his uniform and listened a little to what Oscar had to say. Some of the other players came over and stood brushing their clothes off, too. "Let's go," said one of them.

"It might be dangerous," Oscar was saying. "I could use maybe half a dozen men. You know how well the big shots are guarded." The captain picked a splinter out of his knee and shook his head. There was a squabble of laughing and pushing behind him. Finally a roosterish lieutenant said, "Where is this castle?" Then he added, "How do we know it's in our territory?" "Yes!" said the captain, smiling for the first time. "How do we even know it's in our territory?"

When we had all trooped into the other room Oscar found what he thought might be the location on the German

1/25,000 situation map, which was covered by a transparent sheet marked with flags and lines in grease pencil. "About here." He spotted it with his thumb.

The captain and the lieutenant almost bumped heads; the lieutenant suddenly crowed, "Out of our territory! Six miles out of it." Straightening up, the captain assumed an orientation-lecture manner, faced Oscar and said, "That's right, Captain Hind. You can look right here at the map and you'll see that the dividing line between your divisional area and ours makes a little dip here, putting the place you're talking about definitely outside our territory."

As we went, he smiled again, his mouth the shape of a cookie cutter. "I'd give you some of my men but who knows? Something might break right here and then I'd be caught short." When Oscar was going out the door, the captain yelled, "I hope you get the old boy." Then we could hear him calling signals again in the schoolroom.

Larry was leaning forward, his arms folded over the wheel. Gillespie talked to some kids who wanted gum; the old man sat bolt upright in the back seat. "No dice?" asked Stein.

"No dice and no remarks. We're going to carry out this mission if—if—"

"We have to do it ourselves?"

"Yes," said Oscar as he climbed in. "If we have to do it ourselves."

Stein started for the main road; we traveled for over two hours. The old man kept directing Stein, leaning forward to exude his greasy whisper. Right, left there, now cross the bridge. At last we came to a little crossroads and the old man thought he'd missed a turn. We slammed to a stop. Stein turned around at him and said, "All right, you dumb bastard, you trot back and look at the sign again."

When he ran he cantered; he was like a barrel knocked end over end. He finally got to the crossroads, stared at the guidepost, came clattering back at us again. "*Richtig!*" he yelled from twenty feet away, then scrambled for the jeep, all knees and elbows, as if we might jettison him yet. "These goddamn stupid Heinies," said Stein. "*Was?*" said the old man.

We had some low hills to cross, then the road took a sickle-blade slope into a village; we could see what had happened there from a long way off. It was one of those isolated spots where some local party member, some gray-haired Volksturm lieutenant had rounded up, perhaps, a few men from the town, a dozen farmers, a Russian slave laborer or two, served out some rifles and a *Panzerfaust* and told them to fight.

It was strange the way our artillery had smashed the near end of the town like a baseball bat swung down on a tray of tumblers. The rest of it, tall brown jugs, squat jars, fat bottles, seemed to have been barely jiggled.

Out in the street at the end of hill there was a gang of prisoners in gray-green tunics shoveling up dirt and broken stone. Larry stepped on the gas and we headed for them as fast as we could. But at the last moment the bunch split up like figures in an old Harold Lloyd movie and went tumbling and diving into the rubbish on the side of the road.

The pfc. in charge of them yelled at us and Oscar, too late, said, "Slow up, slow up." Somebody told me once that Stein had killed a prisoner that way in Neustadt.

So we slowed up, we eased by the foundation-mouths surrounded by walls like broken molars with the wrecks of chimneys (shattered canines) sticking up here and there. Old women picked and searched about in these ruins and old men, ahead of us, pushed wheelbarrows of poor retrieved household stuff down the street. Stein drove on as if he would have spilled them, too, if he dared.

A block away I could see one strange place where shells had peeled away nine-tenths of a house and left the side wall standing there alone, an amazed white rind. Three feet of each floor had been preserved, and on the first story a little cupboard and a bowlegged table with a phonograph atop it huddled together like wooden children on that odd shelf.

Then I saw him; there he was. On the second story the white wallpaper with its juicy roses was quite unsmeared and in the corner stood a walnut washstand with a white towel on its arm. But in the middle of the wall staring out from behind a black frame square was our fugitive, with his shiny cap and his famous face.

It was there he was hiding, in full view yet out of reach, perched in the ruins quite safe after all, unviolated by the shell that had smashed his hosts flat into their cellars!

And it seemed that's where he would remain, until time itself obliterated him; perhaps the snow and rain would peel him off the wall like an old circus poster or eventually some wrecking crew would dynamite him down, I don't know. He watched us disappear as the jeep swung around a corner.

When the air-raid siren sounded and the iron shells (or bombs, perhaps) came down on the chinaware village, did he tremble on his wall, was he afraid? Did someone, after the family was all gathered in the air-raid shelter in the cellar, remember him and want to go back? And did somebody else viciously point out the obvious truth? What did he do when the shell hit?

Are the neighbors (if there were any afterwards) scandalized to see that he was left alive after the family was squashed by its own roof and tumbled walls? Or did they say, "Poor fellow" and wish the best for him? I wish we had stayed for the answers.

But instead we went on into the unwrecked part of town, jounced through the humpbacked streets and finally came out on a country road which we followed for three-quarters of an hour. At last the old man asked Stein to stop. He pointed ahead and to the left where the towers of a castle on a tall hill looked pink in the sun like wax candles on a birthday cake. He said he would wait for us until we brought the prisoner back. Then he would claim his reward. He sat down by the side of the road and even Oscar was glad to get rid of him.

In ten minutes we were on the road that squirmed upwards

from the base of the hill towards the now unseen castle. The meadows gradually lowered themselves and became indistinct; after a long low-gear period, the road at last began to level off.

From there it crossed a bridge and lifted up across a little slope to a wide crested gate. All this in soft focus: colors were like paint smears; the air was full of dust and sun, three white geese wandered on the arched stone bridge, the trees wavered in the breeze, a white pompom of a cloud floated over the castle. In a moment Jeanette MacDonald, dressed in a peasant costume, might have stepped out to sing. But instead it was a tall old man in black, carrying a canvas case; we nearly ran him down.

The brakes agonized shrilly; we all bounced forward when the jeep's heels dug in, the geese ran in flop-winged panic, the old man staggered and dropped his little bag. Oscar swiveled the muzzle of a submachine gun at his stomach.

The dust settled for a minute. Now what? "Put down that gun," the old man said. His authority was native because you saw it in his face and eyes while Oscar had only his captain's bars, a poor ersatz at best, so Oscar lowered the M-3 back to its place beside the seat. The old man did not move out of his place in the road. He was very tall in a way both ministerial and military. He had white ogive eyebrows; he looked a little like Norman Thomas.

Now he was smiling; he picked up his canvas case again. "And who are you, sir?" he said, quite naturally taking the question that belonged to Oscar. Respectfully Oscar told him. (Oscar seemed to be reminding himself that, even though captured, he did not legally have to tell more than his name, rank and serial number.)

"And what do you want?"

Not one of us had ever imagined the moment of our being asked that awful, that ridiculous question. It was the trick cigar that blew up in Oscar's face (getting us all a little black). For the first time, I think, since the old man had stepped into the office, Oscar saw clear. But it was too late. All he could do was mumble and look at his hands.

After three or four minutes it was Stein who finally had to say it. We were all startled at last when the name came out. It sounded like an obscenity that has long since passed out of use.

The old man had picked up a caterpillar from a leaf in the meantime, but when he heard that name he was suddenly affected with humor. He dropped the caterpillar and staggered back against a tree, surrounding it with his black broadcloth arm and giving a pleasant andante laugh.

At last he saw how impolite he was being, for we all sat there frozen and Oscar's face was jerked out of shape with pain. He recovered, he straightened up, he tried to make it seem that he had never laughed at all.

"Gentlemen," he said with grace, "allow me to introduce myself. I am Adrien, the Comte de Montfort, and I am in charge of this property, which belongs to my relatives, the Hohenlohe. I shall be pleased to have you inspect it, by all means. I have several guests at present—refugees from other places—however, you may see for yourself that this person is not among them."

Then he came forward and sat down on the fender of the jeep. Stein started; we rolled across the bridge, up the incline and through the gate into a big bumpy courtyard paved with stone. The castle front that faced us was like a being partly dressed in armor, partly in knee breeches, wearing gaiters, a tuxedo coat and a tricornered hat. Victorian bay windows were cut into battlemented medieval towers and under stretches of mansard roof there were hints of baroque, rococo, the Greek revival.

As we got out of the jeep, the Count motioned toward a gate in a six-foot stone wall. "My friends are in the garden. Perhaps you would like to meet them first? To search there?" Oscar did not dare answer as he followed the Count like a newly captured burglar. But there was no patronizing sound in the Count's voice; it was all hospitality. He even made Oscar enter the gate first.

"This was in medieval times the castle refectory," the Count went on in his bland voice. "The roof was destroyed in a fire and never rebuilt. Later generations established here this delightful English garden."

And, in fact, it was delightful. There were flat little highways of gravel leading through the grass, seats, arbors, great cloudy green bushes, plots of flowers, low-swinging trees and even a fountain that could be heard far away.

There were people moving about near the other end; we saw pastels of gowns and heard their voices. An old lady in a long lavender dress with a figure thin and upright as a twisted paper spill, with a hat like a full platter on her head, came sailing down the lane at us.

A few yards away she called in a delicate voice, "Oh, they are American soldiers, but are the Russians not coming then?" The Count answered, "Do not be afraid, Mathilde. The Russians are not coming. These American gentlemen have simply paid us a visit. They were—looking for a friend."

She had reached us now and the Count made introductions. The Countess Mathilde von Giech, he said. Her face seemed to be made of a fine gray crepe paper, its system of wrinkles was so minute and complex. She had no lips to speak of, a neat blade for a nose and clever buttonhole eyes. Her hands were like ancient ivory keepsakes.

"Do come," she said, selecting my arm, "and have some tea with us." And so we walked down the path towards the tea table, hearing the sound of water from the fountain and the even gentler tones of those noble voices as we came near.

The Count made a courtly occasion of our introduction, giving our full names and presenting each of the old ladies and the old men in the vicinity of the table by his or her title in French. Thus Graf von Hardenberg (cavalry moustaches, clipped white head) became le Comte de Hardenberg; Principe di Castagneto (bone-bald, a doggy, jowly face) became le Prince de Castagneto; and another Italian lady (an Alp for a bosom, waterfall of double chins) became la Marquise de Soragne. We were lost in a snowstorm of names from the *Almanach de Gotha.* I heard Prince Boris Massalsky, le Chevalier de la Tour d'Auvergne, I heard Thurn-und-Taxis, Hohenlohe-Bartenstein, Ehrenreich, Plettenburg-Wittenstein, Wurmbrand, Durcheim and a dozen others, famous and ancient.

Some of the old men and a few of the old women looked haughty and stared, but only for a minute because most of them smiled, bowed a little and several of them began to talk to us all at once as the servant was giving us cups of tea and bread with cherry jam.

None of them was under sixty and most seemed to be nearer seventy or eighty. Their clothes denied any change in fashion since the turn of the century. Their conversation, as it began again, was a concert; their voices rose and fell like virginals and harpsichords, antique but in good tune yet. Here and there among the faded colors of faces and clothes stood out the brilliance of a dyed waxed moustache, a ribbon in a buttonhole, or the glint of a precious stone. But generally everything was subdued, polite and gently obscure; the direct sunlight was never invited here. After the introductions everyone turned to the business of tea.

The Countess Mathilde had drawn me to one side and we were sitting in a little arbor forested on three sides by cool leaves.

"Do you know," she said, "that we have been anxiously listening to the wireless and awaiting you for several weeks?" She smiled into my eyes with just a shred of flirtation.

"Anticipating your coming? Oh my, yes. We talked about it often and the Principe even said that we should repel you with halberds—he was joking, of course. Then when the first of your Americans arrived we could hardly believe that they were soldiers! Such innocents, such smooth-cheeked young boys!" She sat next to me as if she were riding sidesaddle:

balanced, alert, always carrying the reins of conversation lightly in her hand.

"They drove up in your little military automobiles and spoke to Count Adrien—we were all here in the garden. They insisted on searching the Schloss—for hidden Nazis, I suppose.

"And what do you think they did then, sir? None of us would believe it! Somewhere among the goods stored in the cellar they discovered a bag of golf clubs and several balls. So they took them and drove down to the meadow just below the Schloss there and we could see them all afternoon knocking those little golf balls about!" She laughed her pretty canary-bird laugh, pitched at the right gentleness so as not to offend me and ceasing soon enough to avoid all hint of excess.

"My great-grandfather was one of the generals who defeated Napoleon Buonaparte, you know," she said. "He would not have surrendered so easily! I think he would have tried to shoot your soldiers. He might easily have done so too, they were so unaware." She stopped for a moment and considered the toe of her shoe.

"But then, I suppose you would have dropped a bomb on him long before he had a chance to do any harm."

The Count had led Oscar off down a garden path to an aperture in the wall that overlooked the countryside; and there they stood, peering through our field glasses, the Count pointing to certain spots on the plain now and then. Gillespie sat on a long wooden seat with Prince Boris Massalsky, the Chevalier de la Tour d'Auvergne and a small German lady whose veins ran under her transparent skin like blue silk threads. They were speaking rapid French: four violins all going at top speed.

I looked around for Stein and suddenly I saw him. Full of smiles he was approaching the group of old men and ladies seated around the tea table. He was speaking to the Graf von Durcheim, offering a pen and a notebook and I heard him say in a candy voice, "*Entschuldigen, Herr Graf, ich möchte Ihre Unterschrift haben . . .*" He was getting all their autographs.

The Countess Mathilde began to talk again. "In any case, we were overjoyed to see the Americans when they arrived. I was so afraid that it would be the Russians who got here first. Prince Boris has described to us how barbarous the Bolsheviks are—worse than savages or cannibal islanders, he says, and quite capable of killing us all."

"But weren't you sorry to see your country defeated?" I asked.

"My country?"

She looked surprised. "Oh, you must mean Germany. No, I don't think so." There was an old lady in a garden chair who was signaling to her with a handkerchief.

"Our wars were won and lost a long time ago, you know," she said. Then she excused herself to go to her friend.

I talked to the gentleman on my left for a while (his English was not nearly so good); then I looked up to see Oscar, the Count, the Countess Mathilde and Stein together by the entrance to the castle. Oscar was motioning. Gillespie and I excused ourselves and went toward them.

Oscar was trying to get away now and the Count was urging us to tour the castle with him. "It is of a certain historical interest," he was saying, "although it dates from a rather late medieval period."

The Countess drew me aside to say good-bye. She whispered, "The Count has told me whom you are looking for. My dear boy (please don't mind my calling you that), do not believe for a single minute that we would tolerate such a creature here! It's quite impossible!"

She drew herself up straighter than ever and the flora of her hat seemed to tremble with invisible storms. "Not for a minute!" Her whisper was sharper than a saw blade. "You have no idea how ill-bred and vulgar that man is said to be!"

When we had finally said good-bye, the Count took us through the castle. Part was made up of enormous echoing halls, panoplies, rooms with thickets of antlers on the walls, vast stone floors and blackened paneling. We had a look into the other part—the apartments where the guests lived, which were nondescript, Victorian and comfortable. The Count took us up in a tower, showed us a suit of armor an ancestor had been killed in and finally offered to take us through the cellars. Oscar impatiently refused. He kept saying, "Well, it's getting a little late now, I'm afraid . . ." But the Count always had one more wonder.

Finally Oscar said flatly that we must go. The Count raised his hand, smiling around at all of us. "But not yet, gentlemen. I have saved the best for the last. Here is something you must not miss. I should consider myself most ungracious if I allowed you to depart without having seen it." He led us down a hall, unlocked a door and brought us into a large sunny room, lined all around the walls with tall wooden cabinets and having a long trestle table running down the center.

The Count went across to a cabinet by the window and drew from it a shallow wooden tray; he then laid it on the table. The sun struck it and for a moment I thought it was filled with great jeweled brooches and buckles of a shining blue. They were butterflies.

"For, gentlemen," said the Count, "this is one of the finest collections of *Lepidoptera* in the whole world. Here you see an exhibit of *genus morpho*, the beautiful South American creatures—these are the *Didius* and the *Menelaus*." He was bringing out more of the glass-topped trays. "The *Venus* and the *Cacique*," he said. One was a deep blue with two white dotted lines and the other was patterned in blue with white and deep-yellow rings. "Here is the *Sulkowsky*," the Count said, putting another tray on the table, "and the *ega*."

We went on to cases of The Great Peacock Moth, the *Apollo* butterfly (his were the best he knew of) and a great display of bird-winged butterflies that the Count, as a young man, had captured in Asia—the *Croesus, D'Urville's, Priam's,* the *Pegasus.*

As we went around the table we spent exactly the correct time admiring each tray. If we showed a tendency to move away too fast, the Count's long hand would go out and he would commandingly point out this or that unusual marking or some specimen exceptionally rare.

Our impatience grew and grew until it took all of the Count's control to suppress Oscar's long sighs and obvious fidgets. The tide of shadow rose in the room and even the gleam of the bright wings began to be obscured. The Count talked on and on, telling long stories of the hunt and pointing out the beauty of the game. "I associate them with the beauty and glory of the past," he said.

Oscar finally spoke up, rebelled against the soft tyranny. We must leave immediately. He had an appointment this evening. But the Count had been expecting it. "Now!" he said. "The final thing. The dessert, as it were. Five more minutes, gentlemen." He led us over to the far corner of the room, wiped his fingers on his handkerchief and slowly and ceremoniously drew a black frame, narrow and longer than the others, from a drawer.

At first all we could make out underneath the glass was a black tangle of lines, a huge arabesque. The Count waited a moment before he explained.

"This," he said, "was presented to me by an admirer, a Swiss schoolteacher to whom I once showed my collection and who, in gratitude, constructed this unusual memento."

"But what is it?" asked Stein.

The Count smiled in his satiric way at Oscar. But I think he was really smiling at all of us.

"Don't you see?" he asked. "It is my initials—*A,* small *d, M* —written out in flowing script by means of a splendidly matched series of marching earwigs and stag beetles."

Mexican Hayride

WILLARD MARSH

NIGHT LAY OVER LAKE CHAPALA WITH THE PERMANENCE OF settled ruins. There were no sounds to it, no future. Creased shadows in the hills denied the moon to certain tilted cornfields, bared others to the granite evening. It could have been the San Francisco headlands, and Warner waited for the fog's far harbingers: its first deep diaphones speaking profoundly from Point Bonita to Mile Rock to Lime Point to the great orange Bridge itself, then all the littler heralds urging the alarm, hooting from shelf to ship to inlet to pier as startled gulls revolved above the rocking buoys . . . But the only tumult was the mush and oscillation of his own mortality, auricle to ventricle; the only gulls the buzzards in their sere roosts, who by day considered him and took the long view. Now the sky began widening with wind. A night bird entered, whistling up its dinner or its mate. Whistling in echo, but not expecting anything of it, Warner took the cobbled climb from shore.

Farmers and their families were dropping off the buses from outlying villages, setting up their sidewalk emporiums (no taxes, no overhead, out of the high rent district). Avocados stacked in fives, unchanged since the Tarascan bazaars, a peso a pyramid; melons fresh from the vine and scallions clotted with warm earth. The movie had already started, the late arrivals hurrying inside with their chairs. The programs were made up of newsreels, interspliced with a U.S. Western featuring stars long resident in Forest Lawn, but young and fearless here forever. There were occasional Spanish subtitles. Those who could read repeated them in unison for those who couldn't. Now and then the cinema folk would do something immoral or incomprehensible or simply dull, and the Mexicans would whistle severely, the way one does at a bull ring when the matadors refuse to earn their handsome fees. It seemed to have little effect. Warner's countrymen would soon be gathering for canasta or charades, followed by loud bad Bach and bad flat highballs. It was Sunday. But then it's always Sunday in the American colony.

He cut up toward the Spring of Grace. Women were grouped around it balancing water jugs, their strong hips braced against the weight and seeming continuous with their lesser vessels. A packtrain of firewood came jogging through the dusk. The burros passed him with forlorn liquid eyes, like backslid deer in an evil incarnation. Across the street stood a Packard, six years older than it was when it arrived here, but still serviceable. Ask the lady who owns one. The lady was also six years older and could stand it less.

Her house was dark, her door agape, as always. Her dog leaped on Warner in the shadowed hallway, whining with delight and bumping its clumsy butt against him. Warner cuffed it on the snout, and assuming he was playing, it fell into a fit of capering and barking.

"Now, Puppyduckles, quit that ruckus," a sugary voice from inside sang, then: "*Quiennn?*"

"Only us chickens," Warner called, coming up into the patio.

On the rope-bed that doubled as a couch he made out the forms of Victory Richmond and Dionisio Gomez, bundled under a serape. They brought their hands out from beneath—Victory a little self-consciously as she sat forward to light the lamp.

"Well, Warner, I haven't seen you in a month of Sundays."

"How's ever little thang, Miss Victory? *Qué tal, hombre?*" He nodded to Dionisio.

"*Q'hubo*, Huarner?" he answered lazily.

"My, I didn't have the least idea it was so dark. I expect one's eyes get accustomed. We were just sitting here discussing a chair Dionisio's mending for me."

"He's quite a mender," Warner said, taking a cowhide chair opposite them. There was a silence. "Clever with his hands," he clarified.

"Yes, well, and then you know how these things go in Spanish." Victory fanned herself with a magazine. "The time it can consume."

"You mean it takes longer in Spanish? I always heard it was the other way around."

She managed to look maligned. "I don't believe I care for your insinuations, Warner."

"Was I insinuating again? God damnit, I'll never learn to speak directly."

"That's a very definite trait in your character, I've noticed. Suspicion."

He winked at her deliberately. She struggled to remain slurred Southern womanhood, then gave up, laughing.

"Contrary to what you're thinking, I don't spend *all* my time that way."

Quite an attractive lady, this Mrs. Richmond, Warner thought. Rather eerily so, because before too much longer she'd be half a century old. She had one of those lucky complexions that would last as long as she would, plus sensibly cut blonde hair and a durable figure from which she wrung the liquor calories by fanatic afternoons of ping-pong. But it was mostly love and laughter, equally unmotivated, that kept her supple.

"Care for a Pepsi, Warner?" When Victory was on the wagon, everyone was on the wagon.

"No, thanks." He was too lazy to get one from the icebox.

"There's fresh lemonade if you'd prefer. The pitcher's over yonder."

"That's a thought. Got any rum to cut it with?"

"The maid hid it."

"Where?"

"How should I know?"

"I mean, got any ideas?"

She was only politely concerned. "No telling how her mind connives. Reckon you should try the well?"

"The well?" Warner hiked over to it, pulled the bucket up. A wicker jug of Bacardi was nestled in it. A clear case of clairvoyance. It turned out that Victory would also have a little dash of rum, just a smidgen, in her lemonade. Dionisio had his straight.

Absently lowering half her glass, Victory said, "How's your play progressing, Warner?"

"I ought to finish this scene I'm on next month."

"Isn't that just grand?"

Now it was his turn. "How's the sculpting coming?"

"Well, ordinarily, wild horses couldn't drag me from it. But I've had to wear myself to the bone with *this* one," she jabbed an elbow in Dionisio's ribs, "getting him to comprehend the *simplest* work I want done. Honestly, if I waited for him to exercise the least scrap of initiative I'd be dead and buried. Warner honey, would you float a teeny weeny bit of rum on top of this? It's awfully concentrated lemonade."

Bored by all the English, Dionisio picked up the guitar he'd sold Victory and was theoretically teaching her. He began singing, in the pleasant near-falsetto that in Mexico, as well as Ireland, every male seemed born with.

"*Arroz con leche*
Me quiero casar
Con una muñeca
De este lugar . . ."

The village waxed and waned with the lake, and in the dissolutely handsome face of Dionisio Gomez you could read its present level. If it were higher, permitting fishing and swimming, there would be a flood of tourists with chairs requiring mending and occasions requiring street-singers. The merchants would prosper, and Dionisio would be carpentering by day and working the fiestas by night, growing fat and dull and moral. His wife could buy material for twenty dresses if she liked, his children could have toys in abundance. And as for his mistress, she would be a *muñeca* of this locality (as he was singing), shy and unhandled, and speaking only when she was addressed. Instead of this witless pampered whore (as he would put it) who spoke no sense continuously in a barbaric tongue, and from whom he was forced to accept money which, though he more than earned it, was a reflection on his integrity and could only be assuaged by quantities of her rum, which only made him sullen.

"*Qué te parece, hombre?*" Warner asked him. "Will the lake regain its height someday?"

"Why not?" Dionisio said irritably. "If this cuckolding draught abates and there be rains. Provided that your countrymen devise no bigger bombs to change the weather."

"I'll write my senator," Warner told him.

He smiled sourly and shifted into a brisk canteen tune. He played as well as he ever would, since it was beneath a musician's dignity to practice once he got to be a *maestro*.

"*O-lay!*" Victory clapped her hands. "Isn't he just heavenly? It's that Spanish blood, it'll tell every time. If only he didn't incline to drink so heavily." She rumpled his hair reprovingly.

"What is this that she says now?" he asked Warner.

"That you are number one of the guitar."

He grunted. "Your brains come in bottles," he told her, and pointed at the rum jug. "Educate yourself!"

But she was busy studying the flat planes of his face. "If he isn't the *spit*-image of some old Toltec idol. I'm simply going to *have* to do a bust of him."

Warner helped himself to another few inches of Sr. Bacardi's blonde balm. Dionisio was puzzling out the melody line of something, getting as far as the fifth bar when he'd bog down each time. Victory sighed.

"They're just like children, aren't they? Not a solitary grief in all creation. The church baptizes them and the church buries them, and in between it does their thinking." She grabbed Dionisio's hair and shook his head. "Don't you want to *make* something of yourself? Don't you want to go back to America with me and get on television?" He ignored her.

"Just like talking to a stone wall. Look," she told him, "*oo-sted*," she jabbed him in the chest, "you," she prodded her hospitable bosom, "*el Estados Oo-nidos? Mucho dinero?*"

"*Como Diós quiere*," he said dryly. As God wishes.

"There, you see?" Victory said in sad triumph. "I'd give anything if I could have their simple faith. Oh well, I don't care to trouble myself about the hereafter." With the rum beginning to reach her, she turned moody. "I'm a fatalist. There's no way of changing what's to come. Let's live awhile before we have to pay for it."

There was a clatter of feet in the hallway, and Cassius came running in. The dog sprang up, tackling him halfway, and after wrestling with it briefly he broke loose. Thwarted, it doubled back and leaped into Warner's chair. He smacked it heavily in the side and it fell down, wagging its tail and barking frenziedly.

"Now, Warner, don't encourage her," Victory said. "If she gets too excited she makes doo-doo on the mats. Well, young man, it's high time you were coming in for supper."

Cass came on up, panting. He greeted Warner as coolly as he dared with his ten years. Then he edged over to the table and glanced in Victory's glass casually.

"We were taking a little lemonade for refreshment," she said quickly. "There's more in the pitcher."

He picked up her glass and sniffed it.

She took it from him with a silvery laugh. "You don't want

this, dear. I let Warner put a little rum on top to be sociable."

"Better lay off it," Cass said.

"Why, what on earth—I'm *ashamed* I heard you say that," Victory said. "Just what was the nature of that innuendo, pray?"

The boy turned away in defeat. "Listen, I got to have two pesos. I need a tablet for school."

"You do, do you?" she said. "Well, it may interest you to know I'm not putting out one red cent more for tablets. I'll give you the opportunity to speak straightforward. What happened to the one I gave you money for last week?"

Cass was trapped. "Chuey's goat ate it."

Victory laughed, the perspective restored once more between indulgent mother and transparent child.

"How can you keep ahead of them?" she told Warner. "All right, run ask Alberta where my purse is, and tell her to fix you and Warner a plate of whatever's in the oven."

Warner went through the motions of refusing his only meal since breakfast, but to no avail. Back from the kitchen, Cass shyly settled himself at the feet of Dionisio, whom he placed in a stabler category than his mother's other gentlemen callers.

"What must a man do, Dionisio, if insulted by a stronger man?"

"*Pos*, Cass, no man is as strong as the edge of a knife."

"Yes, but I am not yet a man."

"Someone gave you insult?"

"To me, no. To my mother."

"An insult of what nature?"

"That she was a woman of moral irresponsibility, liberal with her body."

"Who said this?"

"The nephew of Eliseo of the goats."

"The fat one with the cockeye?"

"No, the tall one of the measle scars."

"I will speak to Eliseo. There will be no more of this."

"Your word?"

"My word . . ."

Self-consciously, Warner picked up one of Cass's comic books. Soon he was a gullible tourist in a realm where a mouse named Miguelito Ratoncito was the owner of a foolish, talking dog, and a duck known as Pato Pascual went fox hunting. At the bottom of each page there would be inspirational slogans. *Save: you gain and Mexico progresses. Prefer the book that educates, not the alcohol that debases.*

Now Alberta brought their plates in, and Cass kept her running for fresh tortillas. They made pretty fair tacos when the canned pork and beans were rolled in them. They also had pork chops, a little burnt, but more free from trichinosis that way. Cass was talking and waving a taco, and it dribbled on him.

"Cassie dear, I *wish* you could learn to cultivate a few graces at the table," Victory said. "You're getting to be as bad as the Mexicans."

He nodded absently, finished bolting his food and cut for the door.

"Cassius! You're not to leave the house this evening, you hear? You're keeping entirely too late hours, you need the sleep for school."

"I'll be right back," he called. "We got a calf cornered down at Lalo's barn and I have to fight it." And he was gone.

Victory sighed, reaching for the rum. "Sometimes I just can't fathom that child's attitude. Be a lamb, Warner, and fetch the lemonade?"

By the time he got back out on the street, Jesús Ochoa was getting ready to crank down the Virgin-blue riot door of his grocery shop named The Eternal Struggle. A short fat man of military leanings, armed with a moustache like Zapata's, he was scowling hideously at the prosperity of his adjacent competitor, The Sun Shines for All. His vegetables were deployed in tidy ranks, like the bric-a-brac retired colonels use to reconstruct old battles.

"Yes, sir," Warner said. "Another day, another dollar."

Jesús smiled blankly. "*Mánde?*"

"No importance. How is the señora?"

"Well, thanks."

"And the children?"

"Also. Without novelty. And yourself?"

"Equally. And the crops?"

Jesús shrugged. "Average, no more."

"And the midnight crop?" Warner asked delicately.

He assumed a guarded expression. Cautiously, he removed a packet from a locked drawer. Fifty grams' worth. They settled on a price of two pesos, which was put on Warner's tab, along with half a *litro* of cane alcohol. Part way back to Doña Felipe's, the lights went out all over town. Lightning in the mountains, maybe, or just some truck colliding with a pole. Warner eased his way through the extinguished streets, beneath a wind-driven moon, to the *posada* door; felt out the bellrope and leaned on it. After a while the old girl slapped on down to let him in, her lantern shedding a waxen path back to the patio.

From its trellis the *teléfono* vine, the width of Warner's finger, sprawled like a stunned snake, its dark green leaves glistening richly as a pelt. Growing from a deceptively small pot, like a cobra from a basket, it lay in a digestive stupor. Almost half as old as himself, it was, like himself, a carnivore. Doña Felipe treated it regularly to saucers of blood, on which it thrived and fattened and waited through the hungry evenings, its thousand pointed leaves thrust out like tongues.

The *doña* raised her lantern. "Shall I make a little omelette for you, Señor Huarner?" she asked hopefully.

"Thanks, no. I have already eaten."

She left him to the shadows, pleased at having just the one meal on his day's bill. Miz Richmond's imported pork-and-beans were still a gluey filler in his stomach, and he wondered if the *teléfono* vine had done as well. They considered one another in the rustling night. What was it that cannibals called fillet of human? Long pig. Care for a spot of Dr. Livingston's Long Pork and Beans, you bastard? Next time I cut myself shaving I'll give you a break.

Then, dialing the combination lock, Warner let himself into the door of his home and castle.

It was composed of one large room, with adobe walls unadorned except by whitewash. There were no pinups, pots of sweet peas, conversation pieces. Instead, he had four blank screens for the projection of whatever whimsies or horrors he was given by euphoria, either self-induced or chemically assisted. There was a table with a typewriter, a shelf of books. A chair, ashtrays, et cetera, and upstage left a bed, for the development of the Freudian underlife.

Now he took his half a quart of pure cane alcohol, one hundred ninety proof, and mixed it with half a quart of reasonably pure water. This gave him one full quart of ninety-five proof white rum, otherwise known as Old Doc Warner's Sunday Punch. Next, he carefully shook out the packet Jesús had given him. The stuff was unworked, just as it came stripped from the plant. There were seeds with it, about the size of barley, and pieces of stem; but it was mostly dried and crumbled leaves, olive drab, somewhat resembling oregano. A little more piquant, however. By a process of tilting and scraping it the heavier impurities were separated, and he ended up with a tiny mound of powder known to all good Fagins variously as tea, jive, pot, hay, hemp, Maryjane.

Rolling himself a stick of it, Warner lit up and drew a lungful, along with some air for carburetion. He held it as long as he could, gradually exhaled, seeing his streaked breath in the candlelight; got that metallic after-taste, shuddered, coughed and lit a natural cigarette. Three drags later and the chore was done, the psyche cast adrift. For the next odd ninety minutes he would be someone else's creature.

He wound the clock, reality's compass, and arbitrarily set it for midnight. He would be free at 1:30. But if the clock stopped, he was done for; there'd be no way of ever getting back.

The lights came back on, the sudden glare jarring him. He snapped them off, poured a shot of alcohol to set the marijuana, and with the smell of burnt weeds in the air he settled back to wait for news from Shangri-la.

It wasn't long in coming. First, from far away, there was the sound of the sea in his ears, the way you'd hear it through a faulty sea shell. Then this sea gently tugged at his extremities, cooling them and causing them to tingle. The tide rose, gathering and carrying him, and he was lifted from his chair to stand enormous in its seething center, clear-headed, bared and buoyant.

Then in that ever new and startling way, the shift set in. Perspective warped, so imperceptibly that it could only be detected sideways. Contours were softened, but in no way blurred. And now a great inner organ of perception opened, like the engaging of an unused brain lobe. Through it, Warner became minutely aware of himself, the branching of the capillary system, the breathing of the pores, the hustling ganglia and the old persistent heart, revving like a stone engine. He monitored these activities for quite some time (directing them, in fact) in awe and wonder. He expanded with self-appreciation. God *damn*, he thought, this is *some* hay.

Suddenly everything was funny. The way the chair set at such a ludicrous angle to the floor, the silly-assed candle consuming itself, and his drunken, grotesque self. His stomach worked in convulsive spasms of laughter. Then quite abruptly, he was sober.

Warner picked up the clock. It was five past midnight.

He sat down, emptied of any emotion whatsoever, waiting for something he couldn't quite remember—and then it started up again, beginning to lift him on a new and higher wave. He hurried to the typewriter, wanting to be ready when it broke.

It took the damnedest time to get a sheet of paper in the machine. His hands were uncoördinated, like a spastic's; he was way ahead of his body.

Finally Warner groped open his play folder, with its scribbled notes on characters, the half-assembled scenes, the clever exits and the midnight flashes. Ignoring all external trivia such as the interpenetration of his fingers with the space bar, he began to put it all down. There were no doubts now, no reservations. He saw his entire play, from the opening curtain to the last slow close, the action vivid and convincing, the people bursting with life. But the mechanics of translating it to paper kept getting in the way. Each word that leaped to print swarmed with rich new vistas of association, and the exploration of them was compulsive. Simultaneously, there was a canny campaign taking place to resist this compulsion, to smuggle out the message.

Come on, fool, say it. It's never been so comprehensible. Indispensable. Consequenceable, evidenceable, uncondensable— uncon*den*sable? Now really, Warner, what kind of woolly terminology is this? Why, it's beautiful terminology, so I guess you can go poop, Warner. Poop, is it? Just for that I guess you can have a knee in the brisket.

Gradually, a mellow lassitude invaded him, pinning his arms to the table. He'd make it yet, if not tonight some other night. He couldn't miss. . . .

He came back to himself with the feel of boulders being rolled from his chest. His heart was jumping like a rabbit in a sack. He could move again. We've been away for quite a while, haven't we? Next time leave a forwarding address.

The clock read 12:22.

He picked it up in a panic of disbelief, shook it. He'd been completely loaded, *stoned*, for at least one full hour. He *knew* it had been at least an hour. That meant he couldn't trust himself, because he was only twenty-two minutes along, with the peak yet to come. At that rate it might be hours—days, even, before he got in phase with time again. *Maybe never,* a voice chuckled in his skull. After all, it's called loco weed, isn't it? You poor son of a bitch, you've skewed yourself into insanity and you'll never make it back.

Warner sat in quiet terror, up to the forehead, those delicate prefrontal lobes with their fused synapses, in a pool of ice water. Nothing significant in itself had changed. He was aware of shapes and objects, but there was just a terribly thin screen between them and himself.

Then, while he waited in the void, he realized that it was 12:23.

All the filaments of his body brimmed with relief as he watched the clock hand moving, the slow wheel ferrying him home. Only an hour more to go. He'd make it, no matter how long it took. Pushing aside the folder entitled *Six Authors in Search of a Character*, he decided this wasn't his night. Instead, he began another letter to the girl he used to introduce to people as his first wife.

Dear Gerry:
I made a little poem for you, a non-heroic couplet.
G
Me
No period, because it never stops.
Remember Russian Hill in San Francisco, in the rain, the bay full of foghorns and the air with bells? And you, adrift on the up-anchored night beside me, while the lisping rain communicated with the roofs. From the window I could see two muffled stars, enough to steer by. Fresh from the fevered country of your hair, I'd watch your body curving to the mattress' polarity. You slept, the rain's casual syllables went past; while I, child of short memory in the banished wood, would search your pollen-heavy lids & that herbed mouth loose from love's small language, for the warm way back. And now my love the angel bitch, my first and last wife Oh she sleeps in other climates now oh now is the time for all good alienists to come to the aid of a wandering client who can't lie still

long enough to get a Junging, Ranking, Reiching, and most especially a thorough Berglerizing and be robbed of all necessity to be himself?

He cradled his head on the typewriter. It made a Gerry-cold lap for him, and he must have slept a little. Eventually it was 1:30, as it had to be, and he was out of it.

He reached for the lights, but they were off again. As his hand paused above the dwindling candle Warner could see his wrist vein throbbing, and for the first time in his life he understood that some day, between two pulses, it would stop. And now he knew that Victory Richmond understood all this, and more. For once she was dead, she'd have to go to hell.

His pulse picked up its canter, merged with the rhythm of the nightly herd of wild burros as they came galloping down the cobbles, their breaths whuffing in the stone-rung evening. The candle bluttered.

I wish I could tell Victory it's not so bad in hell, he thought. At times it's really not so bad at all.

Man Waiting

WARREN MILLER

HE WAS A COURTEOUS YOUNG MAN AND LIKED, AT LEAST, to give the impression he was listening; but there was Mexico City just at the corner of his eye, seven storeys below, and occasionally he averted his eyes from the lawyer's face and, for a moment only, saw the green Alameda Central and the tops of taxis going past. The lawyer slowly translated for him the documents he would have to sign, and paused and hummed when he could not immediately think of the English word. He sounded, Charles thought, like a faulty generator.

The lawyer held up the document so that Charles could see there was, indeed, writing on it and that the whole thing was not rigged. Charles, of course, knew it was rigged. Signing this paper, he told himself, is not going to change anything. He felt exceedingly remote from the law. With a silver pencil the lawyer underlined each word as he read it. Charles thought he was being treated like a backward student. It is the Remedial Reading class, he told himself; I am bright, but inattentive. I could learn if I really wanted to, but I have a tendency to dream. Charles recalled the Notes from the Teacher on old report cards he had carried home.

And with what kind of a sensation did you carry them home, Charles? he asked himself. I carried them home with a *sinking* sensation, he answered, and smiled, commending himself. You turn a pretty phrase. Teachers had always said of him: Charles could learn if he wanted to. They did not understand that he really did want to. That's the thing, Charles said to himself, thinking about it. That's the thing; I really wanted to. Am I really erratic? he asked himself. Or have I defrauded everyone? Perhaps at bottom I am merely dull. He did not know. He could not decide. He crossed his legs.

The lawyer's silver pencil, U.S. made, moved smoothly across the page and back again. "And you mmmm-ah, you mmmm-ah acted in a manner not husbandly but brutal and mmmm-ah failed to acquit yourself of your duties domestical." The lawyer removed the pencil from the paper, waved it, and shrugged his shoulders; he wanted Charles to know that he himself did not believe these things; he apologised that the courts and laws made such statements necessary.

Out the corner of his eye Charles saw the park again and could hear, when the wind was right, the tatters of the Tchaikovsky piano concerto being played there on the public address system. It was the new recording by Bonćleeborn, the prize-winning pianist from Tayhas; the day before his taxi driver had told him this. Charles had not been surprised; he had been told by many of his friends that culture was a very big thing in Mexico; and one of the first things he had seen—on the road from the airport to the city—was a big sign that said, in a Spanish Charles could read: *Show your culture by observing the signs.* Charles approved of culture, on the whole; it had given him a warm feeling to see such a road sign.

Yes, we can learn a thing or two from these so-called backward countries, he said to himself, putting a sententious look on his face. The lawyer misread the look and stopped reading. He said to Charles: "It is only a technicality. I am your wife's lawyer. There will be another lawyer in the court to represent you. He is a friend of mine; his office is around the corner."

"Will I meet him?" Charles asked.

"Unfortunately, he is out of the city. He is in Acapulco. You have been there?"

Charles said he had not. The lawyer put down the document and looked at Charles with disbelief; he told Charles, at some length, about the beauties of Acapulco and warned Charles he must not leave Mexico without first stopping there. Then he resumed the reading which, at this point, dealt with Charles' behavior as husband and father.

Charles listened attentively; he nodded as each point was made. I am all kinds of a swine, he told himself; and savoured, rather, this new image of himself: nasty, sadistic, irresponsible, brutal, all those things he had never been able to manage to be. When the list of his misdemeanors came to an end, his attention wandered once again. You have this tendency, he warned himself; but to no avail: his mind continued to wander.

As if by way of punishment the lawyer then disposed of Charles' daughters. Charles very carefully did not listen to this paragraph, but heard it anyway. The Tchaikovsky came in waves, as the wind willed, and reminded him of broadcasts heard as a boy on the longwave band, his ear pressed close to the loudspeaker, his head full of the roar and crackle of foreign places. Now I am here, he thought, in one of those places. "Unless the mother is incompetent," the lawyer said. "Or she drinks. Or something like that. Otherwise, she always gets the children."

Charles nodded, indicating he would go along with this traditional practice though as yet, himself, undecided whether it was right or wrong. I am reserving judgment, he told himself.

"I am your wife's lawyer," the lawyer said. He said it apologetically because he knew Charles was going to pay his bill. He hesitated; he raised his eyebrows to show he was hesitating; then he leaned toward Charles. "Does your wife, perhaps, drink?"

"No, she doesn't," Charles told him. "She doesn't do much of anything."

"There is very little divorcing here," the lawyer said to this. It was his way of saying "I do not understand," which he could not bring himself to say. He handed Charles a ball-point pen and Charles signed all the documents on the line with the little *x*. Something has gone out of writing, he thought, now that pens no longer scratch. He believed it ought to make a noise; it should at least hiss; there ought to be something. It was only the finality of this document that made it important; he saw it as close kin to a death warrant. Ah, he sighed, looking at the ballpoint pen, where is all this mmmm-ah progress taking us?

"To all intentsanpurposes, you are now free man," the lawyer said. "In a few days, two-three, maybe four, it become official and I give you your papers."

Well, I'll take them, Charles said to himself, I'll take them, but what have they got to do with me? Nothing. Not a thing. I'm washing my hands of all this, he said.

Before the lawyer let him go he chatted with Charles for a few minutes; it was to show he was not all business and that his interest in Charles went beyond mere documents. They spoke of the revolution in Cuba.

The lawyer assured Charles, who was not surprised, that he was a very conservative man. Charles had met, at home and abroad, a number of rich foreign business and professional men. All had been more American than any Americans he knew; they all belonged to Rotary and expressed themselves fervent supporters of free enterprise. They reminded Charles of characters from the novels of the Twenties: swarthy Babbitts with curious accents; men with three last names, including their mothers', spoke without embarrassment of the American Way of Life. And invariably they let one to know that they had a *subscripçión* to *Time*.

The lawyer removed his green glasses. He looked very tired. Charles thought it must be the strain of speaking English that had so fatigued him. Spaniards tire easily when they must speak any language but their own. The lawyer went on to give his views on revolutions in general. It was his firm belief that before crossing a river, one should know what is on the other side. It was not enough, he said, simply to throw out Batista. What would follow? he asked.

Charles did not know.

"Cows will follow," the lawyer said. Charles nodded. The lawyer nodded, happy they were in accord. "Yes, cows always follow a revolution," he said.

Charles nodded again, wondering at the same time what *cows* meant in Spanish. He would look it up when he got back to his room.

Charles rose, and then gripped the arm of the chair because he thought he was fainting or, perhaps, dying. When the dizziness passed, he was surprised to find himself still standing and the lawyer still smiling, his hand extended. Charles shook the hand and left. While he waited for the elevator he leaned his head against the marble wall and, later, on the street, he walked delicately, having been reminded how very delicate a man's system really is.

On Avenida Juarez, across from the park, he went into a little restaurant to sit down and rest because he was now having some difficulty breathing. The restaurant was painted red and black and the furniture reminded him of the World's Fair at Flushing. Old-fashioned modern was, he decided, the best kind of modern; it had nothing to recommend it but nostalgia, yet that was better than nothing at all.

He ordered a cup of café express from a waiter who was twelve years old, or perhaps younger. When he had drunk it, he was once again assailed by dizziness and, without knowing what he was doing or why, he ordered another cup. "*Otra café,*" he said to the boy, perhaps only wanting someone near. But even the two words spoken caused him to gasp for breath; he took great deep breaths but it did not seem to help. For a moment, he felt quite desperate about it.

The boy asked Charles if he desired anything more; he pulled nervously at the points of the short green jacket he wore. Charles said no, there was nothing else. He noted that he was breathing more easily now. He lit a cigarette, clumsily striking the short waxed match on the side of the box. Raising the match he noticed, without alarm, the curious spots that had appeared on the back of his hand. Round and colorless, they proved soft to the touch and peeled off like a scab. An excrescence of some sort, he thought; and connected it with the dizziness, the shortness of breath, and wondered what disease it might be and how much longer he had to live.

He walked up the avenue toward his hotel; he stayed close to the buildings, in case he fainted, but this made it impossible to hail a taxi. He was light-headed with the dizziness; he saw his image reflected in the shop windows, and studied it as a stranger might. I am not as slim as I used to be, he thought, which was the only thing the stranger would not have known.

Cows always follow a revolution, he thought. He knew the lawyer did not mean cows, but cows was all he could see now: a clay road rutted by wagon wheels, the soldiers of the revolution on horseback, an *x* of bandoliers across their chests, advancing; and behind them, ruminative, without haste, cows.

He passed the Del Prado Hotel where the American tourists stayed. The night he had arrived there was a long banner across the front of the hotel: WELCOME MASONS, it said. Now there was one that read: WELCOME PANTHERS. On the hotel steps the Panthers stood, laughing and talking, dressed in suits of Italian silk that glittered like silverfoil. On their lapels each wore a green card protected by a plastic cover. *Hello! I'm a Panther*.

One of the guides who kept vigil there in front of the hotel walked along now beside Charles. "I am licensed guide," he said. "Hello."

"Hello."

"Would you like cultural tour?"

"No," Charles said. "Thank you," he added. He always got rather tired of saying thank you when he was abroad. He said thank you infinitely more often than he ever did at home. He did not want to be thought an ill bred American.

"Maybe you like to see glass curtain at Palace of Beautiful Arts. Very pretty. Also Diego Rivera murals."

"No, thank you." He gasped for breath.

"Or this afternoon today maybe you like if I take you to University City. Very big mosaics made by famous artists including Diego Rivera and others."

". . . Thank you," Charles said. He did not want to waste breath speaking but was afraid to shake his head.

"Five dollars," the guide said. "And I throw in Floating Gardens and famous Aztec Pyramid."

Charles shook his head, experimentally. It's not so bad, he decided. He shook his head again. The guide continued walking beside him. Charles opened his mouth; he tried breathing that way, but it seemed to offer no real advantages. Well, so this is how it's going to be, he said. They were passing the Fronton now where the jai alai was played every night. Charles meant to go.

"Or maybe you like to go night clubbing. Dinner. Cocktail. Dancing and music. Very nice."

Charles declined.

The guide smiled; now he understood. He offered Charles yet another tour. "Special services. Very nice. Clean. All very refined people from goberment go there."

"No. Thank you." Charles smiled to show there was no ill will. The guide returned the smile and pointed to the button in his lapel. "Official licensed guide," he said. Charles nodded; he was happy for the man, that he had received recognition. "You sure you don't want to see Diego Rivera murals?" When Charles said he was sure, the guide shrugged and gave him up.

Charles' hotel was now only two blocks away. I *think* I'm going to make it, he told himself, urging himself on. His hotel was called The New York. It was a new building and its owners had hoped it would attract many American tourists;

but it did not, because it was too small. Americans liked the old colonial hotels, because they had charm; or they liked the big new modern ones, because they had bigness. The New York was patronized therefore mostly by provincial Mexicans, who liked it because it was new. Quite by chance, the hotel's contractor had built according to specifications; so it did not crack or break in half when the earthquake struck, as the big new modern ones had, mosaics and hand-painted murals and all.

The clerk at the desk was one Charles had not seen before; the night clerk was Chinese and, except for the lawyer, Charles had spoken to no one else in Mexico. He got his key and went up to the third floor in the self-service elevator made by Otis. As it rose, he read the certificate issued by the safety inspector, Engineer Carlos Ruiz Alonzo Espinosa G. Charles thought really it was carrying privacy too far to keep secret one's final last name, to use only the initial as so many Latins did. I know you'll never invite me into your home, Charles said to the elevator safety inspector, or introduce me to your mother and your wife; but at least you could tell me your final last name, man.

In his room, Charles lay down immediately and groaned as if the sight of the ceiling were painful to his eyes. Then he said, Well, Charles Alan T., you made it, you made it after all. He did not say it jubilantly; Charles knew there was no good reason for cheering his own survival. Then he blacked out for a few minutes, or perhaps only fell asleep; he was not sure. He might have napped because he had slept very badly the night before. He woke many times during the night and early morning because he had the impression that bare-chested Aztec Indians, carrying spears, were lined along all the four walls of his room. He woke often, as if to make sure they were still there; and until past dawn they always were.

When he woke from his nap he took two aspirins. First he had to unwrap the drinking glass; it had been sealed in a bag to protect the sterilization. Then he filled the glass with Purified Water from a plastic jug. He decided that, considering it was purified, it didn't taste so bad.

He felt a little better for having napped, or fainted, and thought he would take a bath; it would give him something to do and, besides, the spots on his hands made him feel dirty.

He was not frightened. Since the war he had, in fact, never been frightened of anything. He looked upon the Indians who crowded his bedroom at night with something like interest, like curiosity, but never with fear. What little was left of his fear had crystallized like medicine in the bottom of a bottle. There was that grainy residue, but he was saving it for some really grand occasion.

After dinner, which he ate alone and, as is the custom, late, he walked to the Ciné Paris to stand in line for admittance to a French film, a comedy he wanted to see and had missed in New York. On the marble floor of the lobby an Indian woman, selling lottery tickets, fed her baby milk from an American-made bottle. It was the kind his daughters had used. I Buy Name Brands, he said; and he assumed a sweet-but-firm smile, like the lady in the ads. No one smiled back, or even looked at him. I have the distinct impression, Charles said, that in this queue I would never be missed. All about him people talked to each other and from inside the theatre he could hear the laughter of the audience. He had the impression that his aloneness had made him invisible.

From time to time the line moved one pace forward; it was going to be a long wait, apparently, but Charles did not mind, there was no reason to mind. After a little more than an hour an announcement was made at the head of the line and everyone dispersed. The theatre was full, there would be no more seating. Charles moved off as uncomplaining as everyone else. He started across the wide avenue, heading toward Sanborn's where he would have toast and tea before returning to the hotel. There was heavy traffic, he had to run the last part of it, and hauled up on the pavement gasping for breath, his arm around a telephone pole. It was hardly worth it, he thought.

In Sanborn's, as he sat down under the mural—not Rivera's—which displayed several hundred purple watermelons, he reminded himself he must not forget to buy some paperback books before leaving. He had nothing in his room to read but an Agatha Christie he had picked up on the plane; and he did not like Agatha Christie, and he found Hercule Poirot an officious bore. He could not understand the popularity of such a character. Charles smiled, appreciating himself: I am becoming irascible, he thought.

"*Té y pan tostado*," he said to the waitress.

"Yes sir," she said. "Do you want your tea iced or hot?"

"Hot," he said; and he asked himself, plaintively, Oh why do I *come* to such places? He put down the menu and examined his hands. There were no spots but now he noticed others, on his trousers just below the waistband. Perhaps I am infecting this entire restaurant, he said. He looked around and decided it hardly mattered.

Six Panthers entered and sat at the next table. They discussed at length the state of their digestion and the disastrous effects that drinking unpurified water will have; and they called the waitress honey, and she did not seem to mind.

The dizziness returned again and Charles drank quickly the last of his tea; it was no longer hot. In Mexico City, he had noticed, food and drink turned cold very quickly. He paid his check and walked carefully out of the restaurant. The ground had tilted outside and he steadied himself against walls, making his way back to the hotel.

The Chinese night clerk was on duty but Charles did not feel up to talking. He merely waved a hand in greeting and went into the elevator. The night clerk said to the porter, "The poor American is suffering from the altitude. He is suffering from it very strongly." The porter nodded, having noticed the symptoms too. "Well," the night clerk said, "he will either get used to it, or he will not."

Charles undressed as soon as he was in his room and examined his stomach to see if there were any marks or spots; he assumed that the soft white spots on his trousers had seeped through from his skin. But there were no marks of any kind on his stomach. Whatever it is, he said, it is evidently seeping through my pores. He knew very well what it was: it was life that was seeping away. He thought it only just; he thought it right and proper he should die, and that it should be here, in Mexico, he die. Because was it not here he had committed the terrible deed? Had signed the papers? And thereby killed his wife? He knew very well what the dizziness was; it was the murderer's vertigo, his soul reeling at the enormity of his crime.

Charles sat naked on the edge of the bed and thought how silly he must look there, examining his belly. Then he remembered he had forgot to buy a book, and he cursed though he knew he might very well be dead by morning and that it hardly mattered. And though it mattered even less he took his Spanish dictionary and looked up *cows*. There was, as he had suspected, no such word. After *covacha*—small cave— there was only *coyote*, which meant coyote.

Charles took a bath, hot as he could stand it. He would open his pores; he determined to get rid of this thing as quickly as possible. Before he got in bed he took the extra blankets from the dresser drawer and added them to the covers on the bed. He would sweat it out. I shall coöperate all I can, he told it. But after a short while he could no longer bear the suffocating closeness and he kicked off all the covers. He sat up and lit a cigarette; he did not notice the wax dripping onto his hands; he would find the spots in the morning. He could not sleep, he believed, until the Indians arrived; he would wait for them. But they did not come until after he had put out his cigarette. I know why you are here, he told them. Not to kill me but to watch me die.

In the morning they were gone. Charles looked at the sunlight, gold behind the wheat-colored curtains. He said, Well, well, I seem still to have this thing.

He dressed quickly and went down to the lobby to ask were there any messages; knowing it was too soon for the lawyer to have called, yet praying desperately for it just the same. He wanted it to be all over and done with. Only the crime is a crime, he assured himself; once it is done it is done and over with.

There were no messages and no letters. He had been expecting a letter from his wife; he had asked her to keep him posted on his daughters' health. He had not really believed she would write. She isn't much for writing letters, he reminded himself. The desk clerk said, "And how are we feeling today, sir?"

"I am coming along nicely," Charles told him. Yes, it won't be long now, he assured himself; another day or two and it will all be over. He had noticed the new spots on the back of his hand. I'm going to lay my burden down real soon, he said as he went through the doors to the street. He walked to a restaurant and ordered what the menu called *Lonch*. Afterwards, he drank three cups of café express. When he got up to leave he had to sit down again because the dizziness had come upon him with great force.

The waitress, a heavy-breasted elderly-looking girl of 19 or, possibly, 20 leaned over him solicitously. She put her hand on his forehead and he felt better for it; he looked at her gratefully. "Poor sick man," she said. "You like water?" He nodded and she brought him some in a pink plastic glass. "Is purify," she said. I will drink it anyway, he told himself. He did not want to offend her.

He walked back to the hotel then. He did not want it to happen while walking in the street; he was afraid he would be taken for a drunk American. He passed a little park and read a sign that said: Child if you love your parents do not molest the flowers. He recalled now Bernal Díaz' description of Mexico City as it had been when Cortez and his men first saw it. He wondered what could have happened to all the lakes and canals. Had they been filled in? Had they dried up? Had a social-minded government banished them by decree? There's a lot you don't know, Charles, he reminded himself.

He went up to his room and found the maid still there, making up his bed. He did not know the Spanish for Don't mind me, and said it all with a gesture she seemed to understand. "You like Mexico?" she asked, for the sake of making conversation.

"Very much," Charles said.

"Is very precious," she agreed; she touched her finger to her lip and blew a kiss to Mexico.

When she was finished with the room she said, "You know my name?"

He said, "No. What is your name?"

"Carmen," she said, and left.

He put in a call to the lawyer. He decided to be Rotarian and cheerful and say something like, "Well! How's everything going?" He gave the operator the number and waited. After several minutes the operator said, "Hello. Are you the man who is waiting?"

"Yes, I am the man who is waiting," he answered. Then all was silent and he lay down on the bed with the receiver on the pillow by his head. Every few minutes the operator asked him was he the man and he always assured her he was. After 20 minutes of this he hung up and read Agatha Christie. Hercule Poirot smote his forehead because he, Hercule Poirot, had overlooked something terribly obvious; Charles could not imagine what in the world it might be.

Later, he stood up and found the dizziness had passed. He moved with the caution of an invalid, as if he were afraid that an abrupt movement might dislodge something vital. I will take a long walk now, he said; perhaps it will tire me.

He went down the avenue. He had done it so many times now that there were no longer even shop windows he could look into; he had seen them all; had studied, even, the merchandise in the window of Sears, wondering always what ever happened to Mr. Roebuck. The guides in front of the Del Prado no longer approached him. Charles thought they had put a cabalistic chalk mark on his back that meant No Dice.

He stopped in at his lawyer's office. The lawyer was not there. He is at the court, the secretary said, and he will not return until the evening.

Well, I've heard they keep queer hours here, Charles said to himself, and left. In the lobby he was depressed by his discovery that it was only three o'clock; he had only with extreme reluctance looked at his watch and now he was sorry. He found also that the walk had more than tired him; he was exhausted, he felt he had been running miles, and he swayed as the building swayed, one sun-darkened hand pressed against the green marble wall that purled like water all around him.

Finally he went outside and found a taxi waiting at the curb. It is a good sign, he told himself. As they passed the Palace of Fine Arts, Charles thought he read an announcement of the ballet. Tonight he would go to the ballet. He felt much better for having found something to do.

In his room again he noticed, gratefully, that new spots had appeared on his hands. "*Es una forma de leprosía*," he said, aloud. "*Si*," he said, studying the spots closely, as if they were hieroglyphs and he had just found the key, "*si, es una forma de leprosía. O, possiblemente, otra cosa.*" In any case, it was something rare and uncurable; he was sure of that. Again he drew a bath and immersed himself in it, formally, with the sense of a ritual served. He watched the white spots disappear in the hot water; they seemed to melt away. "*Muy interesante*," he commented.

After toweling himself thoroughly he powdered his body with finicky care and then laid it gently on the bed; he had given up ownership, it was nothing to him now but he treated it carefully as one does with something borrowed. When the room began to drift, became unmoored and spun gently, he went with it. He did not fight but rode it out. I want to go quietly, he said.

When he woke from the nap he was only a little surprised to be still alive. He dressed his body with care and walked it down the steps to the lobby. The Chinese night clerk was on duty.

"Good evening, good evening," he said. He spoke English very well, having graduated from a Catholic college near New Orleans.

Charles put his hand to his heart because at that moment it had begun to act in a strange manner, as if some small bird had blundered into it and was now trying to find its way out. Charles stood with his hand on his chest; he looked about to take an oath but only said, "I was thinking of going to the Palace to see the ballet."

"But it is not tonight," the clerk said, full of regret. "The announcement is there but the ballet is not there. The ballet comes next month."

Charles was sorry to hear it.

"And yet, I have an idea," the clerk said, raising his hand. He opened a newspaper and began to look for something. When he found it, he said, "Ah ha!" He folded the paper and showed Charles the announcement of a ballet company's performance for that night. The company had a Russian name.

"Are they good?" Charles wanted to know.

The clerk said, "I have not seen it myself because of the nature of my work, but it is said this company had a triumph in Jalapa last month." He tore out the announcement and gave it to Charles, who thanked him.

The clerk said, "Well, have you seen Floating Gardens yet and University City?"

Charles was too embarrassed to admit he had not. "I saw the mural by Diego Rivera," he said.

"That sure is something, isn't it?" the clerk said. "Did you notice all the historical figures? Juarez and Carlmarss? You notice Cortez?"

Charles said he had.

"Is monumental," the clerk said. "It sure is something. Listen, you been to night clubs yet? I have here a card will introduce you to very famous night club. Just show them this card." Charles took the card and put it in his pocket but not without noticing that the club was named Uncle Sam's.

"Tonight," Charles said, "I think I'll go to the ballet."

"Good idea, sir. Uncle Sam's can be gone to any night, including Sunday and all nights."

At dinner, Charles changed his mind; he would, after all, go to Uncle Sam's. I ought to get out more, he told himself, it would be better for me if I mingled. I want you to get out there, fella, and mingle. And after he had eaten his New York steak with potato baked in aluminum foil, he sat over his tea a long time, considering yet again this problem: the ballet or Uncle Sam's.

There's plenty of time for mingling, he decided finally. You can mingle tomorrow, he told himself, and overtipping the waitress, he went out to the avenue and found a taxi. The theatre was on the other side of town; Charles slouched across the back seat and listened to the meter clicking off centavo after centavo, hundreds of them, and thought, Well here I am in Mexico City on my way to the ballet having just divorced my wife. Yes, you've come a long way, fella, he told himself; and stared out the window at the neon-lighted churches and the great dark houses.

The theatre turned out to be the auditorium of a social club, a place where, ordinarily, the men of a certain Spanish province got together and talked about better days. It was old and dark and there were no murals; startlingly white, a program lay folded on the seat of every chair. Charles sat down and began to read the program notes. The dance was based on a Mexican legend, even though all the dancers had

Russian names. Part I featured a high priest and a sacrificial virgin; in spite of the priest's love for her he sees his duty plain and, though his heart is sick, he plunges the stone knife into her breast. Charles nodded understandingly. That's the way it goes, he said.

Part I was danced to the music of The Preludio of Federico Chopin; the record they used was apparently very old and, at times, the music was hardly audible under the roar and hiss of the surface noise. The leading female dancer entered on short legs and immediately declared her love for the priest. She was, Charles thought, quite clearly one sacrificial virgin who did not know her place. The priest, danced by a young Indian who wore a turban and bloomerlike pants, was at first torn between love and duty. He made this conflict plain enough by frequently throwing his arm across his eyes.

A whole troupe of sacrificial virgins then entered. They were all very young and were, doubtless, students on loan from a ballet school run by a friend of the producer. Charles thought them charming. He liked the way they smiled at their mistakes and pushed each other like playful cubs. One of them, however, was painfully tall. Charles felt very sorry for her. On her toes, she looked as if she had come without her legs and someone, out of pity, had loaned her stilts. She should be chosen for sacrifice, Charles thought; life does not hold much joy for her anyway.

"Precious! Oh, how precious!" the audience cried, blowing kisses. The girls smiled their thanks and waved to their parents and loved ones. They remained on their toes, it seemed to Charles, an unconscionably long time. He was feeling sick and dizzy again and looked at his watch frequently.

When the young girls had finally cleared the stage—one had dropped her wreath of flowers and returned for it ("Precious!")—a tall young woman with long hair and admirable breasts whirled on stage. Charles did not know who she was supposed to be but, since her costume was similar to the first dancer's, he assumed she was a virgin too. It's so hard to tell these days, he said. She had a very athletic body and Charles half expected that parallel bars or flying rings might be brought out for her at any moment.

She was clearly a great favorite of the audience and when she did something very difficult, such as swinging her body completely around while standing on one toe, they shouted, "*Aí! Linda. Que linda!*" Toward the end of her solo the audience sang her praises when she paused, for a moment, during a precarious turn and waited while the record was turned over. "*Maravaillosa!*" they cried, and Charles saw her poor thigh quiver with the strain.

Part One ended with the death of the virgin, put to the knife, reluctantly and without style, by the bloomered priest. That's the way it goes, Charles said, holding tight to his chair as the floor tilted and began to spin. At the moment of the woman's death, there was a sharp crack and a flare of flame, and grey smoke rose from the cardboard altar. In the excitement, the virgin hid herself behind it. "*Que un efecto!*" the man next to Charles said, hardly able to breathe so exciting was this moment.

The priest displayed his grief by several despondent leaps, there was wild applause as the curtain closed; and two boys appeared with boxes and passed among the audience crying, "Chocolates. Chiclets. Coca-Cola. *Helados.* Chocolates. Chiclets. Coca-Cola. *Helados.*" Charles lit a cigarette and began to read the program notes for the second act. "Two thousand years later," he read, "two lovers appear at the ruins of the temple." Time means nothing to these people, Charles said; they reckon it differently than do we of the West. Part Two was to be danced to the music of Shostakovich.

The athletic girl with the sweet breasts appeared first; she was now the young lover. She was accompanied by a squat man with a heavy Aztec face, broad shoulders and big peasant hands. He was able to lift her and carry her about the stage without losing his smile for an instant. At one point, he held her above his head while standing on one toe. The audience could only sigh; aesthetic pleasure had gone too far for words.

As he lowered her to the floor he turned his head and, looking directly at Charles, he smiled, as if with recognition. And it seemed to Charles that in spite of the green makeup and the Indian features, he knew him. Whenever the Indian faced the audience, his green face turned to Charles, smiling.

I don't know you, Charles said, I don't know you. But he was uncertain, and his uncertainty annoyed him; and when the Indian smiled at him again, he turned his head away. Yet, finally, he had to look again; and turned his head and found the dancer smiling at him, his eyes knowing and sly.

It is the vertigo, Charles told himself. He is not looking at me at all. Or if he is, it is merely an actor's trick. I do not know him; it is only that international smile of his makes me think so. He closed his eyes and grasped tightly the arms of his chair; that way he held the whole building firmly in place, for it threatened to drift away, he saw it hurtling through space on the terrible endless journey.

When Part Two ended—the virgin had risen from the dead and, with no apparent motive, slew the sweet-breasted girl—Charles left. He prayed there would be a taxi; he had no idea where he was. There was none, and he walked toward the streetlight at the corner where two women also waited. They had lank kinky hair and when they smiled at him they looked like sisters. When he was near, the one with the gold tooth stepped forward and with a practiced move gently but firmly grabbed hold of his private parts.

"Allo, American boy," she said; and Charles for a moment could not speak because he was having such a hard time breathing, and his heart beat wildly; yet managed to say to himself: I dare not run. She continued to hold him in her hand; and after a very short time this seemed to Charles the most natural thing in the world, no more unreasonable than holding hands.

Smiling, she offered Charles a wide variety of delights;

and if he did not think she alone was sufficient for his needs—
"Not at all," Charles assured her—why then her friend, who
was more than a friend, more than a sister, would lend her aid.

Charles regretted he could not and thanked her a thousand
times.

Her sister would come along at no increase in price, she
told Charles. And her sister, though too shy to say so herself,
had a very interesting specialty that would give Charles much
pleasure.

"I have no doubt of it," Charles said, but he shook his head
and tried to pull away from the women.

He could see for himself, she said, how clean they were.
We are not ordinary whores, she said; and Charles said yes,
he knew that, he had been able to see it at once.

And if one dollar and fifty cents for both herself and her
sister was considered too high, why then—because he was so
cute—she would let it go for one dollar and twenty-five
American.

Charles assured her that she and her sister were very appeal-
ing—precious, he said—and he had no doubt in the world
they were very clean and very special, but he was sick.

Such a pity, she said, taking her hand away. Perhaps there
was something else they could do for him?

I have a vertigo, he told her, a very strong vertigo.

Such a thing made her very sad to hear, she said.

I think I have not much longer to live, he told her, pleased
that he had someone to talk to at last.

And so young and pretty, she said, turning to her sister for
confirmation. She wished him good luck with his sickness and
asked for a cigarette. When she saw they were Mexican cigarettes, she said, "A thousand thanks, but no." And he left
them there, smiling sweetly under the light. He regretted it
but did not turn back, knowing that with them his disgust
would overwhelm every other feeling. He was sorry about it;
he wished it were not so and that he were the kind of man
who went to whores.

He found a taxi on the next street and, though he thought he was hungry, returned directly to the hotel and soaked himself in the steamy water till all the spots had melted off his hands. He powdered himself and went to bed and, on the edge of sleep, came wide awake. "Chaos!" he said. "*Chaos! it is chaos* that follows a revolution. That is what he meant." He laughed, but was rather disappointed after all; he would have preferred cows. When he woke again the Indians were there. "Soon," he told them, "soon," making it a promise. And when he woke in daylight he lay for a long time looking at the ceiling, which swung to the left and then returned, making a small arc. It won't be long now, he told himself. He reached for the phone to call his lawyer and remembered it was Sunday. "Oh God," he said, "it's Sunday."

When he had finished eating breakfast at Sanborn's the dizziness struck him with redoubled force; he slid down in his chair and rested his head on the back for a few minutes. Then, embarrassed, he left and made his way back to his room, struggling for breath, and jubilant, as if he were carrying good news.

In the afternoon he took a taxi to the Plaza de Toros; the desk clerk had got him a ticket. Charles had asked for a ticket for the sunny side, where the Mexicans sat, because he had been told it was no good in the shade where the Americans sat. The bull was never killed on that side because, while the foreigners liked to see it, they did not like to see it too close. The clerk warned Charles that it was sometimes rowdy on the Mexican side; but Charles insisted. The clerk said, "Well, at least they don't throw bottles any more; because the beer now is served only in paper cups."

Charles found that his ticket entitled him to a first row seat; he was going to be very close to the bull. He had not expected that. Neither had he expected that in the center of the ring there would be a large Pepsi-Cola bottle; it was about ten feet high, a replica perfect in every detail. He looked across to where the Americans sat, armed with cameras; there was a surprising lot of them.

The rows behind him filled quickly; by the time the band began to play the famous music, the steep tiers were loud with people. Men with buckets and columns of waxed paper cups moved sideways between the rows selling beer and Pepsi-Cola. Charles was relieved to note that before the first bull was let out, two men in white came and carried out the Pepsi bottle.

There were to be six bulls and three matadors; the matadors were novices. The first one was a tall and ungainly fellow whose uniform seemed to be made of solid gold. He kept a comfortable distance between himself and the animal; and some members of the audience, seated directly behind and around Charles, suggested that if he felt that way about it he should use a telephone. After the cape work and the business with the horse and the placing of the pics, the matador tried to kill the bull. He found it no easy task. The bull showed a disinclination to die. Several times the matador had to pull his sword out of the bull and thrust it in again; and still the bull refused to lie down.

The crowd in Charles' section voiced disapproval of the matador's behavior. They then began to throw things, such as horse manure, which they had brought in bags expressly, it appeared, for this purpose. After the matador, in the manner of an unskilled butcher, had at last killed the bull, he made a circle of the ring to accept the plaudits of the crowd. The crowd, however, continued to throw horse manure, spoiled heads of lettuce, and other rotting vegetables; some even insulted the state of Chihuahua from whence the matador came. This angered him and he picked up bits of manure and threw it back at the crowd. Some of this material, as it was hurled back and forth, fell on Charles' head and shoulders.

The next two matadors were a little better. One, however, was apparently too graceful and the crowd reminded him that the plaza was not a dance hall. When the first matador returned to dispatch his second bull, the crowd welcomed him with whistles. Charles had been told this was not, in Mexico, a sign of approbation. The matador also had ill luck with his picadors, one of whom fell off his horse; the bull then knocked down the horse. The crowd whistled. The matador failed to draw the bull away from the horse; he stood there with his hands on his hips, his golden chest heaving, and looked down at the ground. Charles was quite surprised at the amount of material the crowd had held in reserve for just such an occasion. He pulled his jacket over his head while others, more experienced, huddled under plastic sheets they had brought with them. When the men sitting near Charles had exhausted all the manure and vegetables, they urinated into the waxed paper cups and threw them at the matador. Most of these cups fell short of the ring and this caused many arguments and one fight with knives. A man who smelled strongly of wine fell on top of Charles. "Hola, Garee Coopair," he said, smiling up at Charles.

After the fifth bull Charles made his way out of the plaza. He brushed the manure out of his hair and, carrying his jacket stained with beer and urine, slowly pushed toward the exit. Members of the audience called after him. They thought he did not know and told him there was to be yet another bull. Charles smiled graciously and waved his hand, signalling that he had heard. "Hold onto your wallet, Garee," one called, "we are all pickpockets." They hoped the bullfighting had not made him sick. They waved good-bye and laughed.

Outside, just past the heroic statue of the matador and the dying bull, Charles got into a taxi. He had now a very bad headache. It was, he decided, the worst he had ever had. As soon as he was back in his room he took two aspirins and soaked himself for a long time in the bath. Then he got under the shower and washed his hair. After he had lain on the bed for half an hour listening to his head throb and watching the room tilt and swing in its arc, he took two more aspirins and a sleeping pill. He woke an hour later. He still had the headache.

He said to himself: Well, this headache is something new. It is a good sign, perhaps the beginning of the end. It cannot be much longer now.

He felt too sick to go out; his headache did not permit him to read, even if he had remembered to buy a book. He lay on the bed and smoked cigarettes. Spots appeared on his hands. He sat on the chair. He studied his face in the mirror. At two in the morning he found himself reading the notice on the wall. It was in Spanish and had been placed there by the Administration of Licenses. It pleased Charles that he could understand the Spanish so well and, for a few minutes, he forgot his headache and the dizziness and the fact he had committed murder and was now dying.

I accept these rules, he read aloud, feeling an inordinate pride in his accomplishment. I must inscribe my true name in the hotel register. I must not bring pets or other classes of animals into my rooms; neither may I make a fire. My use of the furniture must be rational. Nobody but myself is responsible for any loss I might suffer here. Not permitted are women of bad conduct or with contagious sicknesses. Also I must not use medicines of bad odor which make disagreeable the habitation to others, nor heroic drugs which are damaging to nature.

It all seems very fair and eminently reasonable, Charles said. I will show my culture by observing these rules. We've got to have something to live by, men.

At three in the morning, the room full of Indians, he overcame his scruples and took the second sleeping pill. It was almost noon when he woke. I still seem to have this thing with me, he said. Well, he said, I suppose I shall just have to get used to it.

The Artificial Nigger

FLANNERY O'CONNOR

MR. HEAD AWAKENED TO DISCOVER THAT THE ROOM WAS full of moonlight. He sat up and stared at the floor boards— the color of silver—and then at the ticking on his pillow, which might have been brocade, and after a second, he saw half of the moon five feet away in his shaving mirror, paused as if it were waiting for his permission to enter. It rolled forward and cast a dignifying light on everything. The straight chair against the wall looked stiff and attentive as if it were awaiting an order and Mr. Head's trousers, hanging to the back of it, had an almost noble air, like the garment some great man had just flung to his servant; but the face on the moon was a grave one. It gazed across the room and out the window where it floated over the horse stall and appeared to contemplate itself with the look of a young man who sees his old age before him.

Mr. Head could have said to it that age was a choice blessing and that only with years does a man enter into that calm understanding of life that makes him a suitable guide for the young. This, at least, had been his own experience.

He sat up and grasped the iron posts at the foot of his bed and raised himself until he could see the face on the alarm clock which sat on an overturned bucket beside the chair. The hour was two in the morning. The alarm on the clock did not work but he was not dependent on any mechanical means to awaken him. Sixty years had not dulled his responses; his physical reactions, like his moral ones, were guided by his will and strong character, and these could be seen plainly in his features. He had a long tube-like face with a long rounded open jaw and a long depressed nose. His eyes were alert but quiet, and in the miraculous moonlight they had a look of composure and of ancient wisdom as if they belonged to one of the great guides of men. He might have been Vergil summoned in the middle of the night to go to Dante, or better, Raphael, awakened by a blast of God's light to fly to the side of Tobias. The only dark spot in the room was Nelson's pallet, underneath the shadow of the window.

Nelson was hunched over on his side, his knees under his chin and his heels under his bottom. His new suit and hat were in the boxes that they had been sent in and these were on the floor at the foot of the pallet where he could get his hands on them as soon as he woke up. The slop jar, out of the shadow and made snow-white in the moonlight, appeared to stand guard over him like a small personal angel. Mr. Head lay back down, feeling entirely confident that he could carry out the moral mission of the coming day. He meant to be up before Nelson and to have the breakfast cooking by the time he awakened. The boy was always irked when Mr. Head was the first up. They would have to leave the house at four to get to the railroad junction by five-thirty. The train was to stop for them at five forty-five and they had to be there on time, for this train was stopping merely to accommodate them.

This would be the boy's first trip to the city though he claimed it would be his second because he had been born there. Mr. Head had tried to point out to him that when he was born he didn't have the intelligence to determine his whereabouts but this had made no impression on the child at all and he continued to insist that this was to be his second trip. It would be Mr. Head's third trip. Nelson had said, "I will've already been there twice and I ain't but ten."

Mr. Head had contradicted him.

"If you ain't been there in fifteen years, how you know you'll be able to find your way about?" Nelson had asked. "How you know it hasn't changed some?"

"Have you ever," Mr. Head had asked, "seen me lost?"

Nelson certainly had not but he was a child who was never satisfied until he had given an impudent answer and he replied, "It's nowhere around here to get lost at."

"The day is going to come," Mr. Head prophesied, "when you'll find you ain't as smart as you think you are." He had been thinking about this trip for several months but it was for the most part in moral terms that he conceived it. It was to be a lesson that the boy would never forget. He was to find out from it that he had no cause for pride merely because he had been born in a city. He was to find out that the city is not a great place. Mr. Head meant him to see everything there is to see in a city so that he would be content to stay at home for the rest of his life. He fell asleep thinking how the boy would at last find out that he was not as smart as he thought he was.

He was awakened at three-thirty by the smell of fatback frying and he leaped off his cot. The pallet was empty and the clothes boxes had been thrown open. He put on his trousers and ran into the other room. The boy had a corn pone on cooking and had fried the meat. He was sitting in the half-dark at the table, drinking cold coffee out of a can. He had on his new suit and his new gray hat pulled low over his eyes. It was too big for him but they had ordered it a size large because they expected his head to grow. He didn't say anything but his entire figure suggested satisfaction at having arisen before Mr. Head.

Mr. Head went to the stove and brought the meat to the table in the skillet. "It's no hurry," he said. "You'll get there soon enough and it's no guarantee you'll like it when you do neither," and he sat down across from the boy whose hat teetered back slowly to reveal a fiercely expressionless face, very much the same shape as the old man's. They were grandfather and grandson but they looked enough alike to be brothers, and brothers not too far apart in age, for Mr. Head had a youthful expression by daylight, while the boy's look was ancient, as if he knew everything already and would be pleased to forget it.

Mr. Head had once had a wife and daughter, and when the wife died, the daughter ran away and returned after an interval with Nelson. Then one morning, without getting out of bed, she died and left Mr. Head with sole care of the year-old child. He had been born in Atlanta. If he hadn't told him that, Nelson couldn't have insisted that this was going to be his second trip.

"You may not like it a bit," Mr. Head continued. "It'll be full of niggers."

The boy made a face as if he could handle a nigger.

"All right," Mr. Head said. "You ain't ever seen a nigger."

"You wasn't up very early," Nelson said.

"You ain't ever seen a nigger," Mr. Head repeated. "There hasn't been a nigger in this country since we run that one out twelve years ago and that was before you were born." He looked at the boy as if he were daring him to say he had ever seen a Negro.

"How you know I never saw a nigger when I lived there before?" Nelson asked. "I probably saw a lot of niggers."

"If you seen one you didn't know what he was," Mr. Head said, completely exasperated. "A six-month-old child don't know a nigger from anybody else."

"I reckon I'll know a nigger if I see one," the boy said and got up and straightened his slick, sharply creased gray hat and went outside to the privy.

They reached the junction some time before the train was due to arrive and stood about two feet from the first set of tracks. Mr. Head carried a paper sack with some biscuits and a can of sardines in it for their lunch. A coarse-looking orange-colored sun coming up behind the east range of mountains was making the sky a dull red behind them, but in front of them it was still gray and they faced a gray transparent moon, hardly stronger than a thumbprint and completely without light. A small tin switch box and a black fuel tank were all there was to mark the place as a junction; the tracks were double and did not converge again until they were hidden behind the bends at either end of the clearing. Trains passing appeared to emerge from a tunnel of trees and, hit for a second by the cold sky, vanish terrified into the woods again. Mr. Head had had to make special arrangements with the ticket agent to have this train stop and he was secretly afraid it would not, in which case he knew Nelson would say, "I never thought no train was going to stop for you." Under the useless morning moon the tracks looked white and fragile. Both the old man and the child stared ahead as if they were awaiting an apparition.

Then suddenly, before Mr. Head could make up his mind to turn back, there was a deep warning bleat and the train appeared, gliding very slowly, almost silently around the bend of trees about two hundred yards down the track, with one yellow front light shining. Mr. Head was still not certain it would stop and he felt it would make an even bigger idiot of him if it went by slowly. Both he and Nelson, however, were prepared to ignore the train if it passed them.

The engine charged by, filling their noses with the smell of hot metal, and then the second coach came to a stop exactly where they were standing. A conductor with the face of an ancient bloated bulldog was on the step as if he expected them, though he did not look as if it mattered one way or the other to him if they got on or not. "To the right," he said.

Their entry took only a fraction of a second and the train was already speeding on as they entered the quiet car. Most of the travelers were still sleeping, some with their heads hanging off the chair arms, some stretched across two seats, and some sprawled out with their feet in the aisle. Mr. Head saw two unoccupied seats and pushed Nelson toward them. "Get in there by the winder," he said in his normal voice, which was very loud at this hour of the morning. "Nobody cares if you sit there because it's nobody in it. Sit right there."

"I heard you," the boy muttered. "It's no use in you yelling," and he sat down and turned his head to the glass. There he saw a pale ghost-like face scowling at him beneath the brim of a pale ghost-like hat. His grandfather, looking quickly too, saw a different ghost, pale but grinning, under a black hat.

Mr. Head sat down and settled himself and took out his ticket and started reading aloud everything that was printed on it. People began to stir. Several woke up and stared at him. "Take off your hat," he said to Nelson and took off his own and put it on his knee. He had a small amount of white hair that had turned tobacco-color over the years and this lay flat across the back of his head. The front of his head was bald and creased. Nelson took off his hat and put it on his knee and they waited for the conductor to come for their tickets.

The man across the aisle from them was spread out over two seats, his feet propped on the window and his head jutting into the aisle. He had on a light blue suit and a yellow shirt unbuttoned at the neck. His eyes had just opened and Mr. Head was ready to introduce himself when the conductor came up from behind and growled, "Tickets."

When the conductor had gone, Mr. Head gave Nelson the return half of his ticket and said, "Now put that in your pocket and don't lose it or you'll have to stay in the city."

"Maybe I will," Nelson said as if this were a reasonable suggestion.

Mr. Head ignored him. "First time this boy has ever been on a train," he explained to the man across the aisle, who was sitting up now on the edge of his seat with both feet on the floor.

Nelson jerked his hat on again and turned angrily to the window.

"He's never seen anything before," Mr. Head continued.

"Ignorant as the day he was born, but I mean for him to get his fill once and for all."

The boy leaned forward, across his grandfather and toward the stranger. "I was born in the city," he said. "I was born there. This is my second trip." He said it in a high positive voice but the man across the aisle didn't look as if he understood. There were heavy purple circles under his eyes.

Mr. Head reached across the aisle and tapped him on the arm. "The thing to do with a boy," he said sagely, "is to show him all it is to show. Don't hold nothing back."

"Yeah," the man said. He gazed down at his swollen feet and lifted the left one about ten inches from the floor. After a minute he put it down and lifted the other. All through the car people began to get up and move about and yawn and stretch. Separate voices could be heard here and there and then a general hum. Suddenly Mr. Head's serene expression changed. His mouth almost closed and a light, fierce and cautious, came into his eyes. He was looking down the length of the car. Without turning, he caught Nelson by the arm and pulled him forward. "Look," he said.

A huge coffee-colored man was coming slowly forward. He had on a light suit and a yellow satin tie with a ruby pin in it. One of his hands rested on his stomach, which rode majestically under his buttoned coat, and in the other he held the head of a black walking stick that he picked up and set down with a deliberate outward motion each time he took a step. He was proceeding very slowly, his large brown eyes gazing over the heads of the passengers. He had a small white mustache and white crinkly hair. Behind him there were two young women, both coffee-colored, one in a yellow dress and one in a green. Their progress was kept at the rate of his and they chatted in low throaty voices as they followed him.

Mr. Head's grip was tightening insistently on Nelson's arm. As the procession passed them, the light from a sapphire ring on the brown hand that picked up the cane reflected in Mr. Head's eye, but he did not look up nor did the tremendous man look at him. The group proceeded up the rest of the aisle and out of the car. Mr. Head's grip on Nelson's arm loosened. "What was that?" he asked.

"A man," the boy said and gave him an indignant look as if he were tired of having his intelligence insulted.

"What kind of a man?" Mr. Head persisted, his voice expressionless.

"A fat man," Nelson said. He was beginning to feel that he had better be cautious.

"You don't know what kind?" Mr. Head said in a final tone.

"An old man," the boy said and had a sudden foreboding that he was not going to enjoy the day.

"That was a nigger," Mr. Head said and sat back.

Nelson jumped up on the seat and stood looking backward to the end of the car but the Negro had gone.

"I'd of thought you'd know a nigger since you seen so many when you was in the city on your first visit," Mr. Head continued. "That's his first nigger," he said to the man across the aisle.

The boy slid down into the seat. "You said they were black," he said in an angry voice. "You never said they were tan. How do you expect me to know anything when you don't tell me right?"

"You're just ignorant is all," Mr. Head said and he got up and moved over in the vacant seat by the man across the aisle.

Nelson turned backward again and looked where the Negro had disappeared. He felt that the Negro had deliberately walked down the aisle in order to make a fool of him and he hated him with a fierce raw fresh hate; and also, he understood now why his grandfather disliked them. He looked toward the window and the face there seemed to suggest that he might be inadequate to the day's exactions. He wondered if he would even recognize the city when they came to it.

After he had told several stories, Mr. Head realized that

the man he was talking to was asleep and he got up and suggested to Nelson that they walk over the train and see the parts of it. He particularly wanted the boy to see the toilet so they went first to the men's room and examined the plumbing. Mr. Head demonstrated the ice-water cooler as if he had invented it and showed Nelson the bowl with the single spigot where the travelers brushed their teeth. They went through several cars and came to the diner.

This was the most elegant car in the train. It was painted a rich egg-yellow and had a wine-colored carpet on the floor. There were wide windows over the tables and great spaces of the rolling view were caught in miniature in the sides of the coffee pots and in the glasses. Three very black Negroes in white suits and aprons were running up and down the aisle, swinging trays and bowing and bending over the travelers eating breakfast. One of them rushed up to Mr. Head and Nelson and said, holding up two fingers, "Space for two," but Mr. Head replied in a loud voice, "We eaten before we left!"

The waiter wore large brown spectacles that increased the size of his eye whites. "Stan' aside then please," he said with an airy wave of the arm as if he were brushing aside flies.

Neither Nelson nor Mr. Head moved a fraction of an inch. "Look," Mr. Head said.

The near corner of the diner, containing two tables, was set off from the rest by a saffron-colored curtain. One table was set but empty but at the other, facing them, his back to the drape, sat the tremendous Negro. He was speaking in a soft voice to the two women while he buttered a muffin. He had a heavy sad face and his neck bulged over his white collar on either side. "They rope them off," Mr. Head explained. Then he said, "Let's go see the kitchen," and they walked the length of the diner but the black waiter was coming fast behind them.

"Passengers are not allowed in the kitchen!" he said in a haughty voice. "Passengers are *not* allowed in the kitchen!"

Mr. Head stopped where he was and turned. "And there's good reason for that," he shouted into the Negro's chest, "because the cockroaches would run the passengers out!"

All the travelers laughed and Mr. Head and Nelson walked out, grinning. Mr. Head was known at home for his quick wit and Nelson felt a sudden keen pride in him. He realized the old man would be his only support in the strange place they were approaching. He would be entirely alone in the world if he were ever lost from his grandfather. A terrible excitement shook him and he wanted to take hold of Mr. Head's coat and hold on like a child.

As they went back to their seats they could see through the passing windows that the countryside was becoming speckled with small houses and shacks and that a highway ran alongside the train. Cars sped by on it, very small and fast. Nelson felt that there was less breath in the air than there had been thirty minutes ago. The man across the aisle had left and there was no one near for Mr. Head to hold a conversation with so he looked out the window, through his own reflection, and read aloud the names of the buildings they were passing. "The Dixie Chemical Corp!" he announced. "Southern Maid Flour! Dixie Doors! Southern Belle Cotton Products! Patty's Peanut Butter! Southern Mammy Cane Syrup!"

"Hush up!" Nelson hissed.

All over the car people were beginning to get up and take their luggage off the overhead racks. Women were putting on their coats and hats. The conductor stuck his head in the car and snarled, "Firstoppppmry," and Nelson lunged out of his sitting position, trembling. Mr. Head pushed him down by the shoulder.

"Keep your seat," he said in dignified tones. "The first stop is on the edge of town. The second stop is at the main railroad station." He had come by this knowledge on his first trip when he had got off at the first stop and had had to pay a man fifteen cents to take him into the heart of town. Nelson sat

back down, very pale. For the first time in his life, he understood that his grandfather was indispensable to him.

The train stopped and let off a few passengers and glided
on as if it had never ceased moving. Outside, behind rows of
brown rickety houses, a line of blue buildings stood up, and
beyond them a pale rose-gray sky faded away to nothing. The
train moved into the railroad yard. Looking down, Nelson
saw lines and lines of silver tracks multiplying and criss-
crossing. Then before he could start counting them, the face
in the window stared out at him, gray but distinct, and he
looked the other way. The train was in the station. Both he
and Mr. Head jumped up and ran to the door. Neither noticed that they had left the paper sack with the lunch in it on
the seat.

They walked stiffly through the small station and came out
of a heavy door into the squall of traffic. Crowds were hurrying to work. Nelson didn't know where to look. Mr. Head
leaned against the side of the building and glared in front of
him.

Finally Nelson said, "Well, how do you see what all it is
to see?"

Mr. Head didn't answer. Then as if the sight of people passing had given him the clue, he said, "You walk," and started
off down the street. Nelson followed, steadying his hat. So
many sights and sounds were flooding in on him that for the
first block he hardly knew what he was seeing. At the second
corner, Mr. Head turned and looked behind him at the station they had left, a putty-colored terminal with a concrete
dome on top. He thought that if he could keep the dome always in sight, he would be able to get back in the afternoon
to catch the train again.

As they walked along, Nelson began to distinguish details
and take note of the store windows, jammed with every kind
of equipment—hardware, dry goods, chicken feed, liquor.
They passed one that Mr. Head called his particular atten-

tion to where you walked in and sat on a chair with your feet upon two rests and let a Negro polish your shoes. They walked slowly and stopped and stood at the entrances so he could see what went on in each place but they did not go into any of them. Mr. Head was determined not to go into any city store because on his first trip here he had got lost in a large one and had found his way out only after many people had insulted him.

They came in the middle of the next block to a store that had a weighing machine in front of it and they both in turn stepped up on it and put in a penny and received a ticket. Mr. Head's ticket said, "You weigh 120 pounds. You are upright and brave and all your friends admire you." He put the ticket in his pocket, surprised that the machine should have got his character correct but his weight wrong, for he had weighed himself on a grain scale not long before and knew he weighed one hundred ten. Nelson's ticket said, "You weigh ninety-eight pounds. You have a great destiny ahead of you but beware of dark women." Nelson did not know any women and he weighed only sixty-eight pounds but Mr. Head pointed out that the machine had probably printed the number upside down meaning the nine for a six.

They walked on and at the end of five blocks the dome of the terminal sank out of sight and Mr. Head turned to the left. Nelson could have stood in front of every store window for an hour if there had not been another more interesting one next to it. Suddenly he said, "I was born here!" Mr. Head turned and looked at him with horror. There was a sweaty brightness about his face. "This is where I come from!" he said.

Mr. Head was appalled. He saw the moment had come for drastic action. "Lemme show you one thing you ain't seen yet," he said and took him to the corner where there was a sewer entrance. "Squat down," he said, "and stick you head in there," and he held the back of the boy's coat while he got down and put his head in the sewer. He drew it back quickly, hearing a gurgling in the depths under the sidewalk. Then Mr. Head explained the sewer system, how the entire city was underlined with it, how it contained all the drainage and was full of rats and how a man could slide into it and be sucked along down endless pitchblack tunnels. At any minute any man in the city might be sucked into the sewer and never heard from again. He described it so well that Nelson was for some seconds shaken. He connected the sewer passages with the entrance to hell and understood for the first time how the world was put together in its lower parts. He drew away from the curb.

Then he said, "Yes, but you can stay away from the holes," and his face took on that stubborn look that was so exasperating to his grandfather. "This is where I came from!" he said.

Mr. Head was dismayed but he only muttered, "You'll get your fill," and they walked on. At the end of two more blocks he turned to the left, feeling that he was circling the dome; and he was correct for in a half-hour they passed in front of the railroad station again. At first Nelson did not notice that he was seeing the same stores twice, but when they passed the one where you put your feet on the rests while the Negro polished your shoes, he perceived that they were walking in a circle.

"We done been here!" he shouted. "I don't believe you know where you're at!"

"The direction just slipped my mind for a minute," Mr. Head said and they turned down a different street. He still did not intend to let the dome get too far away and after two blocks in their new direction, he turned to the left. This street contained two- and three-story wooden dwellings. Anyone passing on the sidewalk could see into the rooms and Mr. Head, glancing through one window, saw a woman lying on an iron bed, looking out, with a sheet pulled over her. Her knowing expression shook him. A fierce-looking boy on a bicycle came driving down out of nowhere and he had to jump to the side to keep from being hit. "It's nothing to them if they knock you down," he said. "You better keep closer to me."

They walked on for some time on streets like this before he remembered to turn again. The houses they were passing now were all unpainted and the wood in them looked rotten; the street between was narrower. Nelson saw a colored man. Then another. Then another. "Niggers live in these houses," he observed.

"Well come on and we'll go somewheres else," Mr. Head said. "We didn't come to look at niggers," and they turned down another street but they continued to see Negroes everywhere. Nelson's skin began to prickle and they stepped along at a faster pace in order to leave the neighborhood as soon as possible. There were colored men in their undershirts standing in the doors and colored women rocking on the sagging porches. Colored children played in the gutters and stopped what they were doing to look at them. Before long they began to pass rows of stores with colored customers in them but they didn't pause at the entrances of these. Black eyes in black faces were watching them from every direction. "Yes," Mr. Head said, "this is where you were born—right here with all these niggers."

Nelson scowled. "I think you done got us lost," he said.

Mr. Head swung around sharply and looked for the dome. It was nowhere in sight. "I ain't got us lost either," he said. "You're just tired of walking."

"I ain't tired, I'm hungry," Nelson said. "Give me a biscuit."

They discovered then that they had lost the lunch.

"You were the one holding the sack," Nelson said. "I would have kep aholt of it."

"If you want to direct this trip, I'll go on by myself and leave you right here," Mr. Head said and was pleased to see the boy turn white. However, he realized they were lost and drifting farther every minute from the station. He was hungry himself and beginning to be thirsty and since they had been in the colored neighborhood, they had both begun to sweat. Nelson had on his shoes and he was unaccustomed to them. The concrete sidewalks were very hard. They both wanted to find a place to sit down but this was impossible and they kept on walking, the boy muttering under his breath, "First you lost the sack and then you lost the way," and Mr. Head growling from time to time, "Anybody wants to be from this nigger heaven can be from it!"

By now the sun was well forward in the sky. The odor of dinners cooking drifted out to them. The Negroes were all at their doors to see them pass. "Whyn't you ast one of these niggers the way?" Nelson said. "You got us lost."

"This is where you were born," Mr. Head said. "You can ast one yourself if you want to."

Nelson was afraid of the colored men and he didn't want to be laughed at by the colored children. Up ahead he saw a large colored woman leaning in a doorway that opened onto the sidewalk. Her hair stood straight out from her head for about four inches all around and she was resting on bare brown feet that turned pink at the sides. She had on a pink dress that showed her exact shape. As they came abreast of her, she lazily lifted one hand to her head and her fingers disappeared into her hair.

Nelson stopped. He felt his breath drawn up by the woman's dark eyes. "How do you get back to town?" he said in a voice that did not sound like his own.

After a minute she said, "You in town now," in a rich low tone that made Nelson feel as if a cool spray had been turned on him.

"How do you get back to the train?" he said in the same reed-like voice.

"You can catch you a car," she said.

He understood she was making fun of him but he was too paralyzed even to scowl. He stood drinking in every detail of her. His eyes traveled up from her great knees to her forehead and then made a triangular path from the glistening sweat on her neck down and across her tremendous bosom

223

and over her bare arm back to where her fingers lay hidden in her hair. He suddenly wanted her to reach down and pick him up and draw him against her and then he wanted to feel her breath on his face. He wanted to look down and down into her eyes while she held him tighter and tighter. He had never had such a feeling before. He felt as if he were reeling down through a pitchblack tunnel.

"You can go a block down yonder and catch you a car take you to the railroad station, Sugarpie," she said.

Nelson would have collapsed at her feet if Mr. Head had not pulled him roughly away. "You act like you don't have any sense!" the old man growled.

They hurried down the street and Nelson did not look back at the woman. He pushed his hat sharply forward over his face, which was already burning with shame. The sneering ghost he had seen in the train window and all the foreboding feelings he had on the way returned to him and he remembered that his ticket from the scale had said to beware of dark women and that his grandfather's had said he was upright and brave. He took hold of the old man's hand, a sign of dependence that he seldom showed.

They headed down the street toward the car tracks where a long yellow rattling trolley was coming. Mr. Head had never boarded a streetcar and he let that one pass. Nelson was silent. From time to time his mouth trembled slightly but his grandfather, occupied with his own problems, paid him no attention. They stood on the corner and neither looked at the Negroes who were passing, going about their business just as if they had been white, except that most of them stopped and eyed Mr. Head and Nelson. It occurred to Mr. Head that since the streetcar ran on tracks, they could simply follow the tracks. He gave Nelson a slight push and explained that they would follow the tracks on into the railroad station, walking, and they set off.

Presently to their great relief they began to see white people again and Nelson sat down on the sidewalk against the wall of a building. "I got to rest myself some," he said. "You lost the sack and the direction. You can just wait on me to rest myself."

"There's the tracks in front of us," Mr. Head said. "All we got to do is keep them in sight and you could have remembered the sack as good as me. This is where you were born. This is your old home town. This is your second trip. You ought to know how to do," and he squatted down and continued in this vein but the boy, easing his burning feet out of his shoes, did not answer.

"And standing there grinning like a chim-pan-zee while a nigger woman gives you directions. Great Gawd!" Mr. Head said.

"I never said I was nothing but born here," the boy said in a shaky voice. "I never said I would or wouldn't like it. I never said I wanted to come. I only said I was born here and I never had nothing to do with that. I want to go home. I never wanted to come in the first place. It was all your big idea. How you know you ain't following the tracks in the wrong direction?"

This last had occurred to Mr. Head too. "All these people are white," he said.

"We ain't passed here before," Nelson said. This was a neighborhood of brick buildings that might have been lived in or might not. A few empty automobiles were parked along the curb and there was an occasional passerby. The heat of the pavement came up through Nelson's thin suit. His eyelids began to droop, and after a few minutes his head tilted forward. His shoulders twitched once or twice and then he fell over on his side and lay sprawled in an exhausted fit of sleep.

Mr. Head watched him silently. He was very tired himself but they could not both sleep at the same time and he could not have slept anyway because he did not know where he was. In a few minutes Nelson would wake up, refreshed by his sleep and very cocky, and would begin complaining that he had lost the sack and the way. You'd have a mighty sorry time if

I wasn't here, Mr. Head thought; and then another idea occurred to him. He looked at the sprawled figure for several minutes; presently he stood up. He justified what he was going to do on the grounds that it is sometimes necessary to teach a child a lesson he won't forget, particularly when the child is always reasserting his position with some new impudence. He walked without a sound to the corner about twenty feet away and sat down on a covered garbage can in the alley where he could look out and watch Nelson wake up alone.

The boy was dozing fitfully, half conscious of vague noises and black forms moving up from some dark part of him into the light. His face worked in his sleep and he had pulled his knees up under his chin. The sun shed a dull dry light on the narrow street; everything looked like exactly what it was. After a while Mr. Head, hunched like an old monkey on the garbage can lid, decided that if Nelson didn't wake up soon, he would make a loud noise by bamming his foot against the can. He looked at his watch and discovered that it was two o'clock. Their train left at six and the possibility of missing it was too awful for him to think of. He kicked his foot backwards on the can and a hollow boom reverberated in the alley.

Nelson shot up onto his feet with a shout. He looked where his grandfather should have been and stared. He seemed to whirl several times and then, picking up his feet and throwing his head back, he dashed down the street like a wild maddened pony. Mr. Head jumped off the can and galloped after but the child was almost out of sight. He saw a streak of gray disappearing diagonally a block ahead. He ran as fast as he could, looking both ways down every intersection, but without sight of him again. Then as he passed the third intersection, completely winded, he saw about half a block down the street a scene that stopped him altogether. He crouched behind a trash box to watch and get his bearings.

Nelson was sitting with both legs spread out and by his side lay an elderly woman, screaming. Groceries were scattered about the sidewalk. A crowd of women had already gathered to see justice done and Mr. Head distinctly heard the old woman on the pavement shout, "You've broken my ankle and your daddy'll pay for it! Every nickel! Police! Police!" Several of the women were plucking at Nelson's shoulder but the boy seemed too dazed to get up.

Something forced Mr. Head from behind the trash box and forward, but only at a creeping pace. He had never in his life been accosted by a policeman. The women were milling around Nelson as if they might suddenly all dive on him at once and tear him to pieces, and the old woman continued to scream that her ankle was broken and to call for an officer. Mr. Head came on so slowly that he could have been taking a backward step after each forward one, but when he was about ten feet away, Nelson saw him and sprung. The child caught him around the hips and clung panting against him.

The women all turned on Mr. Head. The injured one sat up and shouted, "You sir! You'll pay every penny of my doctor's bill that your boy has caused. He's a juve-nile delin-quent! Where is an officer? Somebody take this man's name and address!

Mr. Head was trying to detach Nelson's fingers from the flesh in the back of his legs. The old man's head had lowered itself into his collar like a turtle's; his eyes were glazed with fear and caution.

"Your boy has broken my ankle!" the old woman shouted. "Police!"

Mr. Head sensed the approach of the policeman from behind. He stared straight ahead at the women who were massed in their fury like a solid wall to block his escape. "This is not my boy," he said. "I never seen him before."

He felt Nelson's fingers fall out of his flesh.

The women dropped back, staring at him with horror, as if they were so repulsed by a man who would deny his own image and likeness that they could not bear to lay hands on him. Mr. Head walked on, through a space they silently cleared, and left Nelson behind. Ahead of him he saw nothing but a hollow tunnel that had once been the street.

The boy remained standing where he was, his neck craned forward and his hands hanging by his sides. His hat was jammed on his head so that there were no longer any creases in it. The injured woman got up and shook her fist at him and the others gave him pitying looks, but he didn't notice any of them. There was no policeman in sight.

In a minute he began to move mechanically, making no effort to catch up with his grandfather but merely following at about twenty paces. They walked on for five blocks in this way. Mr. Head's shoulders were sagging and his neck hung forward at such an angle that it was not visible from behind. He was afraid to turn his head. Finally he cut a short hopeful glance over his shoulder. Twenty feet behind him, he saw two small eyes piercing into his back like pitchfork prongs.

The boy was not of a forgiving nature but this was the first time he had ever had anything to forgive. Mr. Head had never disgraced himself before. After two more blocks, he turned and called over his shoulder in a high, desperately gay voice, "Let's us go get us a Co'-Cola somewheres!"

Nelson, with a dignity he had never shown before, turned and stood with his back to his grandfather.

Mr. Head began to feel the depth of his denial. His face as they walked on became all hollows and bare ridges. He saw nothing they were passing but he perceived that they had lost the car tracks. There was no dome to be seen anywhere and the afternoon was advancing. He knew that if dark overtook them in the city, they would be beaten and robbed. The speed of God's justice was only what he expected for himself, but he could not stand to think that his sins would be visited upon Nelson and that even now he was leading the boy to his doom.

They continued to walk on block after block through an endless section of small brick houses until Mr. Head almost fell over a water spigot sticking up about six inches off the edge of a grass plot. He had not had a drink of water since early morning but he felt he did not deserve it now. Then he thought that Nelson would be thirsty and they would both drink and be brought together. He squatted down and put his mouth to the nozzle and turned a cold stream of water into his throat. Then he called out in the high desperate voice, "Come on and getcher some water!"

This time the child stared through him for nearly sixty seconds. Mr. Head got up and walked on as if he had drunk poison. Nelson, though he had not had water since some he had drunk out of a paper cup on the train, passed by the spigot, disdaining to drink where his grandfather had. When Mr. Head realized this, he lost all hope. His face in the waning afternoon light looked ravaged and abandoned. He could feel the boy's steady hate, traveling at an even pace behind him, and he knew that (if by some miracle they escaped being murdered in the city) it would continue just that way for the rest of his life. He knew that now he was wandering into a black strange place where nothing was like it had ever been before, a long old age without respect and an end that would be welcome because it would be the end.

As for Nelson, his mind had frozen around his grandfather's treachery as if he were trying to preserve it intact to present at the final judgment. He walked without looking to one side or the other, but every now and then his mouth would twitch and this was when he felt, from some remote place inside himself, a black mysterious form reach up as if it would melt his frozen vision in one hot grasp.

The sun dropped down behind a row of houses and hardly noticing they passed into an elegant suburban section where mansions were set back from the road by lawns with birdbaths on them. Here everything was entirely deserted. For blocks they didn't pass even a dog. The big white houses were like partially submerged icebergs in the distance. There were no sidewalks, only drives, and these wound around and around in endless ridiculous circles. Nelson made no move to come nearer to Mr. Head. The old man felt that if he saw a sewer entrance he would drop down into it and let himself be carried away; and he could imagine the boy standing by, watching with only a slight interest, while he disappeared.

A loud bark jarred him to attention and he looked up to see a fat man approaching with two bulldogs. He waved both arms like someone shipwrecked on a desert island. "I'm lost!" he called. "I'm lost and can't find my way, and me and this boy have got to catch this train and I can't find the station. Oh Gawd I'm lost! O hep me Gawd I'm lost!"

The man, who was bald-headed and had on golf knickers, asked him what train he was trying to catch and Mr. Head began to get out his tickets, trembling so violently he could hardly hold them. Nelson had come up to within fifteen feet and stood watching.

"Well," the fat man said, giving him back the tickets, "you won't have time to get back to town to make this but you can catch it at the suburb stop. That's three blocks from here," and he began explaining how to get there.

Mr. Head stared as if he were slowly returning from the dead and when the man had finished and gone off with the dogs jumping at his heels, he turned to Nelson and said breathlessly, "We're going to get home!"

The child was standing about ten feet away, his face bloodless under the gray hat. His eyes were triumphantly cold. There was no light in them, no feeling, no interest. He was merely there, a small figure, waiting. Home was nothing to him.

Mr. Head turned slowly. He felt he knew now what time would be like without light and what man would be like without salvation. He didn't care if he never made the train and if it had not been for what suddenly caught his attention, like a cry out of the gathering dusk, he might have forgotten there was a station to go to.

He had not walked five hundred yards down the road when he saw, within reach of him, the plaster figure of a Negro sitting bent over on a low yellow brick fence that curved around a wide lawn. The Negro was about Nelson's size and he was pitched forward at an unsteady angle because the putty that held him to the wall had cracked. One of his eyes was entirely white and he held a piece of brown watermelon.

Mr. Head stood looking at him silently until Nelson stopped at a little distance. Then as the two of them stood there, Mr. Head breathed, "An artificial nigger!"

It was not possible to tell if the artificial Negro were meant to be young or old; he looked too miserable to be either. He was meant to look happy because his mouth was stretched up at the corners but the chipped eye and the angle he was cocked at gave him a wild look of misery instead.

"An artificial nigger," Nelson repeated in Mr. Head's exact tone.

The two of them stood there with their necks forward at almost the same angle and their shoulders curved in almost exactly the same way and their hands trembling identically in their pockets. Mr. Head looked like an ancient child and Nelson like a miniature old man. They stood gazing at the artificial Negro as if they were faced with some great mystery, some monument to another's victory that brought them together in their common defeat. They could both feel it dissolving their differences like an action of mercy. Mr. Head had never known before what mercy felt like because he had been too good to deserve any, but he felt he knew now. He looked at Nelson and understood that he must say something to the child to show that he was still wise and in the look the boy returned he saw a hungry need for that assurance. Nelson's eyes seemed to implore him to explain once and for all the mystery of existence.

Mr. Head opened his lips to make a lofty statement and heard himself say, "They ain't got enough real ones here. They got to have an artificial one."

After a second, the boy nodded with a strange shivering about his mouth, and said, "Let's go home before we get ourselves lost again."

Their train glided into the suburb stop just as they reached the station and they boarded it together, and ten minutes before it was due to arrive at the junction, they went to the door and stood ready to jump off if it did not stop; but it did, just as the moon, restored to its full splendor, sprang from a cloud and flooded the clearing with light. As they stepped off, the sage grass was shivering gently in shades of silver and the clinkers under their feet glittered with a fresh black light. The tree tops, fencing the junction like the protecting walls of a garden, were darker than the sky, which was hung with gigantic white clouds illuminated like lanterns.

Mr. Head stood very still and felt the action of mercy touch him again but this time he knew that there were no words in the world that could name it. He understood that it grew out of agony, which is not denied to any man and which is given in strange ways to children. He understood it was all a man could carry into death to give his Maker and he suddenly burned with shame that he had so little of it to take with him. He stood appalled, judging himself with the thoroughness of God, while the action of mercy covered his pride like a flame and consumed it. He had never thought himself a great sinner before but he saw now that his true depravity had been hidden from him lest it cause him despair. He realized that he was forgiven for sins from the beginning of time, when he had conceived in his own heart the sin of Adam, until the present, when he had denied poor Nelson. He saw that no sin was too monstrous for him to claim as his own, and since God loved in proportion as He forgave, he felt ready at that instant to enter Paradise.

Nelson, composing his expression under the shadow of his hat brim, watched him with a mixture of fatigue and suspicion, but as the train glided past them and disappeared like a frightened serpent into the woods, even his face lightened and he muttered, "I'm glad I've went once, but I'll never go back again."

The Rebels

RICHARD POWER

V INCENT CAME DOWN THE ROAD FROM THE CREAMERY,
carefully scuffling his bare feet in the dust of the cart-tracks.
I always waited for him because I was his pal. It meant being
late for school sometimes, but I never got the stick. Vincent
was no bigger than me, but everybody was somehow afraid
of him, even Billy Flahavan who thought himself a man. And
even the master.

I was the only one who knew that his mother made him
wear boots every day. I never let on, even to him, but I
had seen him hiding the boots in a hole in the creamery wall
and then splashing through a puddle to get his feet looking
like everybody else's. I think that was one reason I liked him
so much, knowing that. And, of course, I liked him because
of his mother, a terrible woman who would win a martyr's
crown for any fellow.

He nodded and said "morra" to me, as I jumped up to
join him.

"How's Billy?" I asked. I had heard Billy was in bed after
the beating and was probably at death's door.

Vincent shrugged his shoulders, but he knew. He always
knew more than we did from the talk at the creamery, but
he never let on. It was useless to be asking him.

We stopped at the door of the forge, looking in at the

sparks flying in the darkness, while we nibbled away at the jam sandwiches in our satchels. It was Lent, the hungry time of the year, when a fellow doesn't get half enough to eat and the birds go hopping around the dead branches whenever the sun comes out. It was cold too, even with the sun on our bare feet.

"D'ye think he'll still be mad," I asked, "the master?" I was hoping against hope for the worst, that Billy was lying in bed, dying or already dead. Only the worst was any use to us, for only the gallows would rid us of the master.

Vincent shrugged as if he didn't care. I noticed, though, that he had a good sod of turf under his arm for the school fire, real hard and black, the pick of the big stack in the creamery yard.

Just then the old smith looked up and saw us. "Off to school with ye," he yelled, "ye little tinkers, ye! D'ye want me to tell the master on ye?"

Vincent tossed a crust in over the half-door to make the smith bawl louder, then he began to run. I followed, wishing I could be like him, afraid of no one, not even after the beating.

When we reached the school, we found Chris on his knees by the grate, blowing the embers aflame. He looked up at us with his pink eyes, which were never really dry, waiting for us to toss him our sods of turf. It was Chris who looked after the fire all day, cleaned the blackboard and gave out the copy-books. He also went out to cut and trim the sticks for the master to beat us with. We didn't hold that against him, though. It was his job, and anyway he had a real gift which he wasn't a bit stingy with—he could cry any time we wanted him to. For a penny, he'd let the tears roll down his cheeks, while we stood around him, looking as if we owned him, watching the amazement on the face of some new fellow. Sometimes the tears began to roll when he didn't want them to and they just kept on rolling until his shirt was wet and we began to get frightened, thinking they'd never stop. Maybe that's why the master never asked him a question. It was just as well, because the poor fellow was very ignorant.

We were sitting very quiet when the master came in. He was a big man, with a gold watch-chain on him like the belly-band of a horse and heavy square-toed boots. I never looked much at his face for fear of him noticing me, but it was the color of soda-bread and he had a big bald head on him, which used to go all red and shiny whenever his blood was up. We sat reading as hard as we could until he spoke. When we heard his voice, soft and deep, we knew it would be an easy morning. He asked Vincent all the hard questions, just as if there was an Inspector there, but any one of us would have got full marks that day. We had taken no chances with our home-work. He even cracked a few jokes. When he saw how good the fire was, he said that we must have been keeping the best turf till last. We all split our sides laughing, though most of the fellows didn't know that he was quoting what Our Lord said to the publicans, when He was complaining about the wine.

Just before the break, Billy came in. He was the only fellow in long trousers, but even they didn't hide his stiff walk as he went up to make his excuse.

"Him!" the master shouted, flinging out his arm towards Billy, "Him the Almighty Power hurled headlong flaming from the ethereal sky, with hideous ruin and combustion, down to bottomless perdition . . ." He stopped waving his arm suddenly and said, "Milton! Paradise Lost, Book One! But I might as well be telling the wall!" Then he asked, very serious, "How is it?"

"What, master?"

"Your bottom, boy?"

" 'Tis sore, sir," said Billy, rubbing his trousers and cocking a gamy eye back at us, as we pretended to laugh our heads off. Billy always thought it was he who made a joke.

235

"Sit down, boy," said the master, real solemn, "for your penance, you may sit down."

We all felt Billy's pain, as he lowered himself slowly into his seat. For the rest of the period, we couldn't keep our eyes off those tight trousers, wondering were they stuck to him or was his behind all bandaged up inside them.

Chris went down the road to the master's house to prepare the master's lunch, for the master had no wife. Chris was good at making tea and boiling eggs. He lived with his grandfather, an old soldier of the English army, who used to wander home from the pubs of a Friday after collecting his pension-money, muttering to himself and taking big skelps out of the hedges with his stick. Chris had no mother and no father. Maybe that was why we didn't begrudge him the master.

As it was raining, we had to stay in to eat our sandwiches. We gathered around the fire when the master left, but we kept an eye out for his return. He used to murder us for standing around the fire. He said it made our wits even more sleepy and stupid than God intended.

Billy began telling us how his da had bet hell out of him, because he wouldn't say what the master had bet him for.

"But, sure, ye might as well be flogged by a fly as by my oul' fella," said Billy. "Jeez, I'd make two of him."

"And what did you do, Billy, tell us?" I burst out. I was killed with the curiosity.

"Nothing much," said Billy, in his hoarse bass voice. He had an open mouth like all the Flahavans and a cowlick of hair plastered down with oil (Flahavan's axle-grease, the master called it).

"But you must have done something, Billy?"

"I didn't," said Billy, grinning with that open mouth, "but I might." He stood there, wanting me to keep on asking.

"Go on," I said, "tell us!" I was beginning to get annoyed.

"Ye're too young."

"Was it," cut in Vincent, "a girl?"

"Now ye're talking!"

"But . . ." All sorts of questions were crowding into my head.

". . . what did you do with her, Billy?" was the only question I could ask, very lamely.

"Nothing! Yet! He caught us walking out the Durrow Road. We'll wait till dark the next time, I can tell ye that!"

"You're not going to go out with her again?" It was the first time in my life I'd talked to anyone who had actually walked out with a girl on his own. And who was so sure about walking out again.

"Of course!" He gave me a push. "Go 'way now, little boy, and play!"

"Who is she?" asked Vincent.

"Wouldn't ye like to know now?"

"I knew you were making it up."

"Did ye now? Well, I'll show ye. Look!" He produced a brown shopkeeper's envelope, creased in two. "She even wrote to me." He took out the letter, a page of a jotter, and folded it to cover the signature. "Go on! Read it if ye don't believe me!"

Vincent took it as if he really wasn't much interested. We all crowded round, jostling each other as we tried to read it over his shoulder. All I could make out was "Dear Billy, You'd better not walk out my way tonight, because my Daddy . . ." Then a shadow fell across it.

"What have ye there?" said the master. He made a lunge for the letter, as Vincent tried to hide it behind his back. His big arms closed around Vincent, lifting him from the floor and twisting him around to straddle him. Then the big black thumb-nail levered at Vincent's knuckles, until the hand suddenly opened and the crumpled letter dropped on to the desk. The master laid it out and began to brush it straight with the backs of his fingers.

Vincent's face went red first, then slowly faded to white.

"Give it back," he said, his lips all stiff. We backed away

from him, staring, backed away to leave him facing the master.

"What's that?" The master's voice was quick, almost frightened. His mouth dropped open a moment, showing the saliva welling around his teeth.

"I said 'give it back.' "

The master's hand opened and closed a few times, as if it had lost its nerve. Then it opened out, flat, and swung against Vincent's face. There was a sharp crack. Vincent staggered back against the fireplace, clutching at his cheek. None of us made a move. We watched him run his tongue into his cheek and spit a blood-flecked dollop into the fire. Then he turned and without a word or a look, walked out of the room.

We had a rough afternoon, but as most of us had learned our stuff off backways and skew-ways and everyway, the master couldn't catch us out. He strode up and down the room, banging his fist into his hand and bawling and looking as if he was going to burst right through the walls. I kept my head down, desperately trying to work out a sum the length of my arm. I was nearly sick inside, thinking of Vincent and of what would happen to him.

We stopped at the forge on the way home. We stared in over the half-door, a line of noses sniffing at the thin white smoke of burning hoof as it melted into the darkness. The sledge rang out on the anvil. Our eyes followed the sparks as they went arching up, then quenched themselves disappointingly in the dry, grey, tindery beard of the smith. We were all poised on tiptoe, waiting for him to turn and bawl at us. When he did so, opening his big spade-mouth to show two yellow tusks, we plunged away with squeals of mock terror. We splashed across the stream, then turned to look back at that terrible face suspended in the darkness of the doorway. We weren't really afraid of him. We knew those black hairy hands of his, that rested like legs of mutton on the half-door, had never beaten anyone. And even if they had, we would have understood why. We had often given them good reason.

There was nothing else to do after leaving the forge. I was too excited to head for home. I left the boys and wandered back through the village towards the creamery cross. Vincent was up the side-road, leaning against an old rusty gate. He was looking into a nettle-grown paddock, where battered churns and slag and packing-cases had overflowed from the creamery yard. He kept the red swollen cheek turned away from me.

"You going home?" I asked. I took it for granted he was waiting till the usual time, in case that mother of his asked any questions.

"No." He glanced at me, his eyes cold and clear, as if he hadn't cried at all. "I'm going to get that letter."

"But . . . what d'ye want it for?"

"I want it. That's all."

"How you going to get it, Vince?" I asked after a while. He was looking out over the paddock, as if he'd forgotten all about me.

"In his house, where else? I'm waiting for him to go up to the shop."

We could see the main road from where we were, just the caps and hats and shawls going past and occasionally a cyclist's head flitting silently by.

"What about Chris?" I said. Chris had to put on the kettle for the master's tea and sweep the house out. The master had no other help.

"What about him?" He turned to me suddenly. The master's old green hat had appeared, moving along the hedge. "D'you want to come? Or don't you?"

There was nothing I could say except "yes." My hands began to sweat, though, and the inside of my corduroy pants went warm and wet, then cold.

We waited till the hat swam away over the top of the hedge, then we ran across the fields and vaulted over the fence into the master's garden. I had never been in it before.

I looked around at the little heaps of cinders and the tins and bottles half buried under the bare, crooked apple-tree.

"Come on," said Vincent, "for God's sake!"

The back-door was open. Chris was kneeling halfway up the wooden stairs, sweeping away with a dustpan and brush. When he looked up and saw us, he let a squeak out of him. He tried to draw himself up and away from us, but Vincent caught him hard by the ankle.

"If you open your gob," said Vincent quietly, "d'ye know what I'll do to ye, Chris?"

Chris nodded his head up and down.

"You hear, Chris?"

Chris nodded again, up and down. He looked from one to the other of us with his little red scared eyes. He was too frightened to talk.

We found our copy-books on the table in the livingroom. It was dark there and smelt of mildew. A small flame was licking around the fresh sods of turf, but there was no heat in the room. Vincent started looking through the copy-books, while I wandered around, looking at the big dark books on the shelves and stacked on the floor. I picked up a book and shook the dust off it.

"Look at this," I said, "by Dickens! And here's another! Look, there's dozens of them, all by Dickens!"

"I know," said Vincent, "they're classics. They come in sets. My dad's got one."

On the mantelpiece, between some photographs, was another book by Dickens. It was *David Copperfield* and it had words underlined in it and a lot of writing in the margins. It made me feel good to find out what he was reading. I had finished *David Copperfield* months before.

I had a look at the photographs. One of them showed a few people standing around in a play, all dressed up as actors, the men wearing those sissy suits with silk stockings all the way up. On the back, it said "St. Malachy's Training College Dramatic Society in The Merchant of Venice by William Shakespeare." Underneath was a list of names.

"Hey, Vincent," I said, "look it here! He did Bassanio." And when I took up the next photograph, I shouted, "Hey, here's the girl that did Portia."

Vincent stopped his searching to come over and look.

"Yeah, that's his wife," he said.

"But . . . I didn't know . . ." I felt aggrieved. Nobody told me anything at home. "And where is she?"

"Gone."

"But where to?" I'd never heard of anyone's wife going away, ever before. Alive anyway.

Vincent just lifted his shoulders. "That's all I heard," he said.

"And what about . . ." I made a great effort to stretch my imagination. "What about his children?"

"She must have them," said Vincent, "that's if there are any."

I was trying hard to think of the master as somebody's father. "But, Vincent . . ." I began.

"Come on, will you?" said Vincent. "We'd better get a move on."

It was then that we noticed that Chris had been standing in the doorway, listening. Vincent went up to him and seized him by the shoulder. "Tell us where he put it," he said. "You'd better!"

"Don't ask me," said Chris, "please!" And the tears began to flow, fast and silent.

"Are ye going to tell me?" Vincent raised his hand. And just in time, I found the letter. It was folded roughly and stuck into a tarnished silver jug on the sideboard.

"Give it here to me," said Vincent. He took the letter between finger and thumb. "Where does he sit?" he asked. Chris pointed to a space on the table between the heaps of books and papers. Vincent tore the letter across quickly. Then he tore it again, more deliberately, back and forth into shreds. The little inky scraps of paper floated down over the empty space.

"You're not going to leave them there, man?" I burst out.

"Come on," said Vincent.

"But he'll have your life."

"Come on."

As we went through the kitchen, I noticed the tray that Chris had prepared. There were two cups, two saucers and two plates on it.

"Chris," I said, "you don't eat here? With *him?*"

Chris nodded. He took up the tray quickly and made for the livingroom.

"But, come here, Chris, tell me . . ."

We heard the footsteps outside the front door, his footsteps. I made a dart for the scullery door. Vincent caught my arm and held me back, pressed into the corner by the dresser. A warm patch began to spread again in my corduroys. I heard the footsteps go hollow in the hall, then go sharp on the lino of the livingroom. I heard them stop suddenly.

"Who did this?" It wasn't the voice I had expected. It was deep and quiet, as it had been that morning.

"I don't know." Chris almost whispered it.

"You do know. Who did it?" The voice terrified me more than if it had been a big bawl. I thought of Chris and of those tears silently flowing. I made a move towards the room, I couldn't help it, but Vincent's hand dragged me viciously back.

"I don't know," whispered Chris again, "please!"

There was a long silence. Then the quiet voice said, "All right, boy, you may sit down."

As the chairs were drawn in, I heard the scrape of a match and the globe of the oil-lamp being lifted. Vincent eased the back-door open and next minute, I was out into the air. Vincent led the way round to the front of the house. We crept up to the ivy-covered window-sill. We were just in time to see the master cross from the mantelpiece and toss *David Copperfield* on the table. He sat down under the yellow light of the lamp and began to pour out the tea. Chris opened the book. He began to read, his finger crawling down the page after the words. Every now and then he paused, while the master leant over and marked a word with a pencil. Chris would watch, then look up as the master talked, look up right into the master's face. Once he even laughed, not right out, but he laughed as if the master really had said something funny, that a fellow didn't have to pretend to laugh at. I stood there looking at them. I still couldn't believe what I saw, but I liked looking at them. Something made me turn to Vincent, though. When I saw him there, staring, with the corner of his mouth drawn back, I said, "Come on, Vincent, come on, for God's sake."

We had nothing to talk about as we walked home. The hedges on either side of us were alive with small twilight noises. At the creamery cross, we stopped and stood for a while, with our hands in our pockets. I asked Vincent was he going to come to school in the morning, or was he going to mitch.

"Yes," he said and left me before I could ask him which he meant.

He was there before us at the cross next morning, waiting for once. The boys crowded around him, full of questions, then found that they had nothing to say to him.

"Well, lads," he said, glancing around the circle of faces, "so every one of you is carrying his sod!"

Each of us looked at his sod and then looked for Vincent's.

"He'll leather hell out of ye," said I.

"I'm not bringing it."

I lifted my sod and looked at it. It was a good sod to look at, but not so good in the hand, heavy and soft after the winter rains. I couldn't even, for Vincent, throw it down.

"Jeez, man!" Billy always swore like that. He never said

the full word because he thought it was a mortal sin. Venial sins he didn't mind. " 'Tis not going to stand up to him ye are?"

"The way you did?" asked Vincent.

"D'ye think I'm mad? What did I get anyway, only a few skelps of an oul' stick? That's all."

"Why though?"

"Because I was caught, that's why. But I won't be caught the next time. I can tell ye that."

"There won't be any next time, for him."

"But he'll kill ye, man. Jeez, he'll tear the windpipe out of ye."

"I know," said Vincent. None of us could take our eyes off him. His face was pale. His eyes were like glass with a greenish light shining through them. He seemed taller than any of us, all drawn out. I felt excited inside, but instead of going tall and thin, I went red all over.

"Then," said I, throwing down my sod, "I'm not taking mine either!"

The boys stared at it a moment, then one by one they began to throw down their sods too.

"Hey!" Vincent was staring at us, real mad. "Take up those sods!"

"No," said I, "we're all in this together. Come on, lads, drop them."

Only Billy tried to keep his. He began to sidle out of the group, but some of the fellows caught him by the wrist and twisted the sod out of his hand.

"He can't beat the lot of us," I said, as a few fellows looked back at the heap of sods, "he can't. He'd get too tired."

Chris's was the only sod in the fireplace, perched on a nest of crumpled papers and wooden cipins. We kept watching it, as the master came in. We couldn't take our eyes off it. That was why he spotted it immediately. The color went slowly up through his face and spread all over the top of his head.

"Step out to the line, the boys who brought no turf."

We all stepped out, trying to look calm, but afraid to look at each other. We were watching that red and shining skull, afraid it would do something, flare out suddenly, maybe, like one of those Japanese flowers that you dip in water. He can't beat us all, I kept saying to myself, please God, he can't beat us all. Oh, God, make him too tired.

He handed Chris a pen-knife and motioned him towards the door. We knew we were for it. While Chris went to cut a new ash-plant, we waited in dead silence, twitching now and then, like sheep waiting for the shearing. I was wondering if it was going to be on the hands or on the behind. Please God, make him think the behind is too much trouble. It was too, because he had to hold our trousers tight so that it hurt more. But please God, make him remember that.

He stood at the window, cracking his fingers and muttering to himself, as he watched Chris below in the copse by the stream. When Chris came back, he grabbed the stick and flexed it a few times between his hands. Then, suddenly, he caught hold of the first fellow in the queue. Without looking to see who it was, he bent the fellow over the desk and raised the stick. The howling began before the first blow landed. With one hand, the master held the trousers tight against the fork of the legs, while with the other, he beat away as if it was an old carpet he had. The howl dwindled into a squeal and then a whimper as the fellow was hauled up and shoved aside. Then the master seized the next fellow.

He worked away like that for a good while, like a red-hot old steam engine. Sometimes, he stopped, gasping for air. Then he was away again on a hack. Gradually, he began to work himself into a good humor. You could see the bald head cooling off. He began to make jokes like "Next, please" and "Step this way, gentlemen" and he bowed to the fellows after he had finished with them. Then he came to Billy.

"Ho," said he, "himself again! Might I recommend, sir, a hair of the dog?"

He laid Billy down with great respect, while we tried to

laugh at the joke. Billy was smart, though, the smartest of the lot of us, though you'd never think it. He waited, very quiet, for the first blow, then he lashed out suddenly with his big boot, which caught the master right in the chest.

"I'm sorry, sir," squawked Billy, in his hoarse man's voice, "honest to God, I never meant it. Please, sir, listen to me, sir . . ." but there was no need to go on. The master had walked slowly over to the window, hunching his shoulders and raising his knees. He stood there a long time, breathing hard and gradually straightening himself up. He turned suddenly to stare at us. His face was terribly pale.

"Is it trying to kill me ye are?" said he, in a whisper.

We didn't know what to say, without telling a downright lie. We just stared back at him.

"All right," said he, his voice a little stronger now, "go, each one of ye, and bring back your sod of turf. And be here in half-an-hour."

We shuffled to our feet. None of us wanted to be the first to go.

"And if one single boy comes back in here without his sod," said he, his voice strengthening all the time, "there'll be skin and hair flying. Every mother's son of ye will be bet again and those that I haven't bet yet will be bet twice over. So away with ye now, ye pack of little divils out of hell!" Then he let a bellow out of him. "Well, what are ye staring at? Get out!"

We made a dive for the door. Chris jumped out of our way to let us pass. He sucked his fingers as he looked after us.

The little stack of turf was still at the creamery cross, where we had left it. We jostled around it, each of us trying to pick out the best sod he could find. The thought of Vincent seemed to strike all of us at once. We stopped and looked up. He was there, watching us.

"Come on, man," Billy said, "get yourself a sod."

Vincent just smiled.

"Come on." Billy crowded up on him with that squaring, swaggering stance of his. "Billy Flahavan is not going to be bet twice. I can tell ye that. Not over you!"

Vincent stayed where he was, waiting. Billy's swagger drooped a bit, pretended to be a twitch of the shoulder-blades. He glanced back to us for encouragement. "Get the bloody thing, man, can't ye?"

"Yes, get it," I shouted. I felt dirty all over, as if part of me was soft and black as a rotting apple. "We've had enough."

There was a murmur from the lads and they pushed forward behind me. "Yes," they said, "go on, man, get it." Vincent stood his ground, as I was pushed against him. His eyes were staring straight into mine. "Get it!" I said, in a whisper. At that moment, I was all set to hit him. My fists were bunched and I was stiff with all the rage inside me.

Just in time, he turned aside. "Hold on a moment," he said. We watched him run away up the lane to the creamery. We began to wonder if we should follow him, to make sure he came back. Then we saw him coming, with three big black sods of turf under his arm.

"Well, come on," said he, running his eyes over us, as he used to do, "if 'tis not afraid ye are?"

"We're not afraid," I said.

"Bloody sure we're not," said Billy.

"Follow me, then," said Vincent, marching off. We fell into step behind him. We wanted to take our time, to drag our feet in the dust, but we didn't dare to in case Vincent turned round.

"What are you going to do, Vince?" I asked, moving up beside him.

"You'll find out!" he said, out loud, so as to lump me in with the rest. "You'll find out, the lot of ye."

The master was at the window, humming a tune as he swished the stick. It was the tune he hummed when he was beating us out of sheer good humor. He used to sing the last line of it, "for you'll remember, you'll remember me," as he brought the stick down hard, emphasizing every syllable. He turned towards us now, as if we had surprised him.

"Ah! So soon, lads? Determined not to miss a good day's sport! Amn't I right, Chris?"

"Yes, master," said Chris, from the seat inside the door.

"Now! Stand out those boys, whose hides haven't yet been properly tanned!"

"Aw! Sir!" pleaded Billy, just as he was easing himself into a seat.

"Aw! Sir! Aw! Sir!" The master swished his stick a few times. "Out to the line, you blackguard!"

"Hey!" called Vincent, who was still standing at the door.

"What's that?" The master turned, staring.

"Don't you want your turf?"

"Sir!" the master shouted. "Say sir!"

"Don't you want your turf?" Vincent was advancing insolently down the room. He stood, weighing a sod in his hand. He had gone very pale.

The master looked at him sharply, snuffing like a bull. He raised the stick and moved forward, his mouth open, spluttering. He ducked just in time, as the sod flew over his head and broke in two against the blackboard. There was silence as the dust drifted down to the floor. Then the master let a roar out of him. He lifted the stick and advanced again.

Vincent's second sod caught him on the forehead, sending his glasses flying. The sharp crack left a thin line of blood. The master dropped the stick. His knuckles dug into his eyes, which were blinded with the dust.

"Look at him!" screamed Vincent, his voice cracking in the middle. "Look at him, now!" He turned towards us. "Come on, lads, quick, belt away!"

"Right!" squawked Billy, lifting his arm. "You oul' bastard!" he yelled as he flung his sod straight into the master's blind face, squashing the nose and mouth. "Now you'll remember me!"

The sods bombarded the master's face from all directions.

He sank into his chair, facing us, his hands still at his eyes, that angry line on his forehead, the blood dripping from nose and chin. A sound midway between a belch and a hiccough burst from him. It was followed by a terrible sound, which stayed the hands of those who had not yet fired. It was a sob, a great shaking sob. It tore out of his chest and was followed by another and then another. We lowered our hands and stared. The sobbing eased a little. It became a long continuous moaning sound, like a baby with the colic. We drew back slowly.

"Come on, you fools," yelled Vincent, "hit him!" He lifted his third sod. Before he could fire it, he was seized from behind. The sod was twisted quickly out of his hand. Chris flung him aside, then stood back panting, with his puny fists up.

"All right, Vincent!" I got between them quickly, as Vincent flung himself viciously forward. "You'd better get out!"

He stopped, staring at me, as if he didn't know me. Then he took a look at the shocked faces all around. He began to tremble all over. Suddenly, he turned and walked out the door.

The rest of us sat down, one by one. Only Chris went up to stand by the blind, naked, bleeding face. He stood by it, wanting to touch it, but afraid to stretch out his hand. The tears had begun to roll down his cheeks, silently rolling as if they would never stop.

I let the sod of turf fall from my hand. I heard it thump on the floor. I'm sure I heard it. In fact, I know I did. But ever since, whenever I look back, I think that I too lifted it and flung it against the face of the master.

The Transfer

BIENVENIDO N. SANTOS

A T THE MEETING OF THE LOCAL CATHOLIC ACTION COMMIT-tee held that Sunday morning at the Bishop's Palace immediately after the high mass, Mr. Conrado Arabia, who was an old government employee as well as chairman of the CAC for the past five years, mentioned casually the need for a practical retirement system for the Church, patterned after the civil service. The committee had met to discuss the final details of the welcome program for the first Bishop of the diocese ever to reside in town.

The Bishop's Palace stood outside the Cathedral grounds. Formerly the mansion of a wealthy Chinese dry goods merchant, it was now ready for its distinguished resident. It still smelled of paint and varnish, but the transformation was complete. The ground floor, formerly a recreation hall and bar, had been partitioned to serve as offices of the Chancery. File cabinets and chairs stood in appropriate corners. A huge mahogany table covered with glass occupied an inner compartment for the Bishop himself. On a wall was a colored painting of His Holiness, the Pope. Typewriters under black leathery hoods, looking like monks asleep at their desks, bookcases with gay jacketed volumes, had replaced the open bar and the wine shelves; religious calendars, each page crowded with pictures of saints and fish in red, now hung on the walls where colorful targets for archery practice used to be. On the first floor, the guest room adjoining the sala was now a chapel, beautiful with imported rugs and gleaming pews. From where he sat, Mr. Arabia could see the altar gravely austere in its simplicity, and the chandeliers, resplendent even in the daytime.

What Mr. Arabia said aroused no end of talk among those who heard him because they knew whom he must have had in mind when he suggested the need for a retirement system for priests.

Father Simplicio Ruivivar had been parish priest of the town for nearly half a century and he was not strong enough any more to carry on the growing complexities of his job. Grown fat and habitually shabby, he waddled about with effort. Old age had impaired his senses. There were old priests who knew when it was time for them to retire and keep to the corner, who allowed younger priests to take over their tasks even while they continued to be nominally, at least, parish priests. But Father Ruivivar refused to acknowledge what was obvious to everybody, that he had become too old for his job. His retort every time someone in the parish dared to brook him or express contrary opinion: "Who are you to say so? You think you are wise, but I am old. Remember, didn't I baptize you myself?" assumed a meaning beyond its implication, that here, indeed, was a priest grown too old for his job.

Something always happened when he said mass that somehow appeared like a desecration for so holy a ritual. Father Ruivivar would suddenly get stuck on a page in the course of the mass. No matter how hard he peered at the lines, he just could not go on and he would stand there, like one petrified, his hands spread apart, fingers pointed upwards, nose glued to the page, stooped and lost, while the acolyte hovered around nervously, holding a short, lighted candle near the page. There was no telling how long the pause would last. It could not have been his glasses or his eyes, for then, all he had to do if that were the case, was to skip the word or the line or even the whole page without anyone noticing it. But there he would stand, in an awkward stoop, unmoving, unmindful of the passing time. At such times perhaps it was his mind that wandered far and took those unnecessary detours into nowhere, but only he could admit this and he would not.

The preparations for the Bishop's arrival swirled about the old parish priest as he walked about or kept to his room, rummaging his rickety bureau for papers that were always getting lost. Actually his assistants did everything, but Father Ruivivar wanted his own way. Sometimes he was only a hindrance. Mr. Arabia, who had to work closely with the church, knew this well and often had to give in to the old priest's wishes even when they were clearly wrong. Nobody dared upbraid him for his faults.

Once the CAC handed Father Ruivivar an amount that was enough to buy the much needed pews of the ruined church. The committee suggested that a local furniture maker be given the job, stipulating the right size and length for each pew. But the old priest had his own plans. He ordered the pews from an out of town carpenter who took a long time finishing them, and when the pews arrived, they were only half the number the committee had expected. The reason soon became clear when the committee saw that they were huge, over-sized pews. The high back almost touched the chins of those who knelt behind. They were pews for giants. But Father Ruivivar liked them that way.

"They are durable," he said, as though size had anything to do with durability.

One thing led to another and Mr. Arabia began thinking aloud how wonderful it would be if they had another parish priest. What he said that Sunday could mean that Mr. Arabia himself might be persuaded to make representations to the Bishop. Somebody at the meeting was quick to suggest that as soon as His Excellency had settled down, Mr. Arabia should seek an audience with him and petition to remove their old parish priest, to retire him to a small, out of the way town.

"But that might appear dictating to the Bishop," Mr. Arabia said. "Besides, coming from us, would it not be unkind?"

Mr. Arabia was referring to those in the organization who, like him, had grown up in the parish, who had been baptized by the parish priest himself whom they were now seeking to retire. Would the act be right, would it not be disloyalty of a sort, a betrayal to memory? What would the old, the truly old, think of it? Would their dead parents (may they rest in peace!), who had been young with this priest, like it this way?

"It is your duty," a member reminded him.

"Your feelings, our feelings, should not count. The good of the parish should be our concern."

"He has only a few more years to live," Mr. Arabia said.

"Meanwhile," said a young lawyer in the group, "we would be in the awkward, unpleasant predicament of waiting for the day of his death, and in our minds, wishing that it would be soon."

"That would be cruel," Mr. Arabia admitted.

"There you are," many voices spoke.

But Mr. Arabia would not promise. He believed that the new Bishop would see the necessity himself before long. Right now, he said, eager to change the subject, there were more pressing problems in connection with the preparations for the Bishop's coming.

As it turned out, when the day came, the parish gave the Bishop a magnificent welcome. Visiting church dignitaries, led by the Papal Nuncio himself, were each given a car, with the name and title of the occupant printed on a sticker in a corner of the windshield. All of them were house guests in the mansions of well-to-do parishioners. There was a long parade from the airport to the Cathedral. Even public school teachers and pupils paused from their rigid routine and rushed to the school gates and waved at the cars. The ecclesiastical colors flew from every window of the houses along the main highway, each one a banner of hope that the new Bishop might soon realize that their old parish priest must go.

Although Mr. Arabia was very busy that day, every time he saw Father Ruivivar he remembered what had been discussed at the committee meeting. The old priest walked with brisk steps towards the Bishop and knelt on his left knee to kiss the proferred ring. He looked solemn all throughout the investiture and enthusiastic, alert to every snag that broke the continuity of the beautiful ritual. It seems he swung the censer at a wilder arc than was necessary. At the formal banquet that night, his face lighted up with a smile at the Papal Nuncio's opening remarks. Somehow it hurt Mr. Arabia to think that there were plans afoot to remove this old priest who could smile so winsomely when a pleasant thought crossed his mind or when a happy word fell upon his good ear. But he must go, Mr. Arabia told himself, for the good of the parish.

Soon the diocese learned what a singular blessing it was for them to have a Bishop in their midst, a humble man of God who was born in one of the outlying barrios of the diocese where he was now Bishop. The parishioners learned to love his humane ways, the simplicity of the man, his understanding. He was a wonderful listener, and, it seemed, he got things done. Yet, after one year, nobody had come to him about Father Ruivivar. There had been changes. The Cathedral had been rebuilt. Pews of the right size had been added. Side altars had been constructed, a new bell now hung from the tower. But the old parish priest was still there.

Instead of quieting down and slackening his pace as suited his age and waning senses, Father Ruivivar seemed eager to make good, but he bungled everything he did. His sermons were longer, they were caustic, often violent. He read lengthy pastoral letters that would have been more effective and better understood if they had been simply summarized; and what was worse, he repeated entire paragraphs without meaning to, maybe, and certainly not for emphasis, as his droning even voice hinted that for him the letter held no meaning; and, as usual, he got stuck somewhere in the missal during the mass. He scolded his parishioners openly, singled out women in the church who wore short-sleeved dresses and low neck-lines. He called the teen-agers' gamin way of doing their hair the "devil's hair-do." Even those who never went to church began to repeat stories they had heard from church-goers, till the stories became mere half-truths and exaggerated anecdotes that delighted many and embarrassed the faithful. But, of course, it was true that Father Ruivivar shouted at the con-fessional especially when he could not hear what the penitent was saying, or he repeated the confession to make certain that he had heard aright, in a voice so loud even those kneel-ing at the pews nearby could hear. Or he would leave the confession booth in the middle of a confession. He was old and grown useless for such delicate things. He could no longer hear what came through the screen in the pained hushed voice of the contrite sinner. He heard other things, perhaps voices from nowhere, to which he made reply as he walked or sat in a crowd or alone in the booth of the confessional. He would shake his head to contradict, to deny, or to refuse what the voices demanded, what they kept saying out of the night of his many years.

Even Mr. Arabia found himself avoiding the masses Father Ruivivar said. He felt guilty about this, but by now he had ceased to have any feeling of remorse over what had already become a general, though not too open, desire on the part of the parish to see Father Ruivivar go.

One day, shortly before the rainy months, Mr. Arabia visited the Bishop at the Palace to deliver a copy of the resolu-tion approved by the CAC, praying the Bishop to give the parish a new head priest. A young lawyer had drafted the resolution and it was worded well. The tone was respectful, no grudges lay hidden between the lines, and the meaning

255

was clear. It was time that Father Ruivivar be retired. As president, Mr. Arabia led the list of signatories.

The Bishop was glad to see him, but Mr. Arabia could not bring himself right away to the subject of the petition. As he talked, he kept touching the envelope in the inside breast pocket of his jacket. He talked of other things: how it was that he had come to "disturb" His Excellency at this time of the day; soon it would be evening. But he had been delayed at the office so he could not come earlier. He was glad to see the Bishop looking well. It seemed the place suited him.

"I'm a native of the parish," the Bishop reminded him, "I'm what you may say, native to the climate. I was born here. I studied in the public elementary school here."

The Bishop tried to recall the names of the men and women whom he still recognized as his former classmates. He remembered one in particular, a former teacher of his in the fourth grade.

"I know him," said Mr. Arabia. "He's an active member of the CAC."

At this point he could have very well added, "Well, that reminds me, Monsignor . . ."

But the Bishop was still talking. Now he was saying: "But I miss the others. A few days after my arrival, I walked through the Cathedral and read the names on each marble tablet. Some of them bore recent dates and familiar names. And there are other resting places I have not been to. But that is how it is. God in His divine wisdom allows some of us to tarry longer here, but we get old, and something goes even before the end."

The Bishop paused, raising his head, and gazed towards the Cathedral grounds as though expecting someone. Mr. Arabia found himself saying almost in a whisper, "Yes, Monsignor, something goes even before the end."

The door opened and Father Ruivivar entered. He was smiling as he approached the Bishop, stooping low to kiss his hand.

The Bishop was unsmiling and direct. As soon as the old priest had taken a seat, he said, "Father Ruivivar, I've decided to transfer you to Malabo. You need rest. Malabo is a beautiful town by the sea."

Mr. Arabia raised a trembling hand to his breast and felt the envelope there. He wanted to excuse himself. He had no right staying. The envelope felt heavy like a rock.

Father Ruivivar must have failed to hear what the Bishop had just said. He sat nodding as though in full agreement with what the Bishop was saying. The smile had not left his face.

Sensing perhaps that the priest had not fully understood what he had just said, the Bishop repeated the words slowly and aloud, almost, Mr. Arabia thought, in anger.

The smile disappeared from the old man's face. He tilted his gray head to one side and murmured, "Malabo?"

"Yes," the Bishop said. "You will be transferred to Malabo. Prepare to leave at the end of the month. You will like Malabo. You're an old man now, Father Ruivivar. You have served the church well these many years, so I'm asking you to rest. There's no better place for you than Malabo."

Father Ruivivar had been intently listening, his good ear turned slightly toward the Bishop and, it seemed, now he understood every word his superior said.

"Do you understand?" the Bishop asked when Father Ruivivar remained quiet. The old man just sat there for a time, his head bowed, looking at the knuckles of his hands upon his lap. Slowly the old head nodded and kept nodding.

"You will like Malabo," the Bishop was saying. "I have been there, bathed in its hot springs. Good for old men like you and me, Father Ruivivar. Old men like us don't have to work too hard. The old have their peculiar burden. And I don't mean just the years on their back. Some other things, only you and I know, Father Ruivivar. Malabo is a proper sanctuary . . . for the old. Who knows, one of these days I might have to retire myself and find me another Malabo.

It isn't that the baths help truly, but the occasional immersions purify."

The gray head kept nodding until the church bells rang out the vesper hour and the men in the palace stood up and prayed.

"That's all," the Bishop said afterwards and bade them good evening.

Mr. Arabia walked with the priest, who kept stumbling over the weeds and the rubble near the convent. It was dark and the lights were far and dim.

Father Ruivivar was silent all the way except that once in a while he would mutter what sounded like "Malabo." When they came to the convent gate, Mr. Arabia turned to the priest and was about to say: "Good evening, Father," when he realized that Father Ruivivar had not been aware of his presence. There was such a frozen expression on his face, it was deathly pale under the naked bulb over them. Mr. Arabia felt that he should take the old man to his room. He was about to take his arm when the priest turned away from the stairs and walked towards the Cathedral. Mr. Arabia followed him as he walked past the rectory to a side door which opened to a side altar. Father Ruivivar walked past the front altar down the steps. Like an automaton, he turned around facing the altar, which was dark except for a slow burning candle dipped in oil at the foot of the Christ, knelt on one knee and crossed himself. Mr. Arabia watched the old priest go past the communion rail. His white cassock shone like a banner in the darkened Cathedral. Now he didn't seem in a hurry any more, but took his time, walking along the walls as in a procession, but as he walked, Father Ruivivar extended his hand, in the manner of one groping in the dark, but sidewise, as though he could see where he was going, but he just wanted to touch the walls. He made one round, pausing long under the belfry. For a while, Mr. Arabia thought the priest was going to ring the bells as he groped for the rope, tied into a knot around a steel hook in the wall. But he walked on till he came to the side door where Mr. Arabia waited. Now he took his arm and the priest started at his touch, but he let him lead him to his room. There was nobody around. From the light outside the window, Mr. Arabia could see that the room was open and he led Father Ruivivar to it.

"Shall I turn on the light, Father? Where's the switch?" Mr. Arabia asked.

Father Ruivivar looked at him and said, "Huh?"

"The light, Father," Mr. Arabia said. "You must have light in your room."

"Oh," said the priest as though he had just realized that evening had come and it was dark. He walked towards the bed and groped on the wall till his fingers touched the switch and he turned it on.

The room was a mess. Mr. Arabia had been here before, but it had never looked this bad. The bed was unmade and the pillow cases should have been changed a long time ago. They were no longer white. They were shabby like everything in the room, like the cassock of Father Ruivivar which always seemed in need of washing. Strange how it could shine in the dark as it did a while ago.

Used candlesticks lay in a heap in a corner. The big table near the bed was littered with papers, pennants attached to sticks bearing the church colors, fat manila envelopes that must have been new before the last war, robes of different hues which the disciples must have used during the Holy Week, among them a green bag now emptied of its coins and paper money, dangling down the table, the same perhaps he had used some years ago, Mr. Arabia thought, when he walked the streets barefooted seeking alms. He was Judas then, but only for a day . . . only for a day.

Father Ruivivar had sat on the bed and bowed his head, his eyes upon his hands as if he were examining them.

"Good night," Mr. Arabia said, hurrying to the door, clasping the rock upon his breast.

The priest raised his head and said: "Is it the end of the

month now and are we going? Are we coming with me, son?"

He stood up and walked towards Mr. Arabia, saying: "You are coming with me? I'm not going alone? So, I'm not going alone. You're coming with me. But what have you done? You're young. Look at your hands."

Mr. Arabia moved to meet him.

"Father," he cried, embracing the old priest, and he was suddenly aware not so much of the bloated body in his arms as of an odd smell that came to him, staining him forever before his time, like that of age, like his own father's when he lay dying in his arms.

In the Zoo

JEAN STAFFORD

KEENING HARSHLY IN HIS SENILITY, THE BLIND POLAR BEAR slowly and ceaselessly shakes his head in the stark heat of the July and mountain noon. His open eyes are blue. No one stops to look at him; an old farmer, in passing, sums up the old bear's situation by observing, with a ruthless chuckle, that he is a "back number." Patient and despairing, he sits on his yellowed haunches on the central rock of his pool, his huge toy paws wearing short boots of mud.

The grizzlies to the right of him, a conventional family of father and mother and two spring cubs, alternately play the clown and sleep. There is a blustery, scoundrelly, half-likable bravado in the manner of the black bear on the polar's left; his name, according to the legend on his cage, is Clancy, and he is a rough-and-tumble, brawling blowhard, thundering continually as he paces back and forth, or pauses to face his audience of children and mothers and release from his great, gray-tongued mouth a perfectly Vesuvian roar. If he were to be reincarnated in human form, he would be a man of action, possibly a football coach, probably a politician. One expects to see his black hat hanging from a branch of one of his trees; at any moment he will light a cigar.

The polar bear's next-door neighbors are not the only ones who offer so sharp and sad a contrast to him. Across a reach of scrappy grass and litter is the convocation of conceited monkeys, burrowing into each other's necks and chests for fleas, picking their noses with their long, black, finicky fingers, swinging by their gifted tails on the flying trapeze, screaming bloody murder. Even when they mourn—one would think the male orangutan was on the very brink of suicide—they are comedians; they only fake depression, for they are firmly secure in their rambunctious tribalism and in their appalling insight and contempt. Their flibbertigibbet gambolling is a sham, and, stealthily and shiftily, they are really watching the pitiful polar bear ("Back number," they quote the farmer. "That's *his* number all right," they snigger), and the windy black bear ("Life of the party. Gasbag. Low I.Q.," they note scornfully on his dossier), and the stupid, bourgeois grizzlies ("It's feed the face and hit the sack for them," the monkeys say). And they are watching my sister and me, two middle-aged women, as we sit on a bench between the exhibits, eating popcorn, growing thirsty. We are thoughtful.

A chance remark of Daisy's a few minutes before has turned us to memory and meditation. "I don't know why," she said, "but that poor blind bear reminds me of Mr. Murphy." The name "Mr. Murphy" at once returned us both to childhood, which has little to do with hunger; it is not so much food as a sacrament, and in tribute to our sisterliness and our friendliness I break the silence to say that this is the best popcorn I have ever eaten in my life. The extravagance of my statement instantly makes me feel self-indulgent, and for some time I uneasily avoid looking at the blind bear. My sister does not agree or disagree; she simply says that popcorn is the only food she has ever really liked. For a long time, then, we eat without a word, but I know, because I know her well and know her similarity to me, that Daisy is thinking what I am thinking; both of us are mournfully remembering Mr. Murphy, who, at one time in our lives, was our only friend.

This zoo is in Denver, a city that means nothing to my sister and me except as a place to take or meet trains. Daisy lives two hundred miles farther west, and it is her custom when my every-other-year visit with her is over, to come across the mountains to see me off on my eastbound train. We know almost no one here, and because our stays are short, we have never bothered to learn the town in more than the most desultory way. We know the Burlington uptown office and the respectable hotels, a restaurant or two, the Union Station, and, beginning today, the zoo in the city park.

But since the moment that Daisy named Mr. Murphy by name our situation in Denver has been only corporeal; our minds and our hearts are in Adams, fifty miles north, and we are seeing, under the white sun at its pitiless meridian, the streets of that ugly town, its parks and trees and bridges, the bandstand in its dreary park, the roads that lead away from it, west to the mountains and east to the plains, its mongrel and multitudinous churches, its high school shaped like a loaf of bread, the campus of its college, an oasis of which we had no experience except to walk through it now and then, eying the woodbine on the impressive buildings. These things are engraved forever on our minds with a legibility so insistent that you have only to say the name of the town aloud to us to rip the rinds from our nerves and leave us exposed in terror and humiliation.

We have supposed in later years that Adams was not so bad as all that, and we know that we magnified its ugliness because we looked upon it as the extension of the possessive, unloving, scornful, complacent foster mother, Mrs. Placer, to whom, at the death of our parents within a month of each other, we were sent like Dickensian grotesqueries—cowardly, weak-stomached, given to tears, backward in school. Daisy was ten and I was eight when, unaccompanied, we made the long trip from Marblehead to our benefactress, whom we had never seen and, indeed, never heard of until the pastor of our church came to tell us of the arrangement our father had made on his deathbed, seconded by our mother on hers. This man, whose name and face I have forgotten and whose parting speeches to us I have not forgiven, tried to dry our tears with talk of Indians and of buffaloes; he spoke, however, at much greater length, and in preaching cadences, of the Christian goodness of Mrs. Placer. She was, he said, childless and fond of children, and for many years she had been a widow, after the lingering demise of her tubercular husband, for whose sake she had moved to the Rocky Mountains. For his support and costly medical care, she had run a boarding house, and after his death, since he had left her nothing, she was obliged to continue running it. She had been a girlhood friend of our paternal grandmother, and our father, in the absence of responsible relatives, had made her the beneficiary of his life insurance on the condition that she lodge and rear us. The pastor, with a frankness remarkable considering that he was talking to children, explained to us that our father had left little more than a drop in the bucket for our care, and he enjoined us to give Mrs. Placer, in return for her hospitality and sacrifice, courteous help and eternal thanks. "Sacrifice" was a word we were never allowed to forget.

And thus it was, in grief for our parents, that we came cringing to the dry Western town and to the house where Mrs. Placer lived, a house in which the square, uncushioned furniture was cruel and the pictures on the walls were either dour or dire and the lodgers, who lived in the upper floors among shadowy wardrobes and chiffoniers, had come through the years to resemble their landlady in appearance as well as in deportment.

After their ugly-colored evening meal, Gran—as she bade us call her—and her paying guests would sit, rangy and acquiline, rocking on the front porch on spring and summer and autumn nights, tasting their delicious grievances: those slights delivered by ungrateful sons and daughters, those impudences committed by trolley-car conductors and uppity salesgirls in the ready-to-wear, all those slurs and calculated elbow-jostlings that were their daily crucifixion and their staff of life. We little girls, washing the dishes in the cavernous kitchen, listened to their even, martyred voices, fixed like leeches to their solitary subject and their solitary creed—that life was essentially a matter of being done in, let down, and swindled.

At regular intervals, Mrs. Placer, chairwoman of the victims, would say, "Of course, I don't care; I just have to laugh," and then would tell a shocking tale of an intricate piece of skulduggery perpetrated against her by someone she did not even know. Sometimes, with her avid, partial jury sitting there on the porch behind the bitter hopvines in the heady mountain air, the cases she tried involved Daisy and me, and, listening, we travailed, hugging each other, whispering, "I wish she wouldn't! Oh, how did she find out?" How *did* she? Certainly we never told her when we were snubbed or chosen last on teams, never admitted to a teacher's scolding or to the hoots of laughter that greeted us when we bit on silly, unfair jokes. But she knew. She knew about the slumber parties we were not invited to, the beefsteak fries from which we were pointedly left out; she knew that the singing teacher had said in so many words that I could not carry a tune in a basket and that the sewing superintendent had said that Daisy's fingers were all thumbs. With our teeth chattering in the cold of our isolation, we would hear her protestant, litigious voice defending our right to be orphans, paupers, wholly dependent on her—except for the really ridiculous pittance from our father's life insurance—when it was all she could do to make ends meet. She did not care, but she had to laugh that people in general were so small-minded that they looked down on fatherless, motherless waifs like us and, by association, looked down on her. It seemed funny to her that people gave her no credit for taking on these sickly youngsters who were not even kin but only the grandchildren of a friend.

If a child with braces on her teeth came to play with us, she was, according to Gran, slyly lording it over us because our teeth were crooked, but there was no money to have them straightened. And what could be the meaning of our being asked to come for supper at the doctor's house? Were the doctor and his la-di-da New York wife and those pert girls with their solid-gold barrettes and their Shetland pony going to shame her poor darlings? Or shame their poor Gran by making them sorry to come home to the plain but honest life that was all she could provide for them?

There was no stratum of society not reeking with the effluvium of fraud and pettifoggery. And the school system was almost the worst of all: if we could not understand fractions, was that not our teacher's fault? And therefore what right had she to give us F? It was as plain as a pikestaff to Gran that the teacher was only covering up her own inability to teach. It was unlikely, too—highly unlikely—that it was by accident that time and time again the free medical clinic was closed for the day just as our names were about to be called out, so that nothing was done about our bad tonsils, which meant that we were repeatedly sick in the winter, with Gran fetching and carrying for us, climbing those stairs a jillion times a day with her game leg and her heart that was none too strong.

Steeped in these mists of accusation and hidden plots and double meanings, Daisy and I grew up like worms. I think no one could have withstood the atmosphere in that house where everyone trod on eggs that a little bird had told them were bad. They spied on one another, whispered behind doors, conjectured, drew parallels beginning "With all due respect . . ." or "It is a matter of indifference to *me* but . . ." The vigilantes patrolled our town by day, and by night returned to lay their goodies at their priestess's feet and wait for her oracular interpretation of the innards of the butcher, the baker, the candlestick maker, the soda jerk's girl, and the barber's unnatural deaf white cat.

Consequently, Daisy and I also became suspicious. But it was suspicion of ourselves that made us mope and weep and grimace with self-judgment. Why were we not happy when Gran had sacrificed herself to the bone for us? Why did we not cut dead the paper boy who had called her a filthy name? Why did we persist in our willful friendliness with the grocer who had tried, unsuccessfully, to overcharge her on a case of pork and beans?

Our friendships were nervous and surreptitious; we sneaked and lied, and as our hungers sharpened, our debasement deepened; we were pitied; we were shifty-eyed, always on the lookout for Mrs. Placer or one of her tattletale lodgers; we were hypocrites.

Nevertheless, one thin filament of instinct survived, and Daisy and I in time found asylum in a small menagerie down by the railroad tracks. It belonged to a gentle alcoholic ne'er-do-well, who did nothing all day long but drink bathtub gin in rickeys and play solitaire and smile to himself and talk to his animals. He had a little, stunted red vixen and a deodorized skunk, a parrot from Tahiti that spoke Parisian French, a woebegone coyote, and two capuchin monkeys, so serious and humanized, so small and sad and sweet, and so religious-looking with their tonsured heads that it was impossible not to think their gibberish was really an ordered language with a grammar that someday some philologist would understand.

Gran knew about our visits to Mr. Murphy and she did not object, for it gave her keen pleasure to excoriate him when we came home. His vice was not a matter of guesswork; it was an established fact that he was half-seas over from dawn till midnight. "With the black Irish," said Gran, "the taste for drink is taken in with the mother's milk and is never mastered. Oh, I know all about those promises to join the temperance movement and not to touch another drop. The way to Hell is paved with good intentions."

We were still little girls when we discovered Mr. Murphy, before the shattering disease of adolescence was to make our bones and brains ache even more painfully than before, and we loved him and we hoped to marry him when we grew up. We loved him, and we loved his monkeys to exactly the same degree and in exactly the same way; they were husbands and fathers and brothers, these three little, ugly, dark, secret men who minded their own business and let us mind ours. If we stuck our fingers through the bars of the cage, the monkeys would sometimes take them in their tight, tiny hands and look into our faces with a tentative, somehow absent-minded sorrow, as if they terribly regretted that they could not place us but were glad to see us all the same. Mr. Murphy, playing a solitaire game of cards called "once in a blue moon" on a kitchen table in his back yard beside the pens, would occasionally look up and blink his beautiful blue eyes and say, "You're peaches to make over my wee friends. I love you for it." There was nothing demanding in his voice, and nothing sticky; on his lips the word "love" was jocose and forthright, it had no strings attached. We would sit on either side of him and watch him regiment his ranks of cards and stop to drink as deeply as if he were dying of thirst and wave to his animals and say to them, "Yes, lads, you're dandies."

Because Mr. Murphy was as reserved with us as the capuchins were, as courteously noncommittal, we were surprised one spring day when he told us that he had a present for us, which he hoped Mrs. Placer would let us keep; it was a puppy, for whom the owner had asked him to find a home—half collie and half Labrador retriever, blue-blooded on both sides.

"You might tell Mrs. Placer"—he said, smiling at the name, for Gran was famous in the town—"you might tell Mrs. Placer," said Mr. Murphy, "that this lad will make a fine watchdog. She'll never have to fear for her spoons again. Or her honor." The last he said to himself, not laughing but tucking his chin into his collar; lines sprang to the corners of his eyes. He would not let us see the dog, whom we could hear yipping and squealing inside his shanty, for he said that our disappointment would weigh on his conscience if we lost our hearts to the fellow and then could not have him for our own.

That evening at supper, we told Gran about Mr. Murphy's present. A dog? In the first place, why a dog? Was it possible that the news had reached Mr. Murphy's ears that Gran had just this very day finished planting her spring garden, the very thing that a rampageous dog would have in his mind to destroy? What sex was it? A male! Females, she had heard, were more trustworthy; males roved and came home smelling of skunk; such a consideration as this, of course, would not have crossed Mr. Murphy's fuddled mind. Was this young male dog housebroken? We had not asked? That was the limit!

Gran appealed to her followers, too raptly fascinated by Mr. Murphy's machinations to eat their Harvard beets. "Am I being farfetched or does it strike you as decidedly queer that Mr. Murphy is trying to fob off on my little girls a young cur that has not been trained?" she asked them. "If it were housebroken, he would have said so, so I feel it is safe to assume that it is not. Perhaps cannot *be* housebroken. I've heard of such cases."

The fantasy spun on, richly and rapidly, with all the skilled helping hands at work at once. The dog was tangibly in the room with us, shedding his hair, biting his fleas, shaking rain off himself to splatter the walls, dragging some dreadful carcass across the floor, chewing up slippers, knocking over chairs with his tail, gobbling the chops from the platter, barking, biting, fathering, fighting, smelling to high heaven of carrion, staining the rug with his muddy feet, scratching the floor with his claws. He developed rabies; he bit a child, two children! Three! Everyone in town! And Gran and her poor darlings went to jail for harboring this murderous, odoriferous, drunk, Roman Catholic dog.

And yet, astoundingly enough, she came around to agreeing to let us have the dog. It was, as Mr. Murphy had predicted, the word "watchdog" that deflected the course of the trial. The moment Daisy uttered it, Gran halted, marshalling her reverse march; while she rallied and tacked and reconnoitred, she sent us to the kitchen for the dessert. And by the time this course was under way, the uses of a dog, the enormous potentialities for investigation and law enforcement in a dog trained by Mrs. Placer, were being minutely and passionately scrutinized by the eight upright bloodhounds sitting at the table wolfing their brown Betty as if it were fresh-killed rabbit. The dog now sat at attention beside his mistress, fiercely alert, ears cocked, nose aquiver, the protector of widows, of orphans, of lonely people who had no homes. He made short shrift of burglars, homicidal ·maniacs, Peeping Toms, gypsies, bogus missionaries, Fuller Brush men with a risqué spiel. He went to the store and brought back groceries, retrieved the evening paper from the awkward place the boy had meanly thrown it, rescued cripples from burning houses, saved children from drowning, heeled at command, begged, lay down, stood up, sat, jumped through a hoop, ratted.

Both times—when he was a ruffian of the blackest delinquency and then a pillar of society—he was full-grown in his prefiguration, and when Laddy appeared on the following day, small, unsteady, and whimpering lonesomely, Gran and her lodgers were taken aback; his infant, clumsy paws embarrassed them, his melting eyes were unapropos. But it could never be said of Mrs. Placer, as Mrs. Placer her own self said, that she was a woman who went back on her word, and her darlings were going to have their dog, soft-headed and feckless as he might be. All the first night, in his carton in the kitchen, he wailed for his mother, and in the morning, it was true, he had made a shambles of the room—fouled the floor, and pulled off the tablecloth together with a ketchup bottle, so that thick gore lay everywhere. At breakfast, the lodgers confessed they had had a most amusing night, for it had actually been funny the way the dog had been determined not to let anyone get a wink of sleep. After that first night, Laddy slept in our room, receiving from us, all through our delighted, sleepless nights, pats and embraces and kisses and whispers. He was our baby, our best friend, the smartest, prettiest, nicest dog in the entire wide world. Our soft and rapid blandishments excited him to yelp at us in pleased bewilderment, and then we would playfully grasp his muzzle, so that he would snarl, deep in his throat like an adult dog, and shake his head violently, and, when we freed him, nip us smartly with great good will.

He was an intelligent and genial dog and we trained him quickly. He steered clear of Gran's radishes and lettuce after she had several times given him a brisk comeuppance with a strap across the rump, and he soon left off chewing shoes and the laundry on the line, and he outgrew his babyish whining. He grew like a weed; he lost his spherical softness, and his coat, which had been sooty fluff, came in stiff and rusty black; his nose grew aristocratically long, and his clever, pointed ears stood at attention. He was all bronzy, lustrous black except for an Elizabethan ruff of white and a tip of white at the end of his perky tail. No one could deny that he was exceptionally handsome and that he had, as well, great personal charm and style. He escorted Daisy and me to school in the morning, laughing interiorly out of the enormous pleasure of his life as he gracefully cantered ahead of us, distracted occasionally by his private interest in smells or unfamiliar beings in the grass but, on the whole, engrossed in his role of chaperon. He made friends easily with other dogs, and sometimes he went for a long hunting weekend into the mountains with a huge and bossy old red hound named Mess, who had been on the county most of his life and had made a good thing of it, particularly at the fire station.

It was after one of these three-day excursions into the high country that Gran took Laddy in hand. He had come back spent and filthy, his coat a mass of cockleburs and ticks, his eyes bloodshot, loud *râles* in his chest; for half a day he lay motionless before the front door like someone in a hangover, his groaning eyes explicitly saying "Oh, for God's sake, leave me be" when we offered him food or bowls of water. Gran was disapproving, then affronted, and finally furious. Not, of course, with Laddy, since all inmates of her house enjoyed immunity, but with Mess, whose caddish character, together with that of his nominal masters, the firemen, she examined closely under a strong light, with an air of detachment, with her not caring but her having, all the same, to laugh. A lodger who occupied the back west room had something to say about the fire chief and his nocturnal visits to a certain house occupied by a certain group of young women, too near the same age to be sisters and too old to be the daughters of the woman who claimed to be their mother. What a story! The exophthalmic librarian—she lived in one of the front rooms—had some interesting insinuations to make about the deputy marshal, who had borrowed, significantly, she thought, a book on hypnotism. She also knew—she was, of course, in a most useful position in the town, and from her authoritative pen in the middle of the library her mammiform and azure eyes and her eager ears missed nothing—that the fire chief's wife was not as scrupulous as she might be when she was keeping score on bridge night at the Sorosis.

There was little at the moment that Mrs. Placer and her disciples could do to save the souls of the Fire Department and their families, and therefore save the town from holocaust (a very timid boarder—a Mr. Beaver, a newcomer who was not to linger long—had sniffed throughout this recitative as if he were smelling burning flesh), but at least the unwholesome bond between Mess and Laddy could and would be severed once and for all. Gran looked across the porch at Laddy, who lay stretched at full length in the darkest corner, shuddering and baying abortively in his throat as he chased jack rabbits in his dreams, and she said, "A dog can have morals like a human." With this declaration Laddy's randy, manly holidays were finished. It may have been telepathy that woke him; he lifted his heavy head from his paws, laboriously got up, hesitated for a moment, and then padded languidly across the porch to Gran. He stood docilely beside her chair, head down, tail drooping as if to say, "O.K., Mrs. Placer, show me how and I'll walk the straight and narrow."

The very next day, Gran changed Laddy's name to Caesar, as being more dignified, and a joke was made at the supper table that he had come, seen, and conquered Mrs. Placer's heart—for within her circle, where the magnanimity she lavished upon her orphans was daily demonstrated, Mrs. Placer's heart was highly thought of. On that day also, although we did not know it yet, Laddy ceased to be our dog. Before many weeks passed, indeed, he ceased to be anyone we had ever known. A week or so after he became Caesar, he took up residence in her room, sleeping alongside her bed. She broke him of the habit of taking us to school (temptation to low living was rife along those streets; there was a chow —well, never mind) by the simple expedient of chaining him to a tree as soon as she got up in the morning. This discipline, together with the stamina-building cuffs she gave his sensitive ears from time to time, gradually but certainly remade his character. From a sanguine, affectionate, easygoing Gael (with the fits of melancholy that alternated with the larkiness), he turned into an overbearing, military, efficient, loud-voiced Teuton. His bark, once wide of range, narrowed to one dark, glottal tone.

Soon the paper boy flatly refused to serve our house after Caesar efficiently removed the bicycle clip from his pants leg; the skin was not broken, or even bruised, but it was a matter of principle with the boy. The milkman approached the back door in a seizure of shakes like St. Vitus's dance. The metermen, the coal men, and the garbage collector crossed themselves if they were Catholics and, if they were not, tried whistling in the dark. "Good boy, good Caesar," they carolled, and, unctuously lying, they said they knew his bark was worse than his bite, knowing full well that it was not, considering the very nasty nip, requiring stitches, he had given a representative of the Olson Rug Company, who had had the folly to pat him on the head. Caesar did not molest the lodgers, but he disdained them and he did not brook being personally addressed by anyone except Gran. One night, he wandered into the dining room, appearing to be in search of something he had mislaid, and, for some reason that no one was ever able to divine, suddenly stood stock-still and gave the easily upset Mr. Beaver a long and penetrating look. Mr. Beaver, trembling from head to toe, stammered, "Why—er, hello there, Caesar, old boy, old boy," and Caesar charged. For a moment, it was touch and go, but Gran saved Mr. Beaver, only to lose him an hour later when he departed, bag and baggage, for the Y.M.C.A. This rout and the consequent loss of revenue would more than likely have meant Caesar's downfall and his deportation to the pound if it had not been that a newly widowed druggist, very irascible and very much Gran's style, had applied for a room in her house a week or so before, and now he moved in delightedly, as if he were coming home.

Finally, the police demanded that Caesar be muzzled and they warned that if he committed any major crime again— they cited the case of the Olson man—he would be shot on sight. Mrs. Placer, although she had no respect for the law, knowing as much as she did about its agents, obeyed. She obeyed, that is, in part; she put the muzzle on Caesar for a few hours a day, usually early in the morning when the traffic was light and before the deliveries had started, but the rest of the time his powerful jaws and dazzling white sabre teeth were free and snapping. There was between these two such preternatural rapport, such an impressive conjugation of suspicion, that he, sensing the approach of a policeman, could convey instantly to her the immediate necessity of clapping his nose cage on. And the policeman, sent out on the complaint of a terrorized neighbor, would be greeted by this law-abiding pair at the door.

Daisy and I wished we were dead. We were divided between hating Caesar and loving Laddy, and we could not give up the hope that something, someday, would change him back into the loving animal he had been before he was appointed vice-president of the Placerites. Now at the meetings after supper on the porch he took an active part, standing rigidly at Gran's side except when she sent him on an errand.

He carried out these assignments not with the air of a servant but with that of an accomplice. "Get me the paper, Caesar," she would say to him, and he, dismayingly intelligent and a shade smart-alecky, would open the screen door by himself and in a minute come back with the *Bulletin*, from which Mrs. Placer would then read an item, like the Gospel of the day, and then read between the lines of it, scandalized.

In the deepening of our woe and our bereavement and humiliation, we mutely appealed to Mr. Murphy. We did not speak outright to him, for Mr. Murphy lived in a state of indirection, and often when he used the pronoun "I," he seemed to be speaking of someone standing a little to the left of him, but we went to see him and his animals each day during the sad summer, taking what comfort we could from the cozy, quiet indolence of his back yard, where small black eyes encountered ours politely and everyone was half asleep. When Mr. Murphy inquired about Laddy in his bland, inattentive way, looking for a stratagem whereby to shift the queen of hearts into position by the king, we would say, "Oh, he's fine," or "Laddy is a nifty dog." And Mr. Murphy, reverently slaking the thirst that was his talent and his concubine, would murmur, "I'm glad."

We wanted to tell him, we wanted his help, or at least his sympathy, but how could we cloud his sunny world? It was awful to see Mr. Murphy ruffled. Up in the calm clouds as he generally was, he could occasionally be brought to earth with a thud, as we had seen and heard one day. Not far from his house, there lived a bad, troublemaking boy of twelve, who was forever hanging over the fence trying to teach the parrot obscene words. He got nowhere, for she spoke no English and she would flabbergast him with her cold eye and sneer, "*Tant pis.*" One day, this boorish fellow went too far; he suddenly shot his head over the fence like a jack-in-the-box and aimed a water pistol at the skunk's face. Mr. Murphy leaped to his feet in a scarlet rage; he picked up a stone and threw it accurately, hitting the boy square in the back, so hard that he fell right down in a mud puddle and lay there kicking and squalling and, as it turned out, quite badly hurt. "If you ever come back here again, I'll kill you!" roared Mr. Murphy. I think he meant it, for I have seldom seen an anger so resolute, so brilliant, and so voluble. "How dared he!" he cried, scrambling into Mallow's cage to hug and pet and soothe her. "He must be absolutely mad! He must be the Devil!" He did not go back to his game after that but paced the yard, swearing a blue streak and only pausing to croon to his animals, now as frightened by him as they had been by the intruder, and to drink straight from the bottle, not bothering with fixings. We were fascinated by this unfamiliar side of Mr. Murphy, but we did not want to see it ever again, for his face had grown so dangerously purple and the veins of his forehead seemed ready to burst and his eyes looked scorched. He was the closest thing to a maniac we had ever seen. So we did not tell him about Laddy; what he did not know would not hurt him, although it was hurting us, throbbing in us like a great, bleating wound.

But eventually Mr. Murphy heard about our dog's conversion, one night at the pool hall, which he visited from time to time when he was seized with a rare but compelling garrulity, and the next afternoon when he asked us how Laddy was and we replied that he was fine, he tranquilly told us, as he deliberated whether to move the jack of clubs now or to bide his time, that we were sweet girls but we were lying in our teeth. He did not seem at all angry but only interested, and all the while he questioned us, he went on about his business with the gin and the hearts and spades and diamonds and clubs. It rarely happened that he won the particular game he was playing, but that day he did, and when he saw all the cards laid out in their ideal pattern, he leaned back, looking disappointed, and he said, "I'm damned." He then scooped up the cards, in a gesture unusually quick and tidy for him, stacked them together, and bound them with a rubber band. Then he began to tell us what he thought of Gran.

He grew as loud and apoplectic as he had been that other time, and though he kept repeating that he knew *we* were innocent and he put not a shred of the blame on us, we were afraid he might suddenly change his mind, and, speechless, we cowered against the monkeys' cage. In dread, the monkeys clutched the fingers we offered to them and made soft, protesting noises, as if to say, "Oh, stop it, Murphy! Our nerves!"

As quickly as it had started, the tantrum ended. Mr. Murphy paled to his normal complexion and said calmly that the only practical thing was to go and have it out with Mrs. Placer. "At once," he added, although he said he bitterly feared that it was too late and there would be no exorcising the fiend from Laddy's misused spirit. And because he had given the dog to us and not to her, he required that we go along with him, stick up for our rights, stand on our mettle, get up our Irish, and give the old bitch something to put in her pipe and smoke.

Oh, it was hot that day! We walked in a kind of delirium through the simmer, where only the grasshoppers had the energy to move, and I remember wondering if ether smelled like the gin on Mr. Murphy's breath. Daisy and I, in one way or another, were going to have our gizzards cut out along with our hearts and our souls and our pride, and I wished I were as drunk as Mr. Murphy, who swam effortlessly through the heat, his lips parted comfortably, his eyes half closed. When we turned in to the path at Gran's house, my blood began to scald my veins. It was so futile and so dangerous and so absurd. Here we were on a high moral mission, two draggletailed, gumptionless little girls and a toper whom no one could take seriously, partly because he was little more than a gurgling bottle of booze and partly because of the clothes he wore. He was a sight, as he always was when he was out of his own yard. There, somehow, in the carefree disorder, his clothes did not look especially strange, but on the streets of the town, in the barbershop or the post office or on Gran's path, they were fantastic. He wore a pair of hound's-tooth pants, old but maintaining a vehement pattern, and with them he wore a collarless blue flannelette shirt. His hat was the silliest of all, because it was a derby three sizes too big. And as if Shannon, too, was a part of his funny-paper costume, the elder capuchin rode on his shoulder, tightly embracing his thin red neck.

Gran and Caesar were standing side by side behind the screen door, looking as if they had been expecting us all along. For a moment, Gran and Mr. Murphy faced each other across the length of weedy brick between the gate and the front porch, and no one spoke. Gran took no notice at all of Daisy and me. She adjusted her eyeglasses, using both hands, and then looked down at Caesar and matter-of-factly asked, "Do you want out?"

Caesar flung himself full-length upon the screen and it sprang open like a jaw. I ran to meet and head him off, and Daisy threw a library book at his head, but he was on Mr. Murphy in one split second and had his monkey off his shoulder and had broken Shannon's neck in two shakes. He would have gone on nuzzling and mauling and growling over the corpse for hours if Gran had not marched out of the house and down the path and slapped him lightly on the flank and said, in a voice that could not have deceived an idiot, "Why, Caesar, you scamp! You've hurt Mr. Murphy's monkey! Aren't you ashamed!"

Hurt the monkey! In one final, apologetic shudder, the life was extinguished from the little fellow. Bloody and covered with slather, Shannon lay with his arms suppliantly stretched over his head, his leather fingers curled into loose, helpless fists. His hind legs and his tail lay limp and helter-skelter on the path. And Mr. Murphy, all of a sudden reeling drunk, burst into the kind of tears that Daisy and I knew well—the kind that time alone could stop. We stood aghast in the dark-red sunset, killed by our horror and our grief for Shannon and our unforgivable disgrace. We stood upright in a dead faint, and an eon passed before Mr. Murphy picked up Shannon's body and wove away, sobbing, "I don't believe it! I don't *believe* it!"

The very next day, again at morbid, heavy sunset, Caesar died in violent convulsions, knocking down two tall hollyhocks in his throes. Long after his heart had stopped, his right hind leg continued to jerk in aimless reflex. Madly methodical, Mr. Murphy had poisoned some meat for him, had thoroughly envenomed a whole pound of hamburger, and early in the morning, before sunup, when he must have been near collapse with his hangover, he had stolen up to Mrs. Placer's house and put it by the kitchen door. He was so stealthy that Caesar never stirred in his fool's paradise there on the floor by Gran. We knew these to be the facts, for Mr. Murphy made no bones about them. Afterward, he had gone home and said a solemn Requiem for Shannon in so loud a voice that someone sent for the police, and they took him away in the Black Maria to sober him up on strong green tea. By the time he was in the lockup and had confessed what he had done, it was far too late, for Caesar had already gulped down the meat. He suffered an undreamed-of agony in Gran's flower garden, and Daisy and I, unable to bear the sight of it, hiked up to the red rocks and shook there, wretchedly ripping to shreds the sand lilies that grew in the cracks. Flight was the only thing we could think of, but where could we go? We stared west at the mountains and quailed at the look of the stern white glacier; we wildly scanned the prairies for escape. "If only we were something besides kids! Besides girls!" mourned Daisy. I could not speak at all; I huddled in a niche of the rocks and cried.

No one in town, except, of course, her lodgers, had the slightest sympathy for Gran. The townsfolk allowed that Mr. Murphy was a drunk and was fighting Irish, but he had a heart and this was something that could never be said of Mrs. Placer. The neighbor who had called the police when he was chanting the "Dies Irae" before breakfast in that deafening monotone had said, "The poor guy is having some kind of a spell, so don't be rough on him, hear?" Mr. Murphy had become, in fact, a kind of hero; some people, stretching a point, said he was a saint for the way that every day and twice on Sunday he sang a memorial Mass over Shannon's grave, now marked with a chipped, cheap plaster figure of Saint Francis. He withdrew from the world more and more, seldom venturing into the streets at all, except when he went to the bootlegger to get a new bottle to snuggle into. All summer, all fall, we saw him as we passed by his yard, sitting at his dilapidated table, enfeebled with gin, graying, withering, turning his head ever and ever more slowly as he maneuvered the protocol of the kings and the queens and the knaves. Daisy and I could never stop to visit him again.

It went on like this, year after year. Daisy and I lived in a mesh of lies and evasions, baffled and mean, like rats in a maze. When we were old enough for beaux, we connived like sluts to see them, but we would never admit to their existence until Gran caught us out by some trick. Like this one, for example: Once, at the end of a long interrogation, she said to me, "I'm more relieved than I can tell you that you *don't* have anything to do with Jimmy Gilmore, because I happen to know that he is after only one thing in a girl," and then, off guard in the loving memory of sitting in the movies the night before with Jimmy, not even holding hands, I defended him and defeated myself, and Gran, smiling with success, said, "I *thought* you knew him. It's a pretty safe rule of thumb that where there's smoke there's fire." That finished Jimmy and me, for afterward I was nervous with him and I confounded and alarmed and finally bored him by trying to convince him, although the subject had not come up, that I did not doubt his good intentions.

Daisy and I would come home from school, or, later, from our jobs, with a small triumph or an interesting piece of news, and if we forgot ourselves and, in our exuberance, told Gran, we were hustled into court at once for cross-examination.

Once, I remember, while I was still in high school, I told her about getting a part in a play. How very nice for me, she said, if that kind of make-believe seemed to me worth while. But what was my role? An old woman! A widow woman believed to be a witch? She did not care a red cent, but she did have to laugh in view of the fact that Miss Eccles, in charge of dramatics, had almost run her down in her car. And I would forgive her, would I not, if she did not come to see the play, and would not think her eccentric for not wanting to see herself ridiculed in public?

My pleasure strangled, I crawled, joy-killed, to our third-floor room. The room was small and its monstrous furniture was too big and the rag rugs were repulsive, but it was bright. We would not hang a blind at the window, and on this day I stood there staring into the mountains that burned with the sun. I feared the mountains, but at times like this their massiveness consoled me; they, at least, could not be gossiped about.

Why did we stay until we were grown? Daisy and I ask ourselves this question as we sit here on the bench in the municipal zoo, reminded of Mr. Murphy by the polar bear, reminded by the monkeys not of Shannon but of Mrs. Placer's insatiable gossips at their postprandial feast.

"But how could we have left?" says Daisy, wringing her buttery hands. "It was the depression. We had no money. We had nowhere to go."

"All the same, we could have gone," I say, resentful still of the waste of all those years. "We could have come here and got jobs as waitresses. Or prostitutes, for that matter."

"I wouldn't have wanted to be a prostitute," says Daisy.

We agree that under the circumstances it would have been impossible for us to run away. The physical act would have been simple, for the city was not far and we could have stolen the bus fare or hitched a ride. Later, when we began to work as salesgirls in Kress's it would have been no trick at all to vanish one Saturday afternoon with our week's pay, without so much as going home to say good-bye. But it had been infinitely harder than that, for Gran, as we now see, held us trapped by our sense of guilt. We were vitiated, and we had no choice but to wait, flaccidly, for her to die.

You may be sure we did not unlearn those years as soon as we put her out of sight in the cemetery and sold her house for a song to the first boob who would buy it. Nor did we forget when we left the town for another one, where we had jobs at a dude camp—the town where Daisy now lives with a happy husband and two happy sons. The succubus did not relent for years, and I can still remember, in the beginning of our days at the Lazy S 3, overhearing an edgy millionaire say to his wife, naming my name, "That girl gives me the cold shivers. One would think she had just seen a murder." Well, I had. For years, whenever I woke in the night in fear or pain or loneliness, I would increase my suffering by the memory of Shannon, and my tears were as bitter as poor Mr. Murphy's.

We have never been back to Adams. But we see that house plainly, with the hopvines straggling over the porch. The windows are hung with the cheapest grade of marquisette, dipped into coffee to impart to it an unwilling color, neither white nor tan but individual and spitefully unattractive. We see the wicker rockers and the swing, and through the screen door we dimly make out the slightly veering corridor, along one wall of which stands a glass-doored bookcase; when we were children, it had contained not books but stale old cardboard boxes filled with such things as W.C.T.U. tracts and anti-cigarette literature and newspaper clippings related to sexual sin in the Christianized islands of the Pacific.

Even if we were able to close our minds' eyes to the past, Mr. Murphy would still be before us in the apotheosis of the polar bear. My pain becomes intolerable, and I am relieved when Daisy rescues us. "We've got to go," she says in a sudden panic. "I've got asthma coming on." We rush to the nearest exit of the city park and hail a cab, and, once inside it, Daisy gives herself an injection of adrenalin and then leans back. We are heartbroken and infuriated, and we cannot speak.

Two hours later, beside my train, we clutch each other as if we were drowning. We ought to go out to the nearest police-man and say, "We are not responsible women. You will have to take care of us because we cannot take care of ourselves." But gradually the storm begins to lull.

"You're sure you've got your ticket?" says Daisy. "You'll surely be able to get a roomette once you're on."

"I don't know about that," I say. "If there are any V.I.P.s on board, I won't have a chance. 'Spinsters and Orphans Last' is the motto of this line."

Daisy smiles. "I didn't care," she says, "but I had to laugh when I saw that woman nab the redcap you had signalled to. I had a good notion to give her a piece of my mind."

"It will be a miracle if I ever see my bags again," I say, mounting the steps of the train. "Do you suppose that black-guardly porter knows about the twenty-dollar gold piece in my little suitcase?"

"Anything's possible!" cries Daisy, and begins to laugh. She is so pretty, standing there in her bright-red linen suit and her black velvet hat. A solitary ray of sunshine comes through a broken pane in the domed vault of the train shed and lies on her shoulder like a silver arrow.

"So long, Daisy!" I call as the train begins to move.

She walks quickly along beside the train. "Watch out for pickpockets!" she calls.

"You, too!" My voice is thin and lost in the increasing noise of the speeding train wheels. "Good-bye, old dear!"

I go at once to the club car and I appropriate the writing table, to the vexation of a harried priest, who snatches up the telegraph pad and gives me a sharp look. I write Daisy ap-proximately the same letter I always write her under this par-ticular set of circumstances, the burden of which is that noth-ing for either of us can ever be as bad as the past before Gran mercifully died. In a postscript I add: "There is a Roman Catholic priest (that is to say, he is *dressed* like one) sitting behind me although all the chairs on the opposite side of the car are empty. I can only conclude that he is looking over my shoulder, and while I do not want to cause you any alarm, I think you would be advised to be on the lookout for any appearance of miraculous medals, scapulars, papist booklets, etc., in the shops in your town. It really makes me laugh to see the way he is pretending that all he wants is for me to finish this letter so that he can have the table."

I sign my name and address the envelope, and I give up my place to the priest, who smiles nicely at me, and then I move across the car to watch the fields as they slip by. They are alfalfa fields, but you can bet your bottom dollar that they are chockablock with marijuana.

I begin to laugh. The fit is silent but it is devastating; it surges and rattles in my ribcage, and I turn my face to the window to avoid the narrow gaze of the Filipino bar boy. I must think of something sad to stop this unholy giggle, and I think of the polar bear. But even his bleak tragedy does not sober me. Wildly I fling open the newspaper I have brought and I pretend to be reading something screamingly funny. The words I see are in a Hollywood gossip column: "How a well-known starlet can get a divorce in Nevada without her crooner husband's consent, nobody knows. It won't be worth a plugged nickel here."

The Blue-Winged Teal

WALLACE STEGNER

STILL IN WADERS, WITH THE STRING OF DUCKS ACROSS HIS shoulder, he stood hesitating on the sidewalk in the cold November wind. His knees were stiff from being cramped up all day in the blind, and his feet were cold. Today, all day, he had been alive; now he was back ready to be dead again.

Lights were on all up and down the street, and there was a rush of traffic and a hurrying of people past and around him, yet the town was not his town, the people passing were strangers, the sounds of evening in this place were no sounds that carried warmth or familiarity. Though he had spent most of his twenty years in the town, knew hundreds of its people, could draw maps of its streets from memory, he wanted to admit familiarity with none of it. He had shut himself off.

Then what was he doing here, in front of this poolhall, loaded down with nine dead ducks? What had possessed him in the first place to borrow gun and waders and car from his father and go hunting? If he had wanted to breathe freely for a change, why hadn't he kept right on going? What was there in this place to draw him back? A hunter had to have a lodge to bring his meat to and people who would be glad of his skill. He had this poolhall and his father, John Lederer, Prop.

He stepped out of a woman's path and leaned against the door. Downstairs, in addition to his father, he would find old Max Schmeckebier, who ran a cheap blackjack game in the room under the sidewalk. He would find Giuseppe Sciutti, the Sicilian barber, closing his shop or tidying up the rack of *Artists* and *Models* and *The Nudists* with which he lured trade. He would probably find Billy Hammond, the night clerk from the Windsor Hotel, having his sandwich and beer and pie, or moving alone around a pool table, whistling abstractedly, practicing shots. If the afternoon blackjack game had broken up, there would be Navy Edwards, dealer and bouncer for Schmeckebier. At this time of evening there might be a few counter customers and a cop collecting his tribute of a beer or that other tribute that Schmeckebier paid to keep the cardroom open.

And he would find, sour contrast with the bright sky and the wind of the tule marshes, the cavelike room with its back corners in darkness, would smell that smell compounded of steam heat and cue-chalk dust, of sodden butts in cuspidors, of coffee and meat and beer smells from the counter, of cigarette smoke so unaired that it darkened the walls. From anywhere back of the middle tables there would be the pervasive reek of toilet disinfectant. Back of the lunch counter his father would be presiding, throwing the poolhall light switch to save a few cents when the place was empty, flipping it on to give an air of brilliant and successful use when feet came down the stairs past Sciutti's shop.

The hunter moved his shoulder under the weight of the ducks, his mind full for a moment with the image of his father's face, darkly pale, fallen in on its bones, and the pouched, restless, suspicious eyes that seemed always looking for someone. Over that image came the face of his mother, dead now, six weeks buried. His teeth clicked at the thought of how she had held the old man up for thirty years, kept him at a respectable job, kept him from slipping back into the poolroom Johnny he had been when she married him. Within ten days of her death he had hunted up this old failure of a poolhall.

In anger the hunter turned, thinking of the hotel room he shared with his father. But he had to eat. Broke as he was, a student yanked from his studies, he had no choice but to eat on the old man. Beside, there were the ducks. He felt somehow that the thing would be incomplete unless he brought his game back for his father to see.

His knees unwilling in the stiff waders, he went down the steps, descending into the light shining through Joe Sciutti's door, and into the momentary layer of clean bay-rum smell, talcum smell, hair-tonic smell, that rose past the still revolving pole in the angle of the stairs.

Joe Sciutti was sweeping wads of hair from his tile floor, and hunched over the counter beyond, their backs to the door, were Schmeckebier, Navy Edwards, Billy Hammond, and an unknown customer. John Lederer was behind the counter, mopping alertly with a rag. The poolroom lights were up bright, but when Lederer saw who was coming he flipped the switch and dropped the big room back into dusk.

As the hunter came to the end of the counter their heads turned toward him. "Well I'm a son of a bee," Navy Edwards said, and scrambled off his stool. Next to him Billy Hammond half stood up so that his pale yellow hair took a halo from the backbar lights. "Say!" Max Schmeckebier said. "Say, dot's goot, dot's pooty goot, Henry!"

But Henry was watching his father so intently he did not turn to them. He slid the string of ducks off his shoulder and swung them up onto the wide walnut bar. They landed solidly —offering or tribute or ransom or whatever they were. For a moment it was as if this little act were private between the two of them. He felt queerly moved, his stomach tightened in suspense or triumph. Then the old man's pouchy eyes slipped from his and the old man came quickly forward along the counter and laid hands on the ducks.

He handled them as if he were petting kittens, his big white hands stringing the heads one by one from the wire.

"Two spoonbill," he said, more to himself than to the others crowding around. "Shovel ducks. Don't see many of those any more. And two, no, three, hen mallards and one drake. Those make good eating."

Schmeckebier jutted his enormous lower lip. Knowing him for a stingy, crooked, suspicious little man, Henry almost laughed at the air he could put on, the air of a man of probity about to make an honest judgment in a dispute between neighbors. "I take a budderball," he said thickly. "A liddle budderball, dot is vot eats goot."

An arm fell across Henry's shoulders, and he turned his head to see the hand with red hair rising from its pores, the wristband of a gray silk shirt with four pearl buttons. Navy Edwards' red face was close to his. "Come clean now," Navy said. "You shot 'em all sitting, didn't you, Henry?"

"I just waited till they stuck their heads out of their holes and let them have it," Henry said.

Navy walloped him on the back and convulsed himself laughing. Then his face got serious again, and he bore down on Henry's shoulder. "By God, you could've fooled me," he said. "If I'd been makin' book on what you'd bring in I'd've lost my shirt."

"Such a pretty shirt, too," Billy Hammond said.

Across the counter John Lederer cradled a little drab duck in his hand. Its neck, stretched from the carrier, hung far down, but its body was neat and plump and its feet were waxy. Watching the sallow face of his father, Henry thought it looked oddly soft.

"Ain't that a beauty, though?" the old man said. "There ain't a prettier duck than a blue-wing teal. You can have all your wood ducks and redheads, all the flashy ones." He spread a wing until the hidden band of bright blue showed. "Pretty?" he said, and shook his head and laughed suddenly, as if he had not expected to. When he laid the duck down beside the others his eyes were bright with sentimental moisture.

So now, Henry thought, you're right in your element. You always did want to be one of the boys from the poolroom pouring out to see the elk on somebody's running board, or leaning on a bar with a schooner of beer talking baseball or telling the boys about the big German Brown somebody brought in a cake of ice. We haven't any elk or German Browns right now, but we've got some nice ducks, a fine display along five feet of counter. And who brought them in? The student, the alien son. It must gravel you.

He drew himself a beer. Several other men had come in, and he saw three more stooping to look in the door beyond Sciutti's. Then they too came in. Three tables were going; his father had started to hustle, filling orders. After a few minutes Schmeckebier and Navy went into the cardroom with four men. The poolroom lights were up bright again, there was an ivory click of balls, a rumble of talk. The smoke-filled air was full of movement.

Still more people dropped in, kids in high school athletic sweaters and bums from the fringes of skid row. They all stopped to look at the ducks, and Henry saw glances at his waders, heard questions and answers. John Lederer's boy. Some of them spoke to him, deriving importance from contact with him. A fellowship was promoted by the ducks strung out along the counter. Henry felt it himself. He was so mellowed by the way they spoke to him that when the players at the first table thumped their cues, he got off his stool to rack them up and collect their nickels. It occurred to him that he ought to go to the room and get into a bath, but he didn't want to leave yet. Instead he came back to the counter and slid the nickels toward his father and drew himself another beer.

"Pretty good night tonight," he said. The old man nodded

and slapped his rag on the counter, his eyes already past Henry and fixed on two youths coming in, his mouth fixing itself for the greeting and the "Well, boys, what'll it be?"

Billy Hammond wandered by, stopped beside Henry a moment. "Well, time for my nightly wrestle with temptation," he said.

"I was just going to challenge you to a game of call-shot."

"Maybe tomorrow," Billy said, and let himself out carefully as if afraid a noise would disturb someone—a mild, gentle, golden-haired boy who looked as if he ought to be in some prep school learning to say "Sir" to grownups instead of clerking in a girlie hotel. He was the only one of the pool-room crowd that Henry half liked. He thought he understood Billy Hammond a little.

He turned back to the counter to hear his father talking with Max Schmeckebier. "I don't see how we could on this rig. That's the hell of it, we need a regular oven."

"In my room in back," Schmeckebier said. "Dot old electric range."

"Does it work?"

"Sure. Vy not? I tink so."

"By God," John Lederer said. "Nine ducks, that ought to give us a real old-fashioned feed." He mopped the counter, refilled a coffee cup, came back to the end and pinched the breast of a duck, pulled out a wing and looked at the bank of blue hidden among the drab feathers. "Just like old times, for a change," he said, and his eyes touched Henry's in a look that might have meant anything from a challenge to an apology.

Henry had no desire to ease the strain that had been between them for months. He did not forgive his father the poolhall, or forget the way the old man had sprung back into the old pattern, as if his wife had been a jailer and he was now released. He neither forgot nor forgave the red-haired woman who sometimes came to the poolhall late at night and waited on a barstool while the old man closed up. Yet now when

290

his father remarked that the ducks ought to be drawn and plucked right away, Henry stood up.

"I could be doing ten while you were doing one," his father said.

The blood spread hotter in Henry's face, but he bit off what he might have said. "All right," he said. "You do them and I'll take over the counter for you."

So here he was, in the poolhall he had passionately sworn he would never do a lick of work in, dispensing Mrs. Morrison's meat pies and tamales smothered in chile, clumping behind the counter in the waders which had been the sign of his temporary freedom. Leaning back between orders, watching the Saturday night activity of the place, he half understood why he had gone hunting, and why it had seemed to him essential that he bring his trophies back here.

That somewhat disconcerted understanding was still troubling him when his father came back. The old man had put on a clean apron and brushed his hair. His pouched eyes, brighter and less houndlike than usual, darted along the bar, counting, darted across the bright tables, counting again. His eyes met Henry's, and both half smiled. Both of them, Henry thought, were a little astonished.

Later, propped in bed in the hotel room, he put down the magazine he had been reading and stared at the drawn blinds, the sleazy drapes, and asked himself why he was here. The story he had told others, and himself, that his mother's death had interrupted his school term and he was waiting for the new term before going back, he knew to be an evasion. He was staying because he couldn't get away, or wouldn't. He hated his father, hated the poolhall, hated the people he was thrown with. He made no move to hobnob with them, or hadn't until tonight, and yet he deliberately avoided seeing any of the people who had been his friends for years. Why?

He could force his mind to the barrier, but not across it. Within a half minute he found himself reading again, diving deep, and when he made himself look up from the page he stared for a long time at his father's bed, his father's shoes under the bed, his father's soiled shirts hanging in the open closet. All the home he had any more was this little room. He could pretend that as long as he stayed here the fragments of his home and family were held together. He couldn't fool himself that he had any function in his father's life any more, or his father in his, unless his own hatred and his father's uneasy suspicion were functions. He ought to get out and get a job until he could go back to school. But he didn't.

Thinking made him sleepy, and he knew what that was, too. Sleep was another evasion, like the torpor and monotony of his life. But he let drowsiness drift over him, and drowsily he thought of his father behind the counter tonight, vigorous and jovial, Mine Host, and he saw that the usual fretful petulance had gone from his face.

He snapped off the bed light and dropped the magazine on the floor. Then he heard the rain, the swish and hiss of traffic on the wet street. He felt sad and alone, and he disliked the coldness of his own isolation. Again he thought of his father, of the failing body that had once been tireless and bull-strong, of the face before it had sagged and grown dewlaps of flesh on the square jaw. He thought of the many failures, the jobs that never quite worked out, the schemes that never quite paid off, and of the eyes that could not quite meet, not quite hold, the eyes of his cold son.

Thinking of this, and remembering when they had been a family and when his mother had been alive to hold them together, he felt pity, and he cried.

His father's entrance awakened him. He heard the fumbling at the door, the creak, the quiet click, the footsteps that groped in darkness, the body that bumped into something and halted, getting its bearings. He heard the sighing weight of his father's body on the other bed, his father's sighing breath as he bent to untie his shoes. Feigning sleep, he lay unmoving, breathing deeply and steadily, but an anguish of fury had leaped in him as sharp and sudden as a sudden fear, for he smelled the smells his father brought with him: wet wool, stale tobacco, liquor; and above all, more penetrating than any, spreading through the room and polluting everything there, the echo of cheap musky perfume.

The control Henry imposed upon his body was like an ecstasy. He raged at himself for the weak sympathy that had troubled him all evening. One good night, he said to himself now, staring furiously upward. One lively Saturday night in the joint and he can't contain himself, he has to go top off the evening with his girl friend. And how? A drink in her room? A walk over to some illegal after-hours bar on Rum Alley? Maybe just a trip to bed, blunt and immediate?

His jaws ached from the tight clamping of his teeth, but his orderly breathing went in and out, in and out, while the old man sighed into bed and creaked a little, rolling over, and lay still. The taint of perfume seemed even stronger now. The sow must slop it on by the cupful. And so cuddly. Such a sugar baby. How's my old sweetie tonight? It's been too long since you came to see your baby. I should be real mad at you. The check against the lapel, the unreal hair against the collar, the perfume like some gaseous poison tainting the clothes it touched.

The picture of his mother's bureau drawers came to him, the careless simple collection of handkerchiefs and gloves and lace collars and cuffs, and he saw the dusty blue sachet packets and smelled the faint fragrance. That was all the scent she had ever used.

My God, he said, how can he stand himself?

After a time his father began to breathe heavily, then to snore. In the little prison of the room his breathing was obscene—loose and bubbling, undisciplined, animal. Henry with an effort relaxed his tense arms and legs, let himself think. He tried to concentrate on his own breathing, but the other dominated him, burst out and died and whiffled and sighed again. By now he had a resolution in him like an iron bar. Tomorrow, for sure, for good, he would break out of his self-imposed isolation and see Frank, see Welby. They would lend him enough to get to the coast. Not another day in this hateful relationship. Not another night in this room.

He yawned. It must be late, two or three o'clock. He ought to get to sleep. But he lay uneasily, his mind tainted with hatred as the room was tainted with perfume. He tried cunningly to elude his mind, to get to sleep before it could notice, but no matter how he composed himself for blankness and shut his eyes and breathed deeply, his mind was out again in a half minute, bright-eyed, lively as a weasel, and he was helplessly hunted again from hiding place to hiding place.

Eventually he fell back upon his old devices.

He went into a big dark room in his mind, a room shadowy with great half-seen tables. He groped and found a string above him and pulled, and light fell suddenly in a bright cone from the darker cone of the shade. Below the light lay an expanse of dark green cloth, and this was the only lighted thing in all that darkness. Carefully he gathered bright balls into a wooden triangle, pushing them forward until the apex lay over a round spot on the cloth. Quietly and thoroughly he chalked a cue: the inlaid handle and the smooth taper of the shaft were very real to his eyes and hands. He lined up the cue ball, aimed, drew the cue back and forth in smooth motions over the bridge of his left hand. He saw the balls run from the spinning shock of the break, and carom, and come to rest, and he hunted up the yellow 1-ball and got a shot at it between two others. He had to cut it very fine, but he saw the shot go true, the 1 angle off cleanly into the side pocket. He saw the cue ball rebound and kiss and stop, and he shot the 2 in a straight shot for the left corner pocket, putting drawers on the cue ball to get shape for the 3.

Yellow and blue and red, spotted and striped, he shot pool balls into pockets as deep and black and silent as the cellars of his consciousness. He was not now quarry that his mind chased, but an actor, a willer, a doer, a man in command. By an act of will or of flight he focused his whole awareness on the game he played. His mind undertook it with intent concentration. He took pride in little two-cushion banks, little triumphs of accuracy, small successes of foresight. When he had finished one game and the green cloth was bare he dug the balls from the bin under the end of the table and racked them and began another.

Eventually, he knew, nothing would remain in his mind but the clean green cloth traced with running color and bounced by simple problems, and sometime in the middle of an intricately planned combination shot he would pale off to sleep.

At noon, after the rain, the sun seemed very bright. It poured down from a clearing sky, glittered on wet roofs, gleamed in reflection from pavements and sidewalks. On the peaks beyond the city there was a purity of snow.

Coming down the hill, Henry noticed the excessive brightness and could not tell whether it was really as it seemed, or whether his plunge out of the dark and isolated hole of his life had restored a lost capacity to see. A slavery, or a paralysis, was ended; he had been for three hours in the company of a friend; he had been eyed with concern; he had been warmed by solicitude and generosity. In his pocket he had fifty dollars, enough to get him to the coast and let him renew his life. It seemed to him incredible that he had alternated between dismal hotel and dismal poolroom so long. He could not understand why he had not before this moved his legs in the direction of the hill. He perceived that he had been sullen and morbid, and he concluded with some surprise that even Schmeckebier and Edwards and the rest might have found him a difficult companion.

His father too. The fury of the night before had passed, but he knew he would not bend again toward companionship. That antipathy was too deep. He would never think of his father again without getting the whiff of that perfume. Let him have it; it was what he wanted, let him have it. They could part without an open quarrel, maybe, but they would part without love. They could part right now, within an hour.

Two grimy stairways led down into the cellar from the alley he turned into. One went to the furnace room, the other to the poolhall. The iron rail was blockaded with filled ashcans. Descent into Avernus, he said to himself, and went down the left-hand stair.

The door was locked. He knocked, and after some time knocked again. Finally someone pulled on the door from inside. It stuck, and was yanked irritably inward. His father stood there in his shirt sleeves, a cigar in his mouth.

"Oh," he said, "I was wondering what had become of you."

The basement air was foul and heavy, dense with the reek from the toilets. Henry saw as he stepped inside that at the far end only the night light behind the bar was on, but that a light was coming from Schmeckebier's door at this end too, the two weak illuminations diffusing in the shadowy poolroom, leaving the middle in almost absolute dark. It was the appropriate time, the appropriate place, the stink of his prison appropriately concentrated. He drew his lungs full of it with a kind of passion, and he said, "I just came down to . . ."

"Who is dot?" Schmeckebier called out. He came to his door, wrapped to the armpits in a bar apron, with a spoon in his hand, and he bent, peering out into the dusk like a disturbed dwarf in an underhill cave. "John? Who? Oh, Henry. Shust in time, shust in time. It is not long now." His lower lip waggled, and he pulled it up, apparently with an effort.

Henry said, "What's not long?"

"Vot?" Schmeckebier said, and thrust his big head far out. "You forgot about it?"

"I must have," Henry said.

"The duck feed," his father said impatiently.

They stood staring at one another in the dusk. The right moment was gone. With a little twitch of the shoulder Henry let it go. He would wait awhile, pick his time. When Schmeckebier went back to his cooking, Henry saw through the doorway the lumpy bed, the big chair with a blanket folded over it, the roll-top desk littered with pots and pans, the green and white enamel of the range. A rich smell of roasting came out and mingled oddly with the chemical stink of toilet disinfectant.

"Are we going to eat here?" he asked.

His father snorted. "How could we eat in there? Old Maxie lived in the ghetto too damn long. By God, I never saw such a boar's nest."

"Vot's duh matter? Vot's duh matter?" Schmeckebier said. His big lips thrust out, he stooped to look into the oven, and John Lederer went, shaking his head, up between the tables to the counter. Henry followed him, intending to make the break when he got the old man alone. But he saw the three plates set up on the bar, the three glasses of tomato juice, the platter of olives and celery, and he hesitated. His father reached with a salt shaker and shook a little salt into each glass of tomato juice.

"All the fixings," he said. "Soon as Max gets those birds out of the oven we can take her on."

Now it was easy to say, "As soon as the feed's over I'll be shoving off." Henry opened his mouth to say it, but was interrupted this time by a light tapping at the glass door beyond Sciutti's shop. He swung around angrily and saw duskily beyond the glass the smooth blond hair, the even smile.

"It's Billy," he said. "Shall I let him in?"

"Sure," the old man said. "Tell him to come in and have a duck with us."

But Billy Hammond shook his head when Henry asked him. He was shaking his head almost as he came through the door. "No thanks, I just ate. I'm full of chow mein. This is a family dinner anyway. You go on ahead."

"Got plenty," John Lederer said, and made a motion as if to set a fourth place at the counter.

"Who is dot?" Schmeckebier bawled from the back. "Who come in? Is dot Billy Hammond? Set him up a blate."

"By God, his nose sticks as far into things as his lip," Lederer said. Still holding the plate, he roared back, "Catch up with the parade, for Christ sake, or else tend to your cooking." He looked at Henry and Billy and chuckled.

Schmeckebier had disappeared, but now his squat figure blotted the lighted doorway again. "Vot? Vot you say?"

"Vot?" John Lederer said. "Vot, vot, vot? Vot does it matter vot I said? Get the hell back to your kitchen."

He was, Henry saw, in a high humor. The effect of last night was still with him. He was still playing Mine Host. He looked at the two of them and laughed so naturally that Henry almost joined him. "I think old Maxie's head is full of duck dressing," he said, and leaned on the counter. "I ever tell you about the time we came back from Reno together? We stopped off in the desert to look at a mine, and got lost on a little dirt road so we had to camp. I was trying to figure out where we were, and started looking for stars, but it was clouded over, hard to locate anything. So I ask old Maxie if he can see the Big Dipper anywhere. He thinks about that maybe ten minutes with his lip stuck out and then he says, 'I t'ink it's in duh water bucket.' "

He did the grating gutturals of Schmeckebier's speech so accurately that Henry smiled in spite of himself. His old man made another motion with the plate at Billy Hammond. "Better let me set you up a place."

"Thanks," Billy said. His voice was as polite and soft as his face, and his eyes had the ingenuous liquid softness of a girl's. "Thanks, I really just ate. You go on, I'll shoot a little pool if it's all right."

Now came Schmeckebier with a big platter held in both hands. He bore it smoking through the gloom of the poolhall and up the steps to the counter, and John Lederer took it from him there and with a flourish speared, one after another, three tight-skinned brown ducks and slid them onto the plates set side by side for the feast. The one frugal light from the backbar shone on them as they sat down. Henry looked over his shoulder to see Billy Hammond pull the cord and flood a table with a sharp-edged cone of brilliance. Deliberately, already absorbed, he chalked a cue. His lips pursed, and he whistled, and whistling, bent to take aim.

Lined up in a row, they were not placed for conversation, but John Lederer kept attempting it, leaning forward over his plate to see Schmeckebier or Henry. He filled his mouth with duck and dressing and chewed, shaking his head with pleasure, and snapped off a bite of celery with a crack like a breaking stick. When his mouth was clear he leaned and said to Schmeckebier, "Ah, *das schmecht gut*, hey, Maxie?"

"*Ja*," Schmeckebier said, and sucked grease off his lip and only then turned in surprise. "Say, you speak German?"

"Sure I speak German," Lederer said. "I worked three weeks once with an old squarehead brickmason that taught me the whole language. He taught me *sehr gut* and *nicht gut* and *besser* I *bleiben* right *hier*, and he always had his frau make me up a lunch full of *kalter aufschnitt* and *gemixte pickeln*. I know all about German."

Schmeckebier stared a moment, grunted, and went back to his eating. He had already stripped the meat from the bones and was gnawing the carcass.

"Anyway," John Lederer said," *es schmecht* God damn good." He went around the counter and drew a mug of coffee from the urn. "Coffee?" he said to Henry.

"Please."

His father drew another mug and set it before him. "Maxie?"

Schmeckebier shook his head, his mouth too full for a talk. For a minute, after he had set out two little jugs of cream, Lederer stood as if thinking. He was watching Billy Hammond move quietly around the one lighted table, whistling. "Look at the sucker," Lederer said. "I bet he doesn't even know where he is."

By the time he got around to his stool he was back at the German. "Schmeckebier," he said. "What's that mean?"

"Uh?"

"What's your name mean? Tastes? Likes beer?"

Schmeckebier rolled his shoulders. The sounds he made eating were like sounds from a sty. Henry was half sickened, sitting next to him, and he wished the old man would let the conversation drop. But apparently it had to be a feast, and a feast called for chatter.

"That's a hell of a name, you know it?" Lederer said, and already he was up again and around the end of the counter. "You couldn't get into any church with a name like that." His eyes fastened on the big drooping greasy lip, and he grinned.

"Schmeckeduck, that ought to be your name," he said. "What's German for duck? *Vogel?* Old Max Schmeckevogel. How about number two?"

Schmeckebier pushed his plate forward and Lederer forked a duck out of the steam table. Henry did not take a second.

"You ought to have one," his father told him. "You don't get grub like this every day."

"One's my limit," Henry said.

For a while they worked at their plates. Back of him Henry heard the clack of balls hitting, and a moment later the rumble as a ball rolled down the chute from a pocket. The thin abstracted whistling of Billy Hammond broke off, became words:

"Now Annie doesn't live here any more.
So you're the guy that she's been waiting for?
She told me that I'd know you by the blue of your eyes . . ."

"Talk about one being your limit," his father said. "When we lived in Nebraska we used to put on some feeds. You remember anything about Nebraska at all?"

"A little," Henry said. He was irritated at being dragged into reminiscences, and he did not want to hear how many ducks the town hog could eat at a sitting.

"We'd go out, a whole bunch of us," John Lederer said.

"The sloughs were black with ducks in those days. We'd come back with twenty, thirty people. Take a hundred ducks to fill 'em up." He was silent a moment, staring across the counter, chewing. Henry noticed that he had tacked two wings of a teal up on the frame of the backbar mirror, small, strong bows with a band of bright blue half hidden in them. The old man's eyes slanted over, caught Henry's looking at the wings.

"Doesn't seem as if we'd had a duck feed since we left there," he said. His forehead wrinkled; he rubbed his neck, leaning forward over his plate, and his eyes met Henry's in the backbar mirror. He spoke to the mirror, ignoring the gobbling image of Schmeckebier between his own reflection and Henry's.

"You remember that set of china your mother used to have? The one she painted herself? Just the plain white china with the one design on each plate?"

Henry sat stiffly, angry that his mother's name should even be mentioned between them in this murky hole, and after what had passed. Gabble, gabble, gabble, he said to himself. If you can't think of anything to gabble about, gabble about your dead wife. Drag her through the poolroom too. Aloud he said, "No, I guess I don't."

"Blue-wing teal," his father said, and nodded at the wings tacked to the mirror frame. "Just the wings, like that. Awful pretty. She thought a teal was about the prettiest little duck there was."

His vaguely rubbing hand came around from the back of his neck and rubbed along the cheek, pulling the slack flesh and distorting the mouth. Henry said nothing, watching the pouched hound eyes in the mirror.

It was a cold, skin-tightening shock to realize that the hound eyes were cloudy with tears. The rubbing hand went over them, shaded them like a hat brim, the mouth below remained distorted. With a plunging movement his father was off the stool.

"Oh, God damn!" he said in a strangling voice, and went

301

past Henry on hard, heavy feet, down the steps past Billy Hammond, who neither looked up nor broke the sad thin whistling.

Schmeckebier had swung around. "Vot's duh matter? Now vot's duh matter?"

With a short shake of the head, Henry turned away from him, staring after his father down the dark poolhall. He felt as if orderly things were breaking and flying apart in his mind; he had a moment of white blind terror that this whole scene upon whose reality he counted was really only a dream, something conjured up out of the bottom of his consciousness where he was accustomed to comfort himself into total sleep. His mind was still full of the anguished look his father had hurled at the mirror before he ran.

The hell with you, the look had said. The hell with you, Schmeckebier, and you, my son Henry. The hell with your ignorance, whether you're stupid or whether you just don't know all you think you know. You don't know enough to kick dirt down a hole. You know nothing at all, you know less than nothing because you know things wrong.

He heard Billy's soft whistling, saw him move around his one lighted table—a well-brought-up boy from some suburban town, a polite soft gentle boy lost and wandering among pimps and prostitutes, burying himself for some reason among people who never even touched his surface. Did he shoot pool in his bed at night, tempting sleep, as Henry did? Did his mind run carefully to angles and banks and englishes, making a reflecting mirror of them to keep from looking through at other things?

Almost in terror he looked out across the sullen cave above Billy's table, and heard the lugubrious whistling that went on without intention of audience, a recurrent and deadening and only half-conscious sound. He looked toward the back, where his father had disappeared in the gloom, and wondered if in his bed before sleeping the old man worked through a routine of little jobs: cleaning the steam table, ordering a hundred pounds of coffee, jacking up the janitor about the mess in the hall. He wondered if it was possible to wash yourself to sleep with restaurant crockery, work yourself to sleep with chores, add yourself to sleep with columns of figures, as you could play yourself to sleep with a pool cue and a green table and fifteen colored balls. For a moment, in the sad old light with the wreckage of the duck feast at his elbow, he wondered if there was anything more to his life, or his father's life, or Billy Hammond's life, or anyone's life, than playing the careful games that deadened you into sleep.

Schmeckebier, beside him, was still groping in the fog of his mind for an explanation of what had happened. "Vere'd he go?" he said and nudged Henry fiercely. "Vot's duh matter?"

Henry shook him off irritably, watching Billy Hammond's oblivious bent head under the light. He heard Schmeckebier's big lip flop and heard him sucking his teeth.

"I tell you," the guttural voice said. "I got somet'ing dot fixes him if he feels bum."

He too went down the stairs past the lighted table and into the gloom at the back. The light went on in his room, and after a minute or two his voice was shouting, "John! Say, come here, uh? Say John!"

Eventually John Lederer came out of the toilet and they walked together between the tables. In his fist Schmeckebier was clutching a square bottle. He waved it in front of Henry's face as they passed but Henry was watching his father. He saw the crumpled face, oddly rigid, like the face of a man in the grip of a barely controlled rage, but his father avoided his eyes.

"*Kümmel*," Schmeckebier said. He set four ice cream dishes on the counter and poured three about a third full of clear liquor. His squinted eyes lifted and peered toward Billy Hammond, but Henry said, on an impulse, "Let him alone. He's walking in his sleep."

So there were only three. They stood together a moment

and raised their glasses. "Happy days," John Lederer said automatically. They drank.

Schmeckebier smacked his lips, looked at them one after another, shook his head in admiration of the quality of his *kümmel* and waddled back toward his room with the bottle. John Lederer was already drawing hot water to wash the dishes.

In the core of quiet which even the clatter of crockery and the whistling of Billy Hammond did not break into, Henry said what he had to say. "I'll be leaving," he said. "Probably tonight."

But he did not say it in anger, or with the cold command of himself that he had imagined in advance. He said it like a cry, and with the feeling he might have had on letting go the hand of a friend too weak and too exhausted to cling any longer to their inadequate shared driftwood in a wide cold sea.

Arrangements at the Gulf

RICHARD G. STERN

IN LAKE FOREST, MR. LOMAX SCARCELY EVER WENT OUT OF his daughter Celia's house. Most of the day he sat well wrapped up in the upstairs sitting room playing cribbage with his valet, Mr. Toombes. After his morning broth he read half of the *Tribune*, and in the afternoon, after his nap, he read the other half. The only season he remarked was winter, and this began for him when he saw the first snowfall coming down over the lawns. Then he would instruct Mr. Toombes to begin preparations for the trip to Magnolia, the Florida Gulf town where he had spent the last twenty-three of his eighty-six winters. A few days later, that third of his family whose year it was to see him off, gathered around him at the LaSalle Street Station and waved goodby as his train moved down the tracks.

In his last year, Mr. Lomax was annoyed to find that all of his family who lived in or near Chicago—and this was well over two-thirds of it—had come down to say goodby to him.

Later, alone with Mr. Toombes in his compartment, Mr. Lomax mumbled, "Like a golf gallery. Goggled at me like a golf mob."

Mr. Toombes went into the adjoining compartment to brew some tea, but tea did not settle Mr. Lomax this evening.

He waved Mr. Toombes away, saying that he would stay up till nine o'clock.

Mr. Lomax wished to stay up the extra hour in order to consider the annoyance which he had suffered at the station, to consider it with the shame he felt in remembering now that he himself had been the cause of it all. Two weeks before, at the family Thanksgiving Dinner, he had said something out loud which formerly he would not have permitted himself to think. He had been served and was studying a white cut of turkey breast similar to those which he had for some years pretended to enjoy for the sake of the family. They've given me an awfully big slice this year, he was thinking, when his son, Henry, a priggish busybody and alarmist, asked him if the turkey didn't look quite right to him. Mr. Lomax, with the same effort it would have cost him to say, "Yes," said instead, "I think I'm going to die in Florida." The consequence of this irrelevance was that Mr. Lomax's leavetaking had been a kind of informal rehearsal of his funeral. Now, shaking his head, Mr. Lomax made sense of the parting remarks which his children had made to him, Celia's "It's been fun taking care of you, Papa" and Henry's "I'm sorry about the business, Papa." As if he hadn't forced Henry out of the firm thirty-five years ago, and as if Celia had not regarded him for twenty years as an immense burden sufferable only because "she owed it to him."

"A pretty thought," mumbled Mr. Lomax. At least, he thought, his bachelor friend Granville had never had to put up with that sort of smallness. Thinking of Granville, as he would see him the next day waiting at the Magnolia station for him as he had done every other year for the past twenty, Mr. Lomax revived enough so that he almost shuddered at the funeral pageant of which he had been the cause and center.

It was very nearly always Granville, the thought of Granville, which pulled Mr. Lomax up in these last years. They were so different, they had done such different things, that the comparison of their lives—and this is what Mr. Lomax constantly made—was never exhausted. The comparison had roots in both pity and envy, and even now, as his mind wandered, Mr. Lomax pitied what he felt must have been the loneliness of his friend's departure from Philadelphia, and then envied its self-sufficiency.

Mr. Lomax was rather proud of his friendship with Granville—Granville was an author—for although the latter was not well enough known for Mr. Lomax to be distinguished by their mere association, Granville's various learning and energy had been the source of much pleasure for him, in conversation, contemplation, and in Granville's books. From the last, Mr. Lomax had learned a great many things, the history of investment banking, the biographies of New England Colonial preachers, the rivers of California, and the topography of the Gaspé Peninsula. Granville's latest volume—the third he'd completed since his seventieth year—had come in the mail the preceding week, and thinking of this, Mr. Lomax rapped on the compartment door for Mr. Toombes.

"Is anything wrong, sir?"

"You might try me with another half a cup," said Mr. Lomax, handing him up the cup although this was not easy for him, "and I think I'll look through the new book."

Mr. Toombes opened a suitcase and handed Mr. Lomax the book and his magnifying glass.

"Never mind the tea, Toombes," said Mr. Lomax. "I'd better not stay up too late." He had not wanted to bother Mr. Toombes just for the book.

As usual, Granville had inscribed something on the flyleaf. It went, "For my old friend, Frederick Lomax, from his 'young' admirer, Herbert Granville." Mr. Lomax frowned. He disliked his friend's frequent allusions to the decade which separated them, for he sensed in them a possible reflection on the uselessness of his own last years in the light of his friend's striking productiveness.

The book was called *Givings and Misgivings*, and Mr. Lomax, who sometimes read little more of the books than was required for acknowledgement and compliment, could not guess whether it would absorb him on its own account or not.

After a bit, he decided that it would not. It was made up of disconnected paragraphs of advice and comment held together by little more than the calendar: there were 365 paragraphs, each labelled in journal fashion, by a date of the year.

The simplicity, the naïveté even, of this arrangement suggested so much of Granville for him that Mr. Lomax looked toward the dark window as if to see him standing at the station in his English cap and knickers, and, in this movement, he recovered the ease and self-satisfaction which his departure had taken from him.

He turned to the paragraph headed March 11, which was his birthday. It went:

> Nothing honest comes with ease; nothing dishonest brings ease. The pressures of life are life itself, as the pressure of the blood is our pulse, the pressure of lungs our breath. Birth itself is the pressure of new life on old. The people who tell you, "Worry kills. Don't worry," do not realise that they are saying, "Life kills. Don't live."

Mr. Lomax read this through twice and then rapped on the door for Mr. Toombes.

"A pencil please, Mr. Toombes," he said, and, when Toombes was gone again, he made a star by the paragraph and another at the bottom margin, and, by the latter, he wrote, "Nonsense," and then his initials, "F.L."

If he could have managed the pencil, thought Mr. Lomax, he would have written a great deal more. The paragraph had seemed to him almost like "the words of a man whose sole worry in life has been whether it's his year to go to Florida or California, who's never done any work in his life but write books, and never had anything to do with birth except be born."

The imagined counterattack tired Mr. Lomax, and he

leaned back against the chair and closed his eyes. Then he tried another paragraph, June 11, which was the date on which his first wife had died and that, a year later, on which he'd proposed to his second. This paragraph read:

Now that glittering heavens and hot seas warm the blood with feelings deeper than all memory, do not turn away, feeling incapable of such beauty. If unfulfillment is bitter, unacknowledgement is bitterer still. It is men who deny the world, not the world which denies men.

Mr. Lomax shook his head and decided not to write anything after this paragraph. In a moment, though, he thought of something, and, taking up his pencil and making two stars, he wrote after the bottom one, "I wish you could have had one of mine, Herbert. F.L."

When the train arrived in Magnolia the next evening, Mr. Granville in his white cap and knickers waved as Mr. Toombes and the conductor helped Mr. Lomax off the train and into the wheel chair.

"Hello there, Lomax," he called. "It's good to see you again."

Mr. Toombes wheeled Mr. Lomax over and the two old men shook hands. "It's good to see you too," said Mr. Lomax. "You shouldn't have come down to the station."

Granville and Bob, the man from the Inn, helped Mr. Toombes lift Mr. Lomax into the station wagon.

"I took the train down this year, too," said Granville. "Just decided not to drive. My reflexes are as good as ever, but I just decided against it."

"Wise thing," said Mr. Lomax, thinking Granville must have had an accident driving back from California last spring.

When they arrived at the Inn, Mr. Lomax went directly to his room without greeting anybody but the owner, Mrs. Pleasants, who waited on the veranda to welcome him for the twenty-third consecutive season.

He slept through dinner and came out at nine-thirty, just as most of the other guests were going up to bed. Those who knew him stayed with him while he had his bowl of soup, talking about their trips and inquiring about his.

When they had all gone up, Granville wheeled Mr. Lomax out to the long porch which overlooked the Gulf and they sat there alone.

"Here we are again," he said.

"And very good to be here," said Mr. Lomax.

"Lucky as well, I think," said Granville, moving his head slightly in the breeze and wondering whether it was too strong for Mr. Lomax.

"Not you," said Mr. Lomax. "You have some claim on the years yet."

Granville smoked a cigarette, taking care to blow the smoke away from his friend's face. "Funny," he said, following the smoke off the dark porch, "I always think of you when I think of that. I mean, after all, you're here and well here. That's taken a lot of weight off my shoulders."

"I've got good shoulders," said Mr. Lomax.

Granville looked at his friend, small and humped in the chair, and he said, "Of course." After a pause, he added, "You make me envious too, you know, so I don't know whether you do me more harm than good. I sometimes tell myself, 'Granville, even if you went around the world, married a ballet dancer, and did God knows what, you still wouldn't have lived half the life Fred Lomax has.'"

"Work and trouble. That your idea of a full life?" said Mr. Lomax. He shivered a little in the breeze. "Never did anything with real thought in my life and the consequence is I leave nothing worth thinking about behind."

"Children," said Granville, emphatically.

Mr. Lomax grunted. "There were twenty people at the station to see me off and, except for three in-laws, not one of them would have been alive except for me. But that's all, Granville. Could have been any twenty people in the station, any twenty off the Chicago gutters and they would have been as near to me as those. As near and as understanding. The virtue of children is a fiction of bachelors."

"Can you mean it?"

"Can you ask me?"

They didn't talk for a moment but watched the moon coming out of the clouds, lighting the palms along the porch and the boats down by the Inn pier.

"I don't regret being old," said Mr. Lomax, looking up at the moon for a moment. "I don't think much about what comes next. As for what I've done, I did it without much consciousness, so it was mostly painless as well as wrong. I think a lot about mistakes. That and the Gulf. I think a lot about sitting out here with you watching the Gulf." After another pause, he said, "I miss you the odd years."

"Thank you," said Granville smiling. "I think of you often then, too."

Mr. Lomax's hand tightened on the chair. "Do you mind my asking why you go way out there since your sister died?"

Granville got up to put his cigarette out in one of the sanded containers on the porch. "I don't know," he said, sitting down. "It's very pleasant out there. Mostly, I guess, it's because I've worried about getting stiff, old in a bad way. Not like you, of course, but you've had so much more than I."

Mr. Lomax was getting very tired but he wanted to say a little more. "I told Henry, by accident, that I was going to die down here."

Granville knew that Lomax wished him to say something but he could not quite make out what. He stared at one of the buoys trembling in the moonlight.

"I'd been feeling that way," Mr. Lomax went on. "It wasn't to arouse anybody—even if I could at my age." After another pause, he said, "I'd like to die when you're around, Herbert."

"That's a funny thing to say, Fred."

"Well, it is funny, but not really. Old friends are true family, aren't they, and you understand me, don't you? More than they. You meet me in the right way, say the right things, the right way." Then Lomax asked his favor. "If it's not this year, it'll be next."

"I'll come down then, Fred," said Granville.

They sat for a while looking out over the Gulf. Then Granville wheeled Mr. Lomax into his room, and, contrary to their custom, they shook hands as they bade each other "Good night."

The Democrat

LAWRENCE STURHAHN

T HE LAND WAS FLAT, ALMOST BARREN, THE GRASS GROWN wild and untended between the trees which stood spread like outpost sentinels, lonely under the immense sky. He hadn't seen another car, or a house for many miles, and now he was driving very fast on the straight cement road with the black strip of tar down its center. He drew a strange exhilaration from the sound of the engine and the wind roaring around the car; and rushing across this flat land, he felt separate and alone from all people, unresponsible. Then, far ahead, he saw the cross roads and the hitch-hiker standing there, with the suitcase beside him.

I'll pick him up, he thought, deciding quickly, already almost upon the man; and passing him, still slowing the car from high speed, he saw the man sharply for an instant, his coat and tie blowing in the wind and the bright, sunburst decal on the side of the suitcase. When he had stopped, the old man came hurrying to the car, which the driver backed to meet him. And he opened the door, putting the cardboard suitcase with the cheap tin clasps—such as you see in Army-Navy Stores, hung up on racks and always reduced from some maximum price to some minimum one—in the back seat, and got heavily in the car, saying he was going to Tampa.

"Going as far as Sarasota. I'll take you that far."

"Thank you, son," the old man said.

He started talking immediately then; about the weather, and of how he'd served in the First World War, and the driver looking at him saw the withered flesh of his face, the white, shiny scar tissue.

"After the war," the old man said, "I come back and got work in the penitentiary. Knew a whole lot about guns—hate them though, son, I had to carry them so much. When a man packs a gun all his life, and if sometimes he have to use it, it gets so he changes, you know what I mean, boy? It changes him, makes him different, like I say."

They were coming up on another car then, and the hitch-hiker stopped talking suddenly, looking intently at it.

"Take it easy," he said, "you want to watch a guy with tags like that. Might be he's some sort of cop. You see that there X on his tag?"

The driver slowed obligingly, seeing nothing in the other car, which had two children looking out the back window.

"He looks all right," the hitch-hiker said in a minute. The car was an ordinary stock sedan and the driver passed it and pulled away, accelerating again. "You can't never tell about them Xs," the old man said, sitting back in his seat.

"Like I say, it changes a man, always having to carry a gun. Like this'n here, you see?" The driver looked down and saw the heavy pistol he was holding gently in his hand. "I allus carry it," he said. And he smiled as he put it back inside his coat.

"You mind if I smoke, son?"

The driver shook his head, feeling the uncertainty in the car now, the sudden shift of emphasis which the presence of the pistol had brought about. He looks friendly enough, at least not unfriendly, the driver thought, it is hard to tell.

"They's some that do," the old man said, lighting his cigarette with a kitchen match, "though I never saw no harm in it myself. I like to ask, 'specially when I'm in another man's car.

314

"Like I was saying, I live in Florida all my life, working over to the penitentiary after the war, going out with the road gangs."

"The chain gangs?" the driver asked. They had come into a settled area: there were houses by the road, and he saw the rural mail-man driving from box to box, leaning across his front seat to push the mail through the open off-side window. A pretty teen-aged girl was standing by one of the boxes, waiting. Yet a fear existed, amorphous, unspecified; a dark incubus that had come with the old man, disquieting him.

"You might call them that," the hitch-hiker said, nodding his head gravely. "It's a damn sight better'n on the wall walking in the hot sun. On the road you ride the trucks where the wind'll cool you—you seen them with the convicts in the cage on the back, and the other truck following with the guard on the cab roof with a sawed-off 12 gauge. You seen them? Well, that there was me," he said proudly. "It ain't so lonely; you git to be friendly like with them."

"It's a good way to build a road, I guess."

"You're right, sure right."

They were coming into Ft. Meyer and the driver slowed down. It was a quiet town with tall palms along the streets and green lawns in front of the houses. And then they turned north again, crossing the bay on a long silver bridge, while beneath them the water was broken and choppy under the steady Gulf wind.

"This here river," the old man said, "reminds me of once I was in the north, near Tallahassee it was—living up there at the time—it was a Sunday and I was fishing up the river a piece, just moving slow in my punt. It was some hot that day, I'll say, and I was sticking close to the bank trying to keep in some lee—where them trees hang out over the water real thick. When I hears a scratching in the brush and somebody saying:

—you better keep moving along there, buddy.

"So I laughed thinking they was having a joke, or maybe

there was a kid with his sweetie, all nekkid, you know; it was the same to me. I wasn't bothering no one at all. So I laugh, 'n this kid about as old as you, he steps out of the brush and holds a sawed-off shotgun on me.

"You ever hold a gun on a man, son, 'n know you could pull that trigga and shoot him down? It's what I say about making a man different. You got to have a kind of experience to handle it—so you don't shoot no man by accident, you see what I mean. But not this kid, he didn't have no experience. He could of shot me without him having any excuse—it's like that in the beginning—and I was scared.

—you hear what I say, the kid says, you better bug out.

—kid, I'm minding my business doing a little fishing. Don't go fooling with me.

"It was then I started to smell the woodsmoke and I figure it's a still.

—hell, what you got, boy, a still? Don't make a difference to me; I probably bought some of your brew. You just go along and I won't tell no living soul.

—mister, move on. I'm counting and then I'm shooting.

—this here's a free river, boy. I'm fishing and doing you no harm. You just fade off in that brush and I'll forget you held a gun on me or said a lot of fool things.

"Maybe a man shouldn't never get mad," the hitch-hiker said slowly, "maybe it won't never do any good, and just naturally leads to grief. If I was to say anything at all I guess I'd say that first. But I was getting mad then, like I had no control. I was getting that mad and the kid was scared 'n liable to gun me down. I could smell it in him. It was a free river and he was telling me to get off it. He was running a still and I ain't got nothing against that excepting what they does is cheat the government, and I wouldn't care nothing about that except that cheating the government out of the tax means another man got to pay it. Who's that? That's you 'n me, boy. In the end, we's the ones getting reamed. I don't know," he said slowly, "it comes to me now that I didn't have no real choice. A man naturally gets mad. Ain't that so, son? I didn't have no real choice, did I? You tell me."

"No," the driver said, "I guess you didn't."

"The way he waving that gun around he act like a Georgia boy to me, excitable like they is, and unthinking. You ain't a Georgia boy, son?"

"No," he said, "I'm from New York."

"Yankee, eh? They's more Yankees than anybody in this here state, I tell you, though most of them not as young as you.

"This boy though, he's fine strung. Georgia boy sure as shooting I could tell. He says to me:

—you take up them oars and row that tub out of here. Right now, hear? On three I'm pulling this trigga and this gun ain't got no rock salt in it, I'll clue you.

—pull that, you little sonofabitch, 'n you'll wish you was born of another mother.

—what'd you say? What'd you say? this kid yells.

"I seen him start to raise the gun, so I give her a hard scull with the oar I'm holding; same time I duck into the bottom.

"That gun went off, bawaanng . . . right over me, close enough to feel wind of them shot. So I take my pistol and sticking it over the side, I lets one go. I know he's scared then because he fires his other barrel without him even seeing me. And his gun's empty then so I stand up, holding that pistol, and looking at him. I could of killed him right then, but he took off into the brush.

"I was mad, boy, crazy kind of mad. They telling me to move off and then that still. They was rights I had for being an American, wasn't there? What the hell I get shot up in a war for, boy? I ask you? Am I right or wrong? You tell me, about the war'n all, right or wrong?"

The driver nodded, listening intently.

"I move out then," the old man said. "I move down stream and pulling in, I went into the woods. I move pretty fast and quiet in them woods and pretty soon I comes on a smell of that smoke again, and a kind of road running through that brush; directly I almost break out in the clearing where I see the three of them standing round. The kid has the gun and the others're talking to him, nervous like and quick. I give a big yell and everything quits while they look all around and then this kid pulls up the gun. I reach around my tree and fires and the pistol jumping in my hand, it scares me. You know why, boy? It scares me because I like the way it feels. The kid fires then, and I hear the shot arattling round me in the brush, and I step out from that tree then, and holding down with two hands I dropped him.

"I thought right then, that's a good shot; and them other two light out leaving the kid screaming and churning on the ground, till one come back and taking him by the arms, he pulls him along while the other is hunkered down by the truck. I could of got him easy. I could of killed the three of them right then." The hitch-hiker paused, thinking about it, and then he said, very seriously, "I could of killed the three of them, and I most wanted to."

"Holy smokes," the driver said.

"They pulled him into that pick-up and skidded out of there, in second, up that mud track. I'm standing there, laughing, son. It seemed funny to me then.

"But that ain't all," he went on. "You know what I did then?"

"What?" the driver asked, thinking that it wasn't possible to have done much more.

"I went and I look over this outfit they had. It was right big—boiler and run-off vats and a shack where they had it put up in nice wooden barrels. So, I took 'n shot that boiler full of holes. I smash up them coils. I go in the shack and stove in them barrels. They was another gun in there 'n I took and broke the stock offen it against a tree, bent them barrels round a rock. By then I had raw whisky running ass-high all over so I took the kerosene they had for lighting the fire. I spread it around and lit the whole shebang. That fire sure burned good on whisky, son, about half them woods is burning when I left." He was finally, morosely silent.

"My God, that's quite a story," the driver said.

"Boy, that there ain't no story, that's God's honest truth."

Now, near the coast, the land was crowded and there were houses, small and poor, set back from the road. There was a billboard reading: 'Visit Crystal Springs Where The Waters Are Best For *You*,' with the picture of a girl in a tiger-skin bathing suit. The sun was gone and the clouds had come into the sky; the wind was blowing, clutching at the palms and the sharp, evil bayonet grass along the road.

"I moved out of that county, son, right then."

"I don't blame you," the driver said.

"That kid I shot," the hitch-hiker said, not hearing him, "he was the sheriff's son. Can you beat it, the whole kit and caboodle belong to the Sheriff."

"You were lucky then."

"Was having a drink in a roadhouse along there and a state trooper come in I knows. He tells me, says the sheriff's looking for me, but he's afraid to push it out of the county. Everybody thinks it pretty funny, the trooper says; and I guess it was, except for the kid I shot. He ended up crippled."

Oh Jesus, the driver thought, in the army you heard all kinds of stories, about the women and the liquor and the brawling. Nobody would ever admit to any fear, except, perhaps, that it was smart to be afraid of combat, even afraid enough to run . . . But you half believed that nobody ever really told the truth about any of it.

"I was lucky, it's true," the old man said, "must be I live right. They's people now who'd kill me if they saw me. So I allus got this gun. I show you this here gun?" He had it out of his coat again, and was holding it cradled protectively in his hand, "I show you this, didn't I?"

"Yes," the driver said, "yes, I saw it." Or maybe some of what was told, he thought, maybe some of it was also true.

"It sure is funny," the old man mused, thinking about it,

"how it all works out. One thing leading to the next and the boy he's crippled for life. Seems one thing always leads to another, don't it? As though there ain't much a man can do about it. Ain't that so, son? You ever go to one of them colleges so's you could learn why things work like they do?"

"Yes," said the driver, "I went to college before I went in the service."

"What do they call that? I mean they got a name for it, don't they?"

"When a man is trapped and has no choice, you mean? Determinism," he said, "I guess that's it."

"Yeah, well that sound like something. A man should listen hard when he hears them things. I been around a whole lot but I reckon I don't know much about them things. Nor most anything, I guess," he said sadly. "I sure would like to know." He was silent a moment. "All I got is the war. Was you in the war, son?"

"Yes," the driver said, "I was in a war," thinking, why does he ask me this? Why should I have to answer his damned questions? The malaise settled in him now.

"Well," the hitch-hiker said, looking at him, "I guess what's important a man should know what he wants, how he's gonna live. Ain't that true?"

"Yes, I guess so. No," he said sharply, "no, I don't know," denying it all.

"Someday somebody'll show me," the old man said with conviction, and then he was silent while they drove into Sarasota, past all the pretty white resort houses, and down into the town, and after this very long silence he said, as a complete thought in itself, "Maybe."

And the driver said, "I'll take you on through town, put you on the road north."

The old man was silent again until finally the car had stopped and then he got out, taking the suitcase with the garish decal on it.

"I sure do appreciate this lift you give me," he said. "They's people who wouldn't pick up a man looks as bad as I do. Good luck to you, boy," the old man said, standing outside the car, "God bless you."

The driver turned the car around then, leaving him standing on the Tamiami Trail north with the suitcase and the revolver which shielded him; and looking back once he saw the man waiting, while the cars passed him going to Tampa, and then the driver found he was gripping the steering wheel so hard there was pain in his fingers.

The Prayer Meeting

HOLLIS SUMMERS

MRS. BEMIS HAD AS GOOD SENSE AS ANYONE IN LEXINGTON, Kentucky, but she liked to pretend she was crazy. After her husband, the Rev. Alfred Bemis, died; after she stopped going to church because of her blood pressure; after the days were filled only with her daughter's chattering care, Mrs. Bemis was compelled to create entertainment for herself. She planned her projects carefully, stretching them out to cover as much time as possible. She patched the projects together from scraps of the past, but the present was infinitely more attractive than the past had ever been. Nothing annoyed her more than for her daughter, Alphie, to start carrying on about "the other days." Alphie was the limit, five feet seven and every inch a fool. It served her right to be named Alphie. Mrs. Bemis had wanted her second child to be a boy. When the doctor announced a girl, Mrs. Bemis had named her Alphie on the spot. She considered Alphie Bemis the ugliest name she had ever heard.

The first daughter, Anne, had run away and married. She died a long time ago, leaving a son whom Mrs. Bemis considered a half wit. He was twenty-five and still studying to be a church educational director at the seminary in Louisville. Mrs. Bemis ordered Alphie to call him long-distance and invite him to the prayer meeting. But she talked about the prayer meeting for two months before the telephone call. At first she had considered inviting everybody in Lexington. Finally, though, she decided on Alphie, Alfred II, and Martha Wattlington for the congregation.

Number Two was a very conscientious boy, so of course he promised to take the bus clear down from Louisville the very next night. Mrs. Bemis always referred to young Alfred as Two or Number Two. It seemed to get his goat. Alphie kept saying, "Remember the other days," over the telephone. Mrs. Bemis could not hear Number Two's voice, of course, but she felt sure he was saying, "Oh, yes, Aunt Alphie. Oh, yes, I remember the other days."

Mrs. Bemis telephoned fat Martha Wattlington herself. She made Alphie dial the number, of course. Martha said she'd be glad to come, she'd been meaning to get over all week. It was amazing what an old voice Martha had over the telephone. Mrs. Bemis laughed into the receiver in spite of herself. Martha had lived neighbor in Paducah, and now they were all back in Lexington—what was left of them. Martha had a grandson, ten years old, and you'd never think to look at her that she once wore spit curls. Martha was one of the first women in Paducah to get a bob. Rev. Bemis never said a word against Martha's hair, but he raised the roof when Anne had hers cut. Rev. Bemis always said Martha Wattlington was a true Christian gentlewoman.

"You'll get your grandson to come for you," Mrs. Bemis said sweetly to the telephone. O. C. Wattlington often walked Martha home. "It does my heart good to see that child." O. C. looked more like a rabbit than a boy. It was his teeth that did it. Nobody ever had two bigger front teeth than O. C. Wattlington. Mrs. Bemis told Martha she liked to keep in touch with the youngest generation, and Martha said O. C. would be glad to drop by.

Number Two arrived before Martha. The Bemis men were always early. If Rev. Bemis didn't get to church an hour ahead, he thought he was late. Mrs. Bemis barely had time to put on a funny outfit before the doorbell was ringing. She had meant to drape some toilet paper around her neck like a scarf, but there just wasn't time.

Two leaned way over to kiss Mrs. Bemis and he stood straight to kiss Alphie. Alphie cried a little, naturally, and clung to him, and said, "Baby, baby." The boy finally pulled himself away from the snottering Alphie, and he squared his thin shoulders, and he said, "You're looking mighty well, Grandmother."

"Nice or well?" she asked him. She turned around slowly so he could get the full effect of her regalia. Over the yellowed pongee she had bought in Paducah thirty years ago, she had placed one of Rev. Bemis's collarless shirts, and over that a red blouse of Alphie's.

"Both nice and well," Number Two said.

Mrs. Bemis pirouetted faster. She laughed because she was making the church educational director lie in his teeth. She twirled so swiftly that her pigtails stood almost straight out. Alphie had tried to make her put her hair up, but Mrs. Bemis had insisted on the pigtails with yarn bows. "You really think I look nice?" she gasped over the laughter.

"Oh, yes, very nice," Number Two said in his preacher's voice.

When Martha came, Mrs. Bemis acted as if her own layered costume were normal prayer meeting attire. Martha was decked out like a horse and buggy as usual—gloves and purse and perfume smelling to high heaven. She shook Mrs. Bemis's hand for a long time and said, "How good it is to see you!" Martha always did show her gums when she smiled, but it was worse now that she had false teeth.

Alphie wanted to tell people where to sit, but Mrs. Bemis wouldn't let her. She put Alphie and Martha on the piano bench, and Two across the room in the Morris chair. She herself sat on the arm of Number Two's chair.

"Your Granddaddy's back." Mrs. Bemis covered her mouth

with her hand so Martha and Alphie would think she was talking about them.

"Oh?" Two said, straightening the crease in his left trouser leg.

"He's been back from the dead for a week, now." You could tell Number Two almost anything. He looked up at Mrs. Bemis with such trustful cow eyes that Mrs. Bemis had difficulty in keeping her face straight. "I think he's liking me better," she said, which gave her an excuse to laugh.

"That's fine," Two said.

"He doesn't spend so much time with that woman any more down at the hotel. I don't mean Martha Wattlington, I mean the other one, the dancer with bobbed hair." Rev. Bemis had been terribly opposed to dancing. Of all the sins he considered dancing the worst.

"We were going to have a prayer meeting." Two cleared his throat. "Prayer meeting." He didn't spell out the words, but he gave the impression of spelling.

Mrs. Bemis made her eyes go blank. "By the way, I've been wanting to have a prayer meeting." She spoke loudly.

Alphie jumped to her big feet. "Little Mother has been yearning for a prayer meeting." Alphie had tears in her eyes. Alphie enjoyed nothing more than following company to the front door and crying and saying that Mrs. Bemis had to be handled with kid gloves. "You just can't force my little mother," Alphie always told the departing guests. If she'd said it once, she'd said it a thousand times.

"Who?" Mrs. Bemis asked.

"We can have Alfred lead us," Alphie said patiently.

"I don't know anybody else to do it." Mrs. Bemis shook her head. The pigtails on her back swayed. She shook her head harder and the pigtails moved more swiftly. She leaned her head back, and the pigtails waved hilariously.

"Mother," Alphie said. "Little Mother."

Mrs. Bemis pretended to slip from the chair arm. Alphie and Martha and Two were beside her in a flash.

325

"Thank you, thank you," Mrs. Bemis said, making her body as heavy as possible. She allowed them to place her in the Morris chair before she got up to walk over to the sliding doors which led to the dining room.

"Wait until the prayer meeting is over," Two said. There was a touch of impatience in his voice which caused Mrs. Bemis to smile at him over her shoulder.

"It's been a lovely day," Martha Wattlington said.

"Lovely." Alphie was about to cry. You could tell from her voice that she was about to cry. "And how are all your folks?"

Mrs. Bemis stood listening at the sliding door. "I think your father's back there, Alphie," she said. "I wish you'd tell him to come in for the meeting."

"Oh, Mother," Alphie said, but she went.

Martha Wattlington said, "We certainly did use to have some good times together—all our families."

"We certainly did," Mrs. Bemis said, and Alphie was back. It would have been a good opportunity to discuss adultery, but Alphie didn't give them time.

"He wasn't there," Alphie said.

Mrs. Bemis began to breathe heavily. She bit her lips together. It was a trick which always worked on Alphie.

"He was there, but he said he had a headache."

"That's different." Mrs. Bemis smiled at Alphie who was a great fool. "He's just been subject to headaches for the last few days," she explained to Martha. "I hope it isn't his eyes."

Number Two was looking at his wrist watch, so Mrs. Bemis opened the sliding doors into the dining room and told him to follow her.

"You'd better go," Alphie said. "It's probably something about the prayer meeting."

It was difficult to talk to anybody as half-witted as Two without laughing in his face, but Mrs. Bemis managed very nicely. She told him she had been worried about the singers. Two said they had enough singers. Mrs. Bemis told him that the doctor had sung to her yesterday and then pinched her knee. Two looked scared out of his half wits, and led her back into the living room.

Naturally Two sat down at the piano. Mrs. Bemis had always thought it unseemly for a man to play the piano, particularly at prayer meeting. It served Two right to be able to play. She made him get up so she could get the three hymn books out of the bench. She insisted on handing out the books, trading them around several times. Alphie looked as if she were about to go crazy. Mrs. Bemis made Alphie and Martha sit on the couch, and then on the radiator. She stuffed Martha's gloves under the cushion of the Morris chair and sat on them.

"I'm afraid you won't be comfortable there," she told Martha and Alphie. "The couch, please."

"Mother. Little Mother," Alphie said, but she and Martha moved.

" 'Dwelling in Beulah Land.' Number Two Three Seven," Mrs. Bemis said. "The first hymn will be 'Dwelling in Beulah Land.' " It was the hymn she disliked most. Next to "The Star Spangled Banner" she considered it the most impossible song in the English language.

Two's hands were quite large and ugly. He hit the keys as if he were angry at them. Alphie said, "The soft pedal," placing her finger on her lips.

"Everybody sing," Two said.

The singing was a lovely fiasco, of course. Two sang so loudly that you couldn't hear yourself, and Martha held the notes longer than anybody. Mrs. Bemis got the full benefit of both of their dreadful voices. Alphie, of course, never had any voice. She took after her father, and besides she was terribly touched by the occasion. She kept rubbing her eyes with the back of her hand.

"Again," Mrs. Bemis said when they had finished all the verses. "Standing as we sing."

Two struck a chord. "You stand, too, Two," Mrs. Bemis

said, and Two stood too. It was hilarious. Mrs. Bemis laughed until she cried.

"Again," she said. "All the verses." Her plans for the service had included only one singing of the song, but it was all too delightful.

"One more verse. This time, humming the chorus."

Mrs. Bemis would have demanded a fourth complete rendition, but she fagged out with laughing and standing up for so long. "Be seated, please," she said.

Martha Wattlington was fagged out, too. She was breathing as heavily as anybody in the room, and she was twelve and a half years younger than Mrs. Bemis.

"Anne is the angriest girl you ever saw," Mrs. Bemis said, folding her hands over her stomach. "She told me she was going to beat her daddy up. She said she was going to whip him within an inch of his life."

"Please, Grandmother," Two said, swinging his legs to the congregation-side of the piano bench. Two couldn't bear for Mrs. Bemis to talk about his dead mother; he was very sentimental about motherhood. On Mother's Day he always sent Mrs. Bemis a card full of lace and sugar. He even sent Alphie a card, less lace and less sugar, but a card nevertheless, which showed how Two's mind ran.

"Anne said, 'If I can't beat him up myself, I'll make Two help me.'" Mrs. Bemis nodded at Two's legs. "She was sitting right on that very bench. She said it yesterday A.M. at half-past seven."

Two looked down at his legs, as if he expected to find his mother on the floor. Mrs. Bemis feigned a coughing fit. Alphie was at her side, of course, fanning her with an antimacassar. Alphie never could find a fan when she needed one.

"I'm all right, Alphie," Mrs. Bemis said weakly. "Take your seat."

"Don't you want to lie down and rest a while, Little Mother?" Alphie asked. "We mustn't get too excited and hot. It's bad for us if we get too hot."

"Seated," Mrs. Bemis said, refusing to allow anyone to speak until Alphie was back by Martha Wattlington. Two tried to speak. Three times he said, "Prayer meeting." Finally Mrs. Bemis had to say, "Your mother told me to tell you to keep silent."

And, finally, Alphie sat down.

Mrs. Bemis cleared her throat. "I said, 'Go to it, Daughter Anne. I'm with you.' She said, 'Mother, he'll ruin us all with that dancer down at the hotel.' "

"Mother, Mother, please," Alphie said, the tears starting again.

"Well," Mrs. Bemis smoothed the antimacassar over her knees. She didn't look straight at Martha Wattlington, but she snatched little glances at her big fat face. Martha looked scared to death, as well she might. Her mouth was open and her eyes were like holes burned in a blanket. "Well, I heard water running in the bathtub."

"Grandmother, we have come for a prayer meeting." Two was standing now. He had pulled a Bible out of his jacket pocket.

"Please, Two." Mrs. Bemis made her voice sweet and patient. "Please, do not be sacrilegious."

Two sat down all right.

"As I was saying, there was your Grandfather and the dancer in the bathtub, splashing and singing for all they were worth. I was heart-sick. I told Anne not to look. I said, 'Daddy, get out of that tub.' "

"You dreamed it, Mother. You dreamed it." Alphie leaned her head against the back of the couch. At least she didn't stand up, which proved she was smarter than Two.

"They were just splashing away. It was the worst sight I ever saw."

"You know you dreamed it," Alphie said. "The bathtub isn't big enough for two people."

"The dancer is smaller than your father," Mrs. Bemis said patiently.

Alphie didn't answer. She just shook her head against the back of the couch.

"Are you denying that the dancer is smaller?" Mrs. Bemis asked sharply.

"I'm not denying it." Alphie was sometimes difficult to handle, even as a child.

"Excuse me." Mrs. Bemis smiled apologetically first at Martha, then at Two. "Alphie, repeat after me: 'The dancer is smaller than my father.'"

"The dancer is smaller than my father," Alphie said.

Two was up again. He was turning the pages of his Bible. Fortunately, he was all thumbs and the pages stuck together and he couldn't find what he was looking for.

Mrs. Bemis stood, too. "How have you been feeling, Martha?"

"Very well very well very well," Martha said all in a breath. She was holding tight to the arm of the couch. "I've been very well, Mrs. Bemis."

"Do you remember when we lived in Paducah and you had your hair cut?" Mrs. Bemis smiled and nodded at Martha Wattlington.

"Indeed I do, Mrs. Bemis." Martha laughed so loudly that she evidently scared herself. She let go of the couch arm, and she sat very straight.

"We will have silent prayer." Mrs. Bemis seated herself and spread the drapery of Rev. Bemis's shirt tails neatly over her knees. "We will dedicate this meeting to my husband, Rev. Alfred Bemis, who has a headache in the back bedroom."

The group was remarkably cooperative. Once Alphie whispered something to Martha and Martha answered; and twice Two said, "Amen." But you couldn't call them disorderly. Mrs. Bemis said, "Please," squeezing her eyelids so tightly that she saw rainbows. "Please, all of you."

The house was very quiet. If there had been a splashing in the bathtub, they could have heard it. But Mrs. Bemis didn't allow herself to think of the bathtub story; she absolutely refused to laugh during the silent prayer period. Too, it was pleasant to watch the rainbows burst in the darkness of the quiet living room. She probably would have lost track of time if Martha Wattlington's grandson hadn't rung the doorbell.

"Amen," Mrs. Bemis said, and Alphie was out in the foyer in a flash. Alphie loved to answer the door.

"I came for my grandmother," O. C. Wattlington said in his squeaking voice.

Alphie was all over herself being gracious. "Come right in, come right in, O. C." Alphie had her arm around the boy's shoulders. Alphie just couldn't keep her hands off people.

"Shake hands with Mrs. Bemis," Martha said.

In spite of herself, Mrs. Bemis said, "Would you like a carrot, O. C.?"

Alphie said, "Why, mother."

O. C. said, "No thank you, mam."

"Could you sing me a little song?" Mrs. Bemis refused to let go of the boy's hand. He was a patient dull child, and after two or three yanks he let his hand stay in hers.

"Can you sing for Mrs. Bemis?" Martha began to gather herself together. She was looking for the gloves, of course.

"We are having a prayer meeting," Mrs. Bemis said. "Do you know any appropriate prayer meeting songs?"

"I don't think so," O. C. said through his rabbit teeth. He couldn't look you in the eye, and he had an outlandish cowlick. Mrs. Bemis felt sure he was the funniest child she had ever seen, unless it was Two at the same age, but she kept her face straight.

"Your grandmother is a very religious gentlewoman," Mrs. Bemis said. "Are you sure you don't have a single, solitary, prayer meeting song?"

"I don't think so." O. C. pulled at his hand a little, but only a little.

"The prayer meeting is dismissed, then," Mrs. Bemis said. "Did you lose something, Martha?"

"Just gloves," Martha said, wallowing around on the couch.

331

"It doesn't matter. It's been awfully nice seeing you." But Martha still looked for the gloves. She was a great one for her possessions.

"What kinds of songs do you know?" Mrs. Bemis spoke each word slowly. O. C.'s face was getting white under his freckles.

"He knows 'Davy Crockett.' " Martha was exasperated. Her face was red. White O. C. and red Martha made an interesting combination for anybody's eyes.

Mrs. Bemis let go of O. C.'s hand for a moment. She clapped her own hands together, although there was really no need to get the group any quieter. They were as quiet as death already. "We will all stand while Master O. C. Wattlington favors us with 'Davy Crockett.' "

Two had turned around to the keyboard. Two never missed a chance to show off.

"He will sing *a cappella*," Mrs. Bemis said sternly.

"It is very difficult to sing unaccompanied"— Two's Adam's apple worked in his thin throat—"unaccompanied under these conditions."

Mrs. Bemis closed her eyes. "Your mother came from the dead and told me to ask you never to play the piano again."

It was a splendid thing to say. The words just came to Mrs. Bemis. She had planned almost every other detail of the evening, but the piano-business was a lovely bolt from the blue. Two got to his feet as if he were a very old man. Mrs. Bemis liked to hope it would be some time before he returned to his music.

"As soon as your grandmother stands, you may proceed, O. C.," Mrs. Bemis said softly.

"You may proceed."

O. C.'s thin little voice moved painfully from one note to another. His hand worked convulsively in Mrs. Bemis's tight grasp. Once he forgot the words, and Martha, her head bowed, supplied, "His politickin' done." It was a very long song, and hideously rendered.

"Thank you, O. C. Thank you very much," Mrs. Bemis said. "And now, before you release my frail hand, I want you to promise to remember—as long as you live I want you to remember. . . ."

"It's late. He has school tomorrow," Martha Wattlington said, as if she knew what Mrs. Bemis was going to say. She couldn't have known, of course, but she moved quickly, for her bulk, across the room, and she stood breathing heavily beside her rabbit of a grandson.

"Remember that your grandmother took a bath with my husband," Mrs. Bemis said sweetly. "They splashed together."

"Grandmother!" Two shouted.

"She doesn't know what she's saying," Alphie sobbed.

"Oh Mrs. Bemis." Martha's voice was a long wail.

The Rabbit didn't say anything.

Mrs. Bemis sank carefully to the floor. It was really the best place to end the meeting, here, now, in the lovely present. She had planned to close with a solo dance. But she had hexed Two's piano playing, and it was foolish to dance without music. Anyhow, she had already over-exerted herself. Her blood pressure was up again. She could tell when it was up.

She did not bat an eyelash as they carried her to the back bedroom. Two was already promising Alphie he would stand by her. Two had the Bemis loyalty. Mrs. Bemis would be gravely ill for at least several weeks, and Two would get terribly behind with his work at the Seminary—all for the sake of "the other days." Martha Wattlington would send in custard and broth until it was running out of their ears. And Alphie . . . oh, that funny stupid Alphie.

They placed her carefully on the bed. Mrs. Bemis thought about pretending that Rev. Bemis lay on the bed beside her. But she didn't. Instead, she went straight to sleep.

Things Changed

BETTY SUNWALL

IF YOU WERE BORN IN LAKE CHARLES, LOUISIANA, YOU PROB-ably wouldn't think a great deal about the Negroes. You'd know that if you came in town from the north on 66 past what is known as Billy's Hot Dog Place you'd run square into Broad Street, and you'd know that if you turned right off Broad Street you'd hit "Nigger Town." It's all clustered together there—movie, stores, churches and houses. It's not such an undesirable section either, for as I have found in my studies, groups both compensate as well as accommodate. It's not as bad as some white man just passing through might think. The houses are little, sure, but you would know if you had studied sociology as I have, that environmentalism is only one factor influencing the structure of man. After all, I lived there. So I should know. But, as I said, you wouldn't do a great deal of thinking about it anyway.

I know I didn't—leastways, that is, not until I was fifteen. When I was fifteen the high school gang devised a new sort of entertainment. They would roar their cars through "Nigger Town," roll down the windows and throw all kinds of rotten stuff and firecrackers at the Negro kids.

One night I remember in particular. The high school gang waited until about midnight when the Negroes were getting out of their movie. Then they really peppered them with cherry bombs and four-inchers. There was a big racket of noise, light, and niggers hot-footing it in all directions—sort of a unique example of displacement, don't you see. I walked home alone that night and while I walked I did a lot of thinking. As I look back on it I can see that my thinking wasn't at all controlled. Doctor Gibson, head of the sociology department, says that your thinking should be controlled; it should be objective in order to evaluate correct.

In a way my thinking that night was objective, though, because after all I did work out a theory. It is night, I said to myself, and some people are living and some are dead and the Cajuns are back in the bayous but they don't count because you can't find them. You see I meant they lost all, what we call, social significance.

It must be necessary, I thought. That was my theory—that things which happen in the night when you was supposed to be sleeping are necessary. It's necessary for the white boys to throw four-inchers and cherry bombs and it's necessary for the Negroes to run and it's necessary for me to walk home alone and think about it because I'm a Negro too. I knew for sure—yes, I certainly knew—that no Negro could roar a car down Shell Beach Drive and throw stuff at the white kids and get by with it. They couldn't, you see, on account of the public opinion. The social pressures weren't slanted that way. I had a theory and I had a powder burn on my leg too, from a cherry bomb. What's the difference between the white and the black man, I said? It was the difference that bothered me.

The importance of the whole experience was that, as Doctor Gibson would say, it motivated me to enter what we call the field of sociology. That's what it did—it motivated me to enter college and study sociology. That's not such a silly thing either because then I'd be able to come back home and change things—make things better.

Doctor Gibson, head of the sociology department, always points his pencil when he says something significant. "It's necessary to understand the mores, folkways and customs of the culture in order to understand the people." He pointed his pencil at me that day and I felt he was depending on me to make conditions better in the South because I knew the mores, folkways and customs of the Negroes, because I was a Negro and knew the conditions.

Doctor Gibson certainly taught me a good deal. He provided me with the tools and now that I had graduated I had to apply them. I got my degree and I feel right proud of it. I had to study a great many intricate things but it paid off because my grades turned out to be good—in the field of sociology.

I came back home—all the way from Chicago where I had gone to seek my education and improve myself. I came back home to see my folks, but it is most likely appropriate that I tell you how I had made out in Chicago and had improved myself. I did not mind hard work for I know that a person who is not to the manor born and to the rank of privilege has got to work hard for what he gets and for his justice. I had worked hard as a barber shop porter from the age of seven on. That is what a person does if he's from a depressed group. I had saved my money, at least what I had not had to give to my folks when they needed it, and when I got my size on me I went up North for opportunity. I could play the piano as good as the next one though I do not aim to flatter myself. I could play classical compositions and otherwise. So I got me a job in a night spot and sometimes when they turned the lights down low or made the colored ones go on I played classical compositions too. That's how I financed my way through college. I was a major in sociology in college and I did not do badly, if I say so myself, considering my handicaps, though I asked no man for sympathy. That is one of the first things we learn in studying the science of sociology. Sympathy does not do anybody any good. Sympathy relaxes the moral fibers of him who gives and him who receives.

As I have stated, I finished my work and came home. I

arrived in Lake Charles and things seemed mighty changed. Everything was either larger or smaller. Only the air was the same—sweet with flower smells—smells of gardenias and the fish smell off the lake. Yes, the air was the same and I was afraid the ethnocentrism, which is what we call it when a group thinks it's better than other groups, of that community would be the same too. For there had not been time to expect great change, for as Thomas Jefferson, that great champion of democracy, said, "Liberty is gained by inches." It would take a long road in the achieving of visible improvement.

There was not much visible improvement in my house when I stopped in front of it. It is natural, I guess, after four years to expect deterioration but when you see the deterioration it is always somewhat appalling. The yard that had once appeared almost large to me was only ten or twelve feet from the sidewalk. The thick green grass only showed in spurts around the edges of dirt and the front porch had half a plank missing. I thought of the white people's houses along Shell Beach Drive and wondered if they had changed, deteriorated, too. I thought of all the difference between the "whites" and "blacks" which I had learned to discard or correlate. Social assimilation—it is possible—I had learned it was possible— now I would help to make it possible—social assimilation, you see.

It only took six steps to cross the yard and be on the porch. I crossed the safe side and looked in through the open doorway. There was Mama. She still wore galoshes. Mama looked larger than the way I had remembered her. Mama always had been rather large, you see, but now she looked fatter. She was hemming at something, I couldn't make out what. She would take a stitch or two and then pick up the beer bottle from the floor and take a drink. Then she would start to hem again or buckle her galoshes. Mama was always buckling or unbuckling her galoshes. While I was watching Mama, Daddy came into the room. He was carrying his shoes in his hand—his shoes and a rag. Without looking at Mama or nothing else, he sat down at the wood table which I had helped him build when I was twelve, and started to rub the toes of his shoes with the rag.

It was mighty good to be home. I walked in and said, "Hello Mama, hello Daddy." They didn't hear me so I said it louder, "Hello Mama, hello—"

Mama looked up and sort of squealed, "Lord Jesus!"

Then I went to her and kissed her and she kissed me a good deal and I kissed her again.

Daddy was there squeezing my hands in both of his, saying, "My son Charlie, he come home to his daddy. He come home to his daddy."

I hadn't let them know that I was coming. Mama and Daddy didn't read and I wasn't sure or certain that Peanut did, although he was five when I left which would make him nine now, you see. Of course I had written sometimes because I knew they would always be able to find someone to read the letters to them but I hadn't written that I was coming. I guess I had wanted to surprise them.

"My son Charlie come home to his daddy." At first when you come home you can't say much; you just want to look at everything and touch things and then when you're certain you won't cry—over-react emotionally as we would say— then you want to talk. Mama asked if the people up North thought I played good piano, if I would go back or stay home, if I would like some fried chicken and, "Has you grown another foot, boy?" Then she buckled her galoshes. All her life, winter or summer, Mama had worn galoshes every day but while I'd been away at school, studying sociology, I somehow thought of Mama in shoes. Daddy still wore his blue overalls with the red stitching. The same overalls only they'd grown too big for him. He seemed to have to pull them after him when he moved. First Daddy moved, then the overalls moved.

I wanted to tell them everything. I never had, you know.

338

I'd never told them about school and sociology. When I had left I didn't think they'd understand, so I'd just said I was going North to play the piano. But now everything was changed. I had graduated and I would tell them all about it and they would comprehend because it was obvious that they loved me a good deal. They sure had missed me. I could tell.

"Daddy."

"Yes, Charlie boy?"

"While I was in the North I went to school."

Daddy had been smiling at me from the moment he had first seen me. He still smiled, "Well—well."

Mama took the beer bottle from her mouth. "You mean you study piano up North?"

"No, Mama, something else."

"My goodness—something else—ain't that fine!"

"Yes, Mama."

"What something else do you study?"

"Sociology."

"Ain't that fine—sociology—what's that?"

"Sociology is a science—it—well, it teaches you how to help people."

"Sure enough, now I remember."

I didn't know what else to say.

Mama took a drink of beer and Daddy looked at me. "You is learning how to help people. My, my, learning how to help." He thought for a bit, then jumped up and squeezed my hands again. "Sure enough." Daddy turned to Mama. "Charlie is gonna help. He's gonna be like Reverend Allen and lead hymn sings."

"Well, ain't that fine," said Mama. "Just last week Reverend Allen goes on a fine trip way over to New Orleans. He done get a flat tire and we take up a collection to get him back. Between your daddy, Peanut and me we give a whole dollar to get the good Reverend back."

"But I'm not going to be like Reverend Allen, Mama."

"Course not, you is gonna be better."

She looked at Daddy. "Bet our Charlie won't get no flat tires."

Daddy patted me on the back. "You is gonna be a big man, ain't you, Charlie?"

I said I didn't know but what with my training in sociology I—

Daddy pulled his overalls up. "You come with me to Mr. Herbert's tomorrow. He got lots of flowers need tending to." Daddy's smile got even bigger. "Mr. Herbert give me my lunch inside the kitchen now."

For twenty-seven years Daddy had been Herbert's gardener. Each noon the cook would set his lunch on the back porch and he would take it and eat it under the fig tree or in the garage if it was raining—but all that was changed now. I didn't say any more about school. Mama said Peanut was out in back and I went to look for him.

Peanut was lying in a small piece of shade made by the only bush in our back yard. He was whittling at something. I would never have known him if it hadn't been for the scar. When I left he was just a five-year-old; now he was a whopping big fellow of nine. The scar was the same, though—dark and wrinkled. It was because of the scar that he got the name Peanut. When he was just a baby, Mama used to sit him down beside her while she washed over the tubs. One day she put him by the big black kettle where she heats the wash water over a fire. Perhaps Mama had had too much beer, we never knew for sure, but when she took the water off she spilled a good bit of it on the baby. His whole right side was burned and it wrinkled. That's why everybody calls him Peanut—because he's brown and wrinkled.

I walked over to him and said, "Hi Peanut—I'm Charlie—remember?"

He glanced up at me and then looked away, as though he was used to seeing me around and maybe a little bothered by it at that. "Sure I remember," and set to whittling again.

It seemed—well, futile to speak again. Still, I thought I'd give it a try just to see what would happen.

"What are you whittling?"

This time he jerked his head up quick; his eyes got narrow and almost crazy, like pictures I had seen of what we call psychotics in one of my text books.

"A gun!"

"What are you making a gun for?" I knew I had to try to be interested in what he was doing in order to contact him. He had evidently known the answer to that for a long time and he gave it to me straight, without "blocking" as we in sociology would say.

"So's I can kill."

He dropped his head and watched his knife hand chip at the wood. "Course," he said, "I know no silly ol' wood gun like this'll kill. Pretty soon I'll get me a real gun."

"Why do you want a real gun?"

He kept chipping hard at the wood like nothing else mattered.

"Why are you going to kill?"

"Cause they're dirty no-goods that's why!"

I realized we'd both been talking low like we was conspirators, not like a kid and a college graduate, but like we was conspiring against something and I felt guilty to have been forced into that kind of talk by a nine-year-old. So the next time I spoke I spoke loudly, "Listen Peanut, just because they do the things they do, now and then, doesn't mean you should go around shooting all the whites in the world. In the first place you couldn't, in the second place it wouldn't help. But there is a way—"

He laughed. He laughed without rhyme or reason. Then he licked the shavings off the knife blade easy and sure without even thinking of cutting his tongue. He pushed the shavings off his tongue with his teeth at the same time he pushed the words out, "Hell, I ain't gonna kill no white man. I'm gonna kill niggers. Niggers ain't no good nohow. I'll kill 'em, then the white folk'll give me money and like me 'cause I killed 'em and then I'll be just as good as them. Gooder 'cause there ain't no white man got guts enough to kill *all* the niggers."

I stood there for a while—without thinking—without anything—just stood. Peanut was watching me, probably waiting for me to say something. There were so many things I could say. There were a multitude of things in the text books. I knew what Peanut was doing—he was identifying with the white race—he was trying to cross the color line because he hated his own race. He was a lot of things—my brother, too. Maybe a child guidance clinic—there was one in New Orleans. But he couldn't go there so I talked to him with reason to get at the basic causes of things.

"Peanut, if you killed all the Negroes you'd have to kill Mama and Daddy. You'd have to kill me too. Would you like that?"

He looked at his gun and then looked at me without saying nothing.

"Well, O.K., if you're going to kill niggers you might as well kill them all but you have to have a plan. Why don't you let me help you?"

He squinted his left eye and cocked his head back. "How come you wanta help?"

"Why not?"

He worked his tongue back and forth over his lower lip. "You mean you're gonna help me kill niggers?"

"I mean I'm going to help you work out a plan. First we've got to decide exactly why we're going to kill them. If we know that we'll be able to make a better plan."

"Hell, you talk crazy."

I laughed. "Maybe I do."

Then he laughed. His tight mouth sort of spread out into something loose and human and he laughed. "O.K., you and me'll make a plan."

He boosted himself off the ground and shook my hand

very solemnly. I cuffed him on the ear and he pretended not to like it. Then we walked in the house together.

That night I didn't go right to sleep as I usually do when I go to bed. I thought about home, Mama, Daddy, Peanut and all the things I had to do. I hadn't said any more about school and sociology but I would. Tomorrow, I said to myself, I'll tell them all about sociology, explain it so that they'll understand and then I'll get to work on Peanut—condition him to a new way of thinking. There was so much to do and the smell of something frying—have to be conditioned all over.

It was sow belly frying. "Get up, Charlie boy." It was six o'clock and Daddy and sow belly. I got dressed and sat down at the table. Mama was stirring the grits and drinking a bottle of beer.

"Mama?"

She spooned out my grits. "What, Charlie?"

"Do you think it's good for you to drink so much beer?"

"Lord, that's how come I drink it!"

Daddy was smacking on sow belly and didn't pay any attention to our talk.

She brought her beer over to the table and sat down by me. "Your mama is a sick woman."

I asked what she meant.

"Well, you see, my doctor say I got a sick belly. He say nothing agree with it but beer." She took a big mouthful and slushed it around before swallowing.

"What doctor, Mama?"

"My doctor."

"Oh."

She sighed. "I don't like it—but that what the doctor say I gotta do—drink beer all the time."

I said that I had never heard of beer being used for a stomach cure.

She said that was what the doctor told her, that beer was the best medicine. "Because I got a sick belly."

343

I asked how her stomach felt and she said, "Sick. It is so sick that I would die but for the medicine." She told me that sometimes it was hard as a rock, that it got bigger and littler, and caught on fire if she didn't take her medicine.

Daddy finished smacking, put his hand on my shoulder and said, "Time to go to Mr. Herbert's."

At noon we ate inside Herbert's kitchen like Daddy kept saying we would. By three o'clock we had most of the work done. Daddy had worked with the flowers and I had mowed the front and back yard. We were both trimming around the front sidewalk when a big black convertible pulled up to the curb. Daddy looked at the car and then told me, "That's Mr. Jud, Mr. Herbert's son."

Mr. Jud was thin and blond and drunk as all get out. He moved from the car toward us yelling, "Get out of the way, Mat. Here I come and I'm liable to kick hell out of you if you're in my way!"

Daddy pulled himself up as straight as he could and so did I.

Jud looked at me and then at Daddy. "What's wrong, Mat, getting too old to do your work by yourself?"

Daddy said, "No, Mr. Jud, he my boy just got back from playing piano up North."

Mr. Jud said, "You don't say," and started toward the house. Before he got to the door he stopped and looked back at Daddy and me. He walked back toward us a little, then stopped and stared at me. Then he laughed one of those half laughs that white people use when they aren't having a good time but like to pretend they are. That's a form of rationalization, don't you see.

"So you play piano?"

I said, "Yes."

"Where?"

"In a night spot."

"Are you good?"

"As good as the next one, I guess."

344

He laughed some more and I was altruistically happy at being able to provide myself as joke.

"You're just what I'm looking for, piano man. I've got a girl who's never satisfied. She's seen everything there is to see and yet she wants to see more." His eyes closed and he rocked back and forth. "But she's never seen you. She's never seen you." He stopped the rocking. "We'll be over tonight and you'd better play like you've never played before."

He asked Daddy where we lived and Daddy told him.

I knew that if he ever sobered up he wouldn't come. I had known a good many white people in Chicago; some of my friends had been white people and most of my colleagues. But I knew Jud didn't want to be friends and I bet he didn't know about sociology either so he was no colleague. I knew what he wanted—just another dumb nigger—a hot jazz man without a brain in his head. I hoped he'd sober up.

After supper Daddy put on clean overalls. "Well, well, Mama. Mr. Jud is coming to hear Charlie play piano." Mama said she'd fry chicken and Peanut got out his gun collection.

They came about nine-thirty, Jud with his arm around the girl's waist. He wasn't sober and neither was she. They got on the porch and the girl's foot went through the broken plank but Jud pulled her back, laughing, before her complete leg went down. I went to the door.

Jud squeezed his girl to him and said, "Look, sweetheart, meet—what's your name?"

I said, "Charlie."

"Yeah, Charlie, the best piano man in the country, so I've heard."

The girl giggled all over, stretched up and kissed Jud on the cheek, "You're wonderful, darlin'." Then she shinnied up to Jud even more. "Is it all right, darlin', for us—?"

He patted her on the side where his hand was. "Everything's all right when you're with Uncle Jud, baby. Uncle Jud's here." And he patted her some more.

345

They came in and I pulled two of the straight wood chairs out from under the table so they could sit down. Daddy was making some kind of a welcome speech about how nice it was for them to come see us, when the girl, almost choking from so much giggling, pulled at Jud's sleeve. "Did you ever see the like of that?" She pointed to Mama's galoshes and Jud went off into fits of laughing. Eventually even Mama joined in. I seemed to be the only one who didn't. Mama brought out the fried chicken and some of her medicine. Mama, Jud, and the girl, all being in somewhat the same condition, were getting along beautifully—but always at Mama's expense. I could see that though she couldn't. They called her Snow Queenie on account of the galoshes and she told them about her sick belly.

Daddy kept telling them about "my boy, Charlie," how big he was going to be and how he was going to lead hymn sings.

Peanut brought his gun collection over to Jud and stammered out his idea about killing niggers. "If I was a white man I wouldn't come to no nigger's house."

Jud kicked Peanut out of the way with his eyes. "If I were a nigger I wouldn't be telling a white man what to do because the white man might break the nigger in two."

This wasn't at all what Peanut had expected. He slinked over by the piano where I was sitting. I could tell it had been a traumatic experience for him and would like to have said something to him. I thought perhaps he might think better of his own race and less of his plan after this.

Then Jud looked at me. I had been sitting on the piano stool, watching without saying anything. "All right, Charlie, start playing. We want to be entertained—don't we," he said, looking at his girl. She giggled again—or had she ever stopped?— and I turned around on the stool so I faced the piano and ran my fingers up and down improvising my own chords. I watched my hands move and I wondered what right, what justification, there was for their being in our house. They were making fools out of us—out of me. They'd brag about

346

this later on. They'd say, "My God, you haven't seen any-thing until you've seen the way niggers live. Let me tell you —I spent a whole evening with them—the old lady wore galoshes, one of the kids was nuts and—" Why didn't I tell them that I'd been to school, that I'd graduated from college, that I knew as much or more than they did?

I didn't say anything, instead I worked my way out of original into some standard music which I knew they would like better because they'd be able to recognize it. I don't know how long I played.

"That's plenty for one night."

It was Jud who had spoke. Jud ordered me to stop. Jud was standing. I stood too. Jud and his girl were walking to the door.

"We're going to go now," he said. He said it like as if their leaving was an extraordinary event, one that would throw us into the depths of depression from which we never would recover.

My nerves were all rubbing against each other. I knew I should say something but everything I said in my mind was either too high or too low. I listened to myself control the pitch and say, "I was glad to play for you."

"O.K., Charlie, O.K.—just keep playing the piano and you'll be all right."

"Mr. Jud, I certainly am glad you like my piano playing. I always appreciate playing for someone who appreciates my music. But Mr. Jud—?"

"But what?"

"But maybe I want to do something besides playing the piano."

"You play it good, boy. Why don't you want to play the piano?"

I was a fool. I knew it all the time, right that minute, but I was the kind of fool I could not help being, which I will freely admit but without shame.

"Mr. Herbert," I said. I knew I was a fool. "Mr. Herbert,

I believe there are many studies which, if you have the time and interest to investigate, will undoubtedly prove to you that there is no essential difference between one man and another, and I do not mean to say just in the eyes of God, either. I as well as many others, who are far more learned than me, believe that—"

"What the hell are you talking about?" he said, and flushed up.

"—believe that the Negro, given the same advantages as the white man, will be able to contribute much that is worth while to our American society. I myself am a college graduate in sociology and I intend to help my country in every respect and—"

He started toward me and I was trembling. I was not afraid of him; I was just afraid of what I had said. The girl jumped back against the wall like as though she'd seen a water moccasin and Jud was closer to me with his fingers spreading out and in from his side.

Somewhere Mama was saying: "Mr. Jud you ain't gonna—you ain't gonna—"

"The hell I ain't gonna," Mr. Jud said and stepped in.

But Daddy grabbed his arm. "Mr. Jud—Mr. Jud—" Daddy was saying, like in a prayer.

"Take your hands off me, nigger!"

"Mr. Jud you know me—I work for you all—you know—"

"Yeah I know you but I don't know him!"

"You know him, Mr. Jud—he my boy—you know he don't mean nothin'—"

"Well God dammit I do!" And he jerked loose, but Daddy grabbed on again.

"He didn't mean it, Mr. Jud—he didn't mean it."

Then Mama was standing up, still hanging onto her beer bottle and with her eyes popped. "Mr. Jud—Mr. Jud. He didn't mean nothing. I'm his Mama and I know. I know he ain't got good sense—"

Then Daddy said, "That's right—he ain't got no more sense'n Peanut. And you know Peanut."

"Good sense or not I'm gonna teach that black bastard—"

And he called me bastard. He called me that and my Mama standing there. And me standing there and nothing to do.

But Mama was saying, "Mr. Jud, Mr. Jud—a big fine boy like you—you ain't gonna hit a poor little nigger ain't got good sense!"

He didn't hit me.

He didn't hit me. He just looked at me and let his hands sink. Then he said, "Good sense or not—piano or not—he better keep that black mouth shut."

The girl was sort of making a fuss and whimpering.

So Jud looked at her. She looked sure enough like she'd been bit by that snake. "It's all right, honey," he said and he went to her and put his hand on her like he owned her.

Then Daddy took a step toward him.

"Thank you, Mr. Jud, thank you, Mr. Jud," he said.

And Mama was saying, "Thank you, Mr. Jud," over and over.

He turned round and looked at them. "Yeah, you'd better thank me," he said.

Then he was gone. There wasn't a sound, not even Mama slurping beer.

Then I looked at Daddy. "Daddy," I said.

Daddy pulled up one of the straps on his clean Sunday overalls.

I said, "Daddy," again because I didn't want him to be ashamed for what he had done for me. I wanted to let him know how I felt.

Then Daddy said, "Get out."

"He won't be back, Daddy," I said. "He won't hurt me."

"Get out."

"But—"

"Get out!" he said, loud this time.

349

"Get out?"

"Get out for how you talk."

"How I talk?"

"How you talk to Mr. Jud—you ain't got no business—"

"Daddy, Mr. Jud ain't got no business—"

"Get out!"

He said it and I knew what he meant. That poor old nigger —I knew what he meant.

I looked at Mama. "Mama," I said, "Mama."

"You're a bad boy," Mama said.

"But Mama—"

"I thought you be a good boy and come home—be a good boy and lead hymn sings."

"But Mama—"

Then Daddy said, "Get out!"

I heard what he said but I kept on looking at Mama. It didn't do any good to look at her—I just saw what I saw.

"All right," I said. "All right—I'll go."

Then I turned around like I was ready to get my stuff. There was Peanut, looking at me big-eyed.

"Peanut," I said, "Peanut," and I was about to cry seeing him there. I leaned over like I was ready to hug him good-bye.

But he jerked back.

He raised up that silly little old wood gun and pointed it. He pointed it at me. "Bang, bang, bang!" he said.

The Buck in Trotevale's

THOMAS WILLIAMS

I WATCH MY SON PURSUE AN APPLE ACROSS THE FLOOR. HE IS seven months old. He grabs the shiny globe with both hands and puts it to his mouth: *squeak, squeak,* he gums it. There it goes, rolling bumpily beneath a chair, while he gravely watches. Onward! He'll corner the damned thing. Some day he'll get his teeth into such promising fruit. Meanwhile, he tries. And tries again—he won't give up. I am sure that I was never so determined. Although his eyes are mirror images of mine, I am uncomfortably aware of an alien deepness there, as if even now he were governed by a discipline I have never known. He works at his apple as he does at his world, single-mindedly, until it either accommodates him or shows itself to be impervious. Now the apple has escaped him again, and he watches it until it stops rolling, marks it well before arranging himself for the long crawl toward it. He rarely cries . . . and I wonder, knowing that they will always be mine, at the injustice of this stranger's inevitable wounds. . . .

When I was fourteen, coping with that world of benevolent rulers—coping with an instinctive directness much like my son's—Mr. Brown rented our furnished room. Now, I believe Mr. Brown to have been a kind of Yankee, although I didn't at first because he came from the South—from Massachusetts, where all those Massachusetts hunters come from, the ones who park in the middle of the road and shoot heifers for deer, not knowing the difference; proudly (it is said every year) bearing their pied trophies through Leah Town Square on the fenders of their Buicks, deer tags fluttering from bovine ears. I never saw this, myself, but, at fourteen, New Hampshire boys are careful license-plate watchers. *Massachusetts.* I still hear some disapproval echoing in my older voice.

I didn't know Mr. Brown very well at first. He was very quiet, and had a talent for missing squeaky boards and squeaky stairs. I'd see him in the upstairs hall once in a while, between his room and the bathroom. He'd come home from work, wash and change his clothes before walking downstreet to the Welkum Diner for his supper. I can see him walking down Maple Street: tall, superbly balanced, each foot reaching the sidewalk as if searching carefully for purchase. His heels rose lightly before each step, and I believed that if the sidewalk had suddenly tipped right up on its side, Mr. Brown would have been ready for it. He was in his late sixties, I suppose—an almost too-handsome man with his tanned face and thick white hair, his straight shoulders—and yet I like to think of him as being in his seventies. Seventy-seven makes me think of him; the two numerals spare and lean as the man, trim as are most men who grow old and active. He walked a lot. He even skied and on winter Sundays we would see him on Pike Hill doing his graceful old-fashioned christies on the unbroken snow, each long ski under control, his ski clothes fresh and dry. In the summer he hired a high-school boy and a motorboat and water-skied on Lake Cascom. His age was a little more apparent when he wore bathing trunks, of course. His belly bulged out. But even then, seeing that taut little pot, you knew that it contained only enough innards to run the lean body. There was no surplus about Mr. Brown.

He hunted, too. His shotgun was a Purdy. He let me see it in its oak and leather case, luminous as if a fire burned beneath the French walnut stock, the metal covered with delicate

English scrollwork. His deer rifle was almost too beautiful for my young eyes, and I have never seen another like it. It was made in Austria, between the wars, and had two barrels, over and under, like a shotgun, but with a high, carved comb to the stock to bring Mr. Brown's cool eye up to an iron sight. I held this masterpiece, a prince among our common Winchesters and Marlins.

"I have it because, in its own way, it's almost as beautiful as a deer," he said. "I'm sure the deer couldn't care less, but I do."

But precious as it was, I would have chosen my father's Winchester. With that familiar weapon in my hand, my vision of myself as a Yankee boy, thin-lipped and taciturn, was complete. Such foreign beauties as the over-and-under could not seduce me from the common dream.

One conforms, of course, without knowing it—and not only to the common dream, for I was skillfully eased into my after-school job at Trotevale's without once questioning the justice of this sentence. Collusion it was, I know now, between my parents and *their* dream of Education. Mr. Brown was Trotevale's shoe clerk, and that was how I got to know him a little better.

Every day after school, and on the long Saturdays, I found myself a clerk among the socks and shirts, with a button on the cash register sacred to my hesitant finger. Hair combed, white shirt and bow tie, I hid down the long aisles of glass-fronted, varnished counters, pretending to be a customer.

I couldn't find anything. I couldn't tie a knot on a parcel, I counted change too many times before reluctantly giving it up to a customer. "Where are the handkerchiefs?" I would desperately ask a passing clerk. "Where are the boys' blue denim pants sizes three or four, and what does that mean— age, or inches?" All day I trotted back and forth between customer and source of information, and by the end of the first long Saturday I was amazed and a little frightened by the number of things there was to know, just to be a clerk. Having exhausted everyone else's patience (how could they remember how many times I'd asked the same question?), I had taken to asking Mr. Brown everything. He never chided me for my profound lack of interest; he had an extremely dependable fund of gentle patience.

"Don't you have a family?" I asked him once. "Why do you live in our furnished room? Are you going to live here forever?"

"No, I don't have a family," he said, no obvious opinion of families in his voice; "no mother, no father, no wife, no children. And most likely I won't stay here or any place else forever. And that's not such an uncommon way to be." He smiled that private smile of experience. "I'm what you might call an old bastard. Nobody claims me but myself."

I know now that this is not so terribly uncommon. There are many nomadic old bastards come to Leah and pass through, not all of them bums or lumberjacks with a quick eye for a bottle. Many are short-order cooks, those skinny food haters: you can see their bones, their silver identification bracelets, tattoos and spatulas in any diner, their sunken faces framed by the exhaust fan. There are other kinds: awning menders, embalmers, one-shot salesmen fleeing some private suburban nightmare—and clerks, like Mr. Brown. They stay a year or two and head around the circuit once again: Rhode Island, Massachusetts, New Hampshire, Maine, Vermont. Old men, mostly, pretty set in their ways, they almost have to be single. The jobs pay little, but there's always a job somewhere.

Trotevale's store is no longer on Leah's square. A couple of years ago the Cascom Savings Bank, next door, took over both buildings, and now the two look like one. Built in 1854 of wood, modernized by a sheathing of red brick in 1907, they are now modernized again, rather gaudily, in three-colored cathedral stone which seems to be held together by chrome strips, like a modern automobile. You hardly notice the disappearance. Trotevale's sign was black, framed by gilt paint, and the raised gilt letters said TROTEVALE's. That's all. Two counters ran down the middle of the store, piled with sweaters, shirts, gloves and other kinds of "good" clothes. Work clothes were in the basement, piled on plain tables. On the left side of the main floor shoe boxes filled the wall from front to back, and Mr. Brown, if there were no customers, sat composedly in one of the four wooden armchairs. On the right, glass-fronted cases reached to the ceiling, and every ten feet or so a pair of long-handled tweezers, long enough to reach the highest five-dollar Dobbs, leaned against the cabinets. Ladies undisplayables were upstairs, along with the office and the tailor's room, on a wide balcony that went all the way around, close below the stamped-metal ceiling. The balustrade was carved orange cypress: balls, flutes, grapes, Corinthian capitals and Roman arches. The whole store was fine, consistent 1907, except for the surface of the main floor, which had been covered with plastic tile in wide green and white squares. Upon this miraculous surface the old mahogany counters, the cast-iron adjustable tie racks, the jigsawed buttresses and varnished legs all seemed to float, as in a painting by Dali, an inch or so above the floor. It was Trotevale's first concession to those two-page magazine ads (before and after), and of course it wasn't enough. All it did was knock the pins out from under 1907.

Each day after school I'd go home, change my clothes and go to Trotevale's for the two hours until closing time. On Saturday I came in at eight-thirty in the morning. Eleven and a half hours! And those long, dusty afternoons were rarely broken by anything amusing. I watched the second hand of the white-faced clock at the back of the store, and sometimes it stopped dead for what seemed like whole seconds. Long ones they were, too. Sometimes I looked at myself, back, front and sides, in the tricky fitting mirrors, not caring at all for my profile. Better the front view, and I could practice my frigid

Yankee stare—that bright aggressive look I found legitimate upon the faces of my friends—the one that declares equality and asks: *What kind of a damn fool are you?*

At other times, in that mirror, I could wish upon my face bones the crisp dignity of Mr. Brown's straight nose, the regal depth of those blue eyes. Old man that he was, I began to pay him the compliment of imitation. When he spoke—while showing me how to tie the string around a package without having to let go of one end to tie the knot, without asking the customer for the use of a finger—he emitted a low, rather kindly humming sound. "Mmmm," he would croon for "Yes," or for "Oh, is that so?" or for mere wordless sympathy. I believe he meant to let you know that he was listening, or that he understood exactly how you felt, and this nonword was the least interrupting of all assents. I don't know. Perhaps it led to a certain distance between himself and the person he communicated with, as meaningful words would not. But I'd hear it, deep in his chest somewhere, a kind of cellolike vibrato, as hard to locate as a partridge drumming in the deep woods.

I began doing this myself, and found that Mr. Brown's idiosyncrasies and his *presence*, in a way, were noted. "Listen," my father said at supper, "he's doing *that*, like Mr. Brown!" Strangely, I was pleased, rather than embarrassed. But of course I stopped doing it. I developed, instead, a slow smile—one that took several seconds to mature, like Mr. Brown's. My mother's comment was less pleasing: "If I didn't know how old you were, I'd say you were filling your pants."

Bessie Sleeper was the secretary and bookkeeper for Old Man Trotevale, who had shingles and rarely came to the store. Bessie weighed two-hundred pounds, but had tiny feet. In the back of the store an open-shaft service elevator ran from the basement to the office on the balcony, and this was known, not to Bessie, as Bessie's Hoist. It creaked as she stepped upon it and pulled the rope which started huge flywheels in the basement. *Clang* went the collapsible gate that somehow never caught your fingers in its disappearing parallelograms, and Bessie rose. She walked as if she carried a bucket of water in each hand, her face bitterly clenched with effort, her tiny blue eyes stabbing about for a place to sit her burden down. She was always very nice to me. She loved Mr. Brown.

Her feet were truly perfect, he said, and every week she bought a pair of shoes. I can see her, wedged into one of the old wooden armchairs, a spot of molten thrill somewhere deep, deep—certainly not showing—as Mr. Brown, cool in his white shirt and black armgarters, held her foot in his strong, dry hand. She wasn't the only woman in town who bought too many pairs of shoes.

If any one person, in the continuing absence of Old Man Trotevale, ran the store, it was Mr. Hummington, a busy little middle-aged man who wore rimless octagonal glasses the color of an old photograph. You could see his eyes way down in there in the mauve twilight, moving around. They didn't seem to have any whites. He had black hair that seemed to grow all on one side of his head, form a rigid slab across the top and end rootlessly above the opposite ear. I knew his secret: I saw him bend too far over one time, behind the overcoats, and as one expects something to follow when a cover flies open, I half-expected his brains to fall out. He was always busy arranging things, changing things—the plastic floor was his project—marking prices and code upon labels: an expert, a dynamo. It was he who totaled up the cash register and told jokes in a high and businesslike voice. I remember him best in a series of gestures: he breaks a roll of pennies over his finger (it didn't hurt), spills them into a little rubber capsule, slaps the capsule into its carriage and snaps the handle which shoots it on a wire up to Bessie's balcony cash register.

"Was a clerk. Young feller. No longer with us [snicker]. Put a mouse in the tube and sent it up to Bessie!" All this in a tone as smooth as steel, with a look half warning, half prediction. Should I have laughed? Perhaps I tried one of Mr. Brown's slow smiles.

There were other clerks: pale, retail creatures who fade quickly from memory. One was Randall Perkins, whose father owned the Leah Paper Mill. His father, having evidently assessed his son's talents, had arranged the job for him in the restful atmosphere of Trotevale's. A tall, vacant boy, I see him standing with a suit of long winter underwear in limp hands, the virile red wool, the functional flaps in interesting contrast to his ennui.

All this while there have been rumblings from above—a permanent, threatening overtone. In his little enclosure on the balcony my personal ogre was at work, his sewing machine ripping off machine-gun bursts. Oaths and maledictions! I dreaded Mr. Halperin, the tailor. He cursed in odd languages, he sat like a malignant toad and blamed me for the pants I brought him. His wet grey eyes glared across ridges of brown flesh. His head was large, bald, and thrust itself forward from shoulders hardly wider than his neck. His behind was as wide as a woman's, and hid his stool completely, as if the legs went up and stuck right into meat. He always wore a complete black suit, and on the top of his head a black skullcap which I thought to be a mask, like an eye patch, covering some horrible concavity.

"In Berlin I am a tailor! I do not make with such *dreck!*"

I was unused to such foreign behavior. My Yankee family, had it come to such screaming, would have found itself wading in fresh blood. Occasionally I came close to crying under Mr. Halperin's barrages, and I dreaded Mr. Hummington's purposeful approach, suit folded over his arm: "Take this up to the Jew."

"I can't stand it," I said to Mr. Brown. "He *yells* at me."

"Mr. Halperin is a very good tailor," Mr. Brown said.

"Why doesn't he tailor, then, and not yell at me?" To my shame, tears of injustice did come to my eyes.

"Now, now. He doesn't mean anything by it. Mr. Halperin's had a hard life and he's angry about it."

"I don't like him," I said. "I don't like him one little bit." With a bitter look toward the balcony, I retired to my hiding place behind the overcoat racks. Above, the machine rattled viciously.

I held it against Mr. Brown that he and the tailor were friendly. The tailor never screamed at Mr. Brown, nor was he sullen, as he was with Mr. Trotevale and Mr. Hummington. A strange pair they were on the cozy, elm-lined streets of Leah! One was far too handsome, the other far too ugly: both deformed, I'm sure, in Leah's eyes. They were watched and snickered after as they walked, one tall and too smoothly graceful; the other on thick legs, humping along to keep up.

One evening Mr. Brown came downstairs and stood in our livingroom archway, wearing a long, silk smoking jacket. My mother and father immediately stood up, then sat down, embarrassed by their instinctive gesture of respect.

"I came to ask," Mr. Brown said formally, "if it would be all right if Mr. Halperin visited me in my room. We'll play chess, which is a very quiet game, although by nature Mr. Halperin is not always quiet." He smiled.

"Oh, fine! Perfectly all right! Sure!" came from my mother and father at the same time. I'm sure they had hardly heard a word. An exquisite orange and gold dragon climbed about Mr. Brown's chest and breathed scarlet fire over his breast pocket. We were all stunned by this animal.

And so, a few days later, Mr. Brown introduced the old tailor to my mother and father. Mr. Halperin bowed, called my mother something German, and shook hands too much. After the introducing was done there was a short, deep silence while everyone's eyes shifted here and there, and then Mr. Brown took the tailor upstairs.

I didn't consider myself especially sneaky. But there were two of me, and the separation was sometimes hard to mark.

359

Blame could be shifted. And in that constant pursuit of personality I would have done away with one. The other I called Tabber, sort of north-of-Boston Simon Templar, a creature of the erotic or violent night, a cool customer. The window of Mr. Brown's room opened onto the front-porch roof, and so did the window of mine.

Of course I expected to see, in that familiar room, nothing more horrifying than two old men playing chess. But Tabber, a dark blanket wrapped about his shoulders, eased himself along the shingles to his observation post beneath the whicking leaves of the black maple. He was not afraid of the dark. I was, occasionally. He was entirely fascinated by The Abomination. I was afraid of it. In my half-innocent mind the canon of sin was infinitely long: Demonology, Sex, The Elders of Zion, Werewolves, Toads with Jewels in Their Heads, Warts at a Touch, Step on a Crack and Break Your Mother's Back! I didn't want to believe any of it. Tabber depended upon his Winchester, I upon a skepticism that was too much a protest against the ghoulish residue of childhood.

We crouched there in the cool September night, deliciously illegal, hidden from the neighbors by the tree and from Mr. Brown and Mr. Halperin by the photometric qualities of the window screen. My mother had lent Mr. Brown her card table, and there sat the two men. I looked directly over Mr. Brown's square shoulder at the tailor's thick scowl. Two empty beer bottles stood on the dresser, and beside Mr. Brown's walnut chessboard were the two glass steins he had bought for the occasion. Both men smoked pipes, the tailor's a hornlike meerschaum that rested against the knot of his tie, Mr. Brown's a thin briar. Streamers of smoke passed slowly through the window screen and past my face without changing shape, like ghosts passing through a wall.

I watched them for a long time as they played. They hardly spoke. When the tailor drank he didn't take his pipe out of his mouth, just shoved it around to the side with his stein!

"Well?" the tailor said.

Mr. Brown didn't answer for a second or two, then the white head began to nod. I could tell by his ears that he smiled. "Well done," he said; "very well done. I didn't know it had happened to me until just now."

"Four moves," the tailor said.

Mr. Brown kept on nodding. "You are very good, Mr. Halperin."

"From you? A compliment." Somehow the tailor managed to look pleased while still scowling. "You are not bad, Mr. Brown."

"I know that, but I'm nowhere near as good as you."

"It is good that you say it!" The tailor may have tried to smile beneath the rolls of his cheeks. "I knew you would be good, of course," he said.

"You did!"

"Of course I did!"

For some unaccountable reason the tailor was becoming angry. His grey eyes glittered, his baggy lids quivered. Tabber may have reached for his Winchester, but I was glad that the capable back of Mr. Brown screened me, even as little as it did, from the sight of the tailor's anger.

My admiration for Mr. Brown increased, too, because he remained perfectly calm. I could almost hear his basal hum—his sympathetic, yet impersonal purr.

"Tell me why, Mr. Halperin," he said soothingly.

The tailor got up, jarring the card table and teetering the chessmen, and stamped around the room for a while. He began to breathe short, explosive little gasps, and finally he turned toward Mr. Brown. With an ominously quick hand he pulled out his wallet and extracted a photograph in a plastic cover.

"Look at this! Look at it! And tell me if there is no resemblance!"

Mr. Brown took the photograph. Over his shoulder I saw the two men in the picture, one short and one tall. They wore bathing suits with funny tops, like summer underwear, and that was all I could see.

"It is my favorite picture. Why? Because next to me he is Adonis. Such a toad as me!" the tailor said proudly. "He was the same, like you. There are persons who are naturally beautiful, naturally graceful. It is my theory! They are good at everything."

Mr. Brown had been watching the tailor, not the picture, and he said, "Who was he, then?"

The tailor scowled worse than ever, ground his teeth and began to make a high, whining noise, as if he were in terrible pain. He put his hands over his ears and his head began to sway from side to side. "He was my brother. My brother Hy . . ." (My face ached from unconscious imitation, as if I too were bound to speak.) "My brother *Hyman!*" And tears poured, a solid faucet-stream of tears poured down his face. "I am sorry! So stupid! Forgive me!" he said in a voice that seemed to come bubbling up from under water.

Mr. Brown seemed completely unaffected. He gravely studied the photograph. The tailor wiped his face and blew his nose, emerging from this process unscathed, his face exactly as it had been before. Mr. Brown finally looked up.

"Yes, there is a resemblance," he said at last, and handed the picture back with a steady hand. I could see his other hand beneath the table, kneading his thigh.

Beneath my blanket, kneeling on the mossy shingles, I watched and recovered with the tailor. Tabber had returned to his simpler world of bang-you're-dead, and I was alone. I had never seen a man cry. I, myself, hadn't really *cried* for a long time—maybe a whole year. And why were the sloppy tears of this old man, whom I disliked, so catching? I was absolutely disgusted with myself, and with whatever undependable lever had pulled those tears out of me. I felt tricked, unfairly manipulated by the tailor. "God damn you," I whispered, "God damn you old bastard!" and wiped the traitorous tears into my blanket.

The tailor, completely recovered, began to set up the chess-board again, but Mr. Brown said that he was too tired. I retreated into the leaves until they left the room. When Mr. Brown came back, the tailor then walking lumpily beneath the street light on his way home, I came back to the window. Mr. Brown sat down in his easy chair, motionless for a moment, his face tight and unhappy. Then he raised his hands to the level of his eyes. They were shaking. I watched him for a while, but he just sat there, so I left him.

In the afternoons that followed Mr. Halperin's outbreak and on the long Saturdays, he became, as I watched, overly friendly toward Mr. Brown. The tall man was as precisely friendly as before, but the tailor would rush downstairs to talk excitedly, his hands dangerously wild among the racks and stacks of the main floor. He was making Mr. Brown a suit, and to the barely perceptible annoyance of Mr. Brown descended upon him even when he was waiting on a customer, looped a tape about his chest, the thick arms roughly pushing, the ugly face brushing Mr. Brown's ear. Then he whipped the tape off and brought it close to his eyes.

"Forty! Thirty-two!" He roared for everyone in the store to hear. "Magnificent! It is for such men suits should fit!" Humming, nodding, grunting, waving his yellow tape, he rushed back upstairs to his shop.

At times he came to argue, especially when Chief Atmon stopped by to talk to Mr. Brown about guns. The tailor did not like uniforms, and our Chief of Police did little to reassure him. To Chief Atmon the tailor was a living joke, and the sight of him was enough to bring on a ponderous merriment. "*Gay cock off in yawm,*" he would suggest to the infuriated tailor.

"If you are going to speak Yiddish, why don't you correct yourself?" the tailor said.

"I learned it in the Army," Chief Atmon explained.

Mr. Brown would not join the Cascom River Fish and

Game Club, but he did listen—he had little choice—to Atmon's hunting stories. Atmon was a big man, as big as anyone in Leah. His blue uniform fit tightly as the bark of a tree around his great legs and torso. He was an excellent pistol shot, and it was always surprising to see the loud man so steady, so suddenly cool and precise as he fired on the Cascom River range, then bursting again in the vacuum of a crushing bang, breathing the fumes of his smokeless powder, looking for the hole he always found in the black.

When he hunted he cursed the animal he pursued. "There goes the son of a bitch! Kill the bastard!" he would yell as a deer slipped away through the alders. And when he killed: "I got the son of a bitch right in the boiler room! Right in the goddam boiler room!"

He was a successful hunter, hunted legally, and got his deer through study and marksmanship. The boys of Leah admired him for this, and we grimaced painfully but sincerely as our clavicles unbent after one of his whacks on the back. The big man was fierce and loud, but friendly—there was no doubt about that. He even wanted Mr. Halperin to like him—you could see the little eyes up there in the open red face, searching nervously for signs of affection.

"A murderer," Mr. Halperin said, staring at Chief Atmon's departing back and at the huge Colt .44 that Atmon carried tight and black against his hip.

Mr. Brown considered this. "No. But maybe he could be."

"He hates the animals," Mr. Halperin said. "He kills out of hate. He carries proudly his pistol. He plays with it."

"Chief Atmon isn't a bad man, though," Mr. Brown said slowly. "Look how he loves his little beagle. . . ."

"Of course! He is a sentimental slob. The worst kind of murderer. I've seen such swine crying over their dogs while men died. . . . And what is this beagle? A murder dog, meant to break the backs of rabbits!"

"No. A fine little dog, doing what he is meant to do. But Chief Atmon, now," Mr. Brown said thoughtfully, "he loves

364

his little dog. You see, it doesn't run away from him. I suppose he believes the little dog loves him." He smiled. "Don't ever run away from him, Mr. Halperin."

"I have run away from worse than that punchinello," Mr. Halperin said.

"I neither like him nor dislike him," Mr. Brown said. "I don't hunt with him."

"Yes, you hunt, don't you," Mr. Halperin said disgustedly. "How can you? Do you gloat over the red blood you spill?"

"Do you think I do?"

"I cannot think of a reason for murder."

"If you think it is murder I can't begin to explain it to you," Mr. Brown said tolerantly.

"But why? But why?" The tailor waved his hands in Mr. Brown's face. "Look at it! Here is a beautiful deer, a fine animal; he eats only the little grasses, the little twigs from the trees. He hurts nobody. All he asks is to live, to grow tall and beautiful. You sneak to wound him, shoot big balls of lead through his living body. What did he do to you? He has pain! He falls!" The tailor's eyes were full of tears.

"Mr. Halperin," Mr. Brown said calmly (but from my inconspicuous distance I remembered his shaking hands). "A buck is not a man. He is better equipped than a man. If you want to make a man out of him, the man you make will be an unpleasant one. He is murderous in the rut. He lets his does go first across any dangerous ground. He is completely disloyal, completely selfish. I don't make a man out of him, and I don't judge him. He is beautiful and correct for what he is. We've driven off most of his natural enemies, like the wolf, because we thought they threatened us. And now he has two major enemies left, Mr. Halperin. Neither is man. One is starvation, and none of his fine talents give him a chance against that horror. Another is the breeding of the defective among him, which will make him small, ugly and stupid and even wipe him out. Hunting man is the only enemy left that he is equipped to overcome. And if the slow and the feeble among him are not killed, he will no longer be the most beautiful animal on earth."

Mr. Halperin looked away, his head bent, his hands held out, palms up. "I have heard such theories before, in Germany," he said.

"You're talking about people, Mr. Halperin. I'm talking about deer. . . ."

"So there's a difference?" the tailor said, and abruptly turned away.

I had never heard such beautiful theories, but in the town of Leah, where hunting is part of life, where school is for girls on the first of November and the paper mill is closed, we never thought too much about *killing* deer. You *got* a deer, and he was yours. From the wild flash and flag of him, one noise of his canny rush for escape, he changed. He became your own, to touch, to show, and finally to eat. I retreated to my coat-rack hideaway, gloating over Mr. Brown's victorious argument. I went to the fitting mirrors and practiced him, ignoring my pointy profile.

Mr. Halperin didn't speak about hunting again, but if anything his demonstrative affection for Mr. Brown increased. The swoops to measure him, the constant cornerings and contacts began to tell. Once I saw Mr. Brown avoid him—saw him turn and go back to the basement when he saw that Mr. Halperin was waiting for him by the shoe-fitting chairs. The tailor would come up often and put his hand on Mr. Brown's shoulder—a shoulder held rigid. Finally Mr. Brown turned to him and said, in a clear, cold voice, "Don't *lean* on me, Mr. Halperin."

The tailor jumped back, his hand still in the air at the height of Mr. Brown's shoulder. "What? What?" he asked.

Mr. Brown ignored him, and continued to wait on Bessie, who was stolidly buying her weekly pair of shoes—her weekly impersonal foot caress at the hands of Mr. Brown.

At the foot of the stairs the tailor turned around. His eyes were wet again, and he smiled a twisty little smile. "So!" he said to me. "So we know! When didn't it? Look! He waits on that fat pig who has the soul of a garbage can, the mouth like a hemorrhoid!" He shook his head. "Ah, he is so just like! So cold!"

When he had the time he still worked on Mr. Brown's suit, still made the necessary measurements—but formally now, with prior permission. Most of the time he sat in his little room, firing off bursts of stitches, waiting to cuss me out.

Until that morning in November, Leah Town Square was sere, hardened by a morning frost; the tall elms were creaky in the cold sunlight, and I was hardened and hopeless at the beginning of another endless Saturday. I crossed the green but dying grass, passed the empty benches that would soon be taken in. It was the first day of hunting season and I must wear a necktie and white shirt, hear the sporadic shots echoing down from the dark hills of Leah. The deer, jumped by hunters, would be moving nervously through the quiet spruce, leaping past the bright beeches into darkness. And I must wait on people who didn't care enough—who didn't care at all.

From a distance I had seen Bessie and Mr. Brown standing in front of Trotevale's, but the frosty wind made my eyes water, and I kept them down, not bothering to wonder why the two didn't go straight inside on a cold morning. As I came nearer I saw that Bessie was in a state of unrest. Something jiggled that mass, made her stamp her precious feet and open and shut her soundless mouth. Mr. Brown stood next to her, and they both peered in through the big window to the right of the front door. When I came up to them it was a terrible and delicious shock to me, too: the big window was only half there. Slabs and splinters of glass glittered upon the sidewalk, wide sheets of it and millions of jagged darts of it had crushed Mr. Hummington's window display of two-dollar ties and ten-dollar hats.

"Something moving *around* in there!" Bessie whined. Through the unnatural hole we heard bumpings from the rear, thumps and breaking glass.

The rest of the clerks and Mr. Halperin had come by the time Mr. Hummington arrived at a run, his key foremost. "Late! Late!" he explained, as if his lateness were something so odd it must be proclaimed. Then he saw the broken window, and with military precision he stabbed the Yale lock with his key and overran it, nearly shattering the glass of the door with his forehead. We cautiously followed him inside— all except Bessie, who remained outside uttering complaining little squeaks.

The glass case that had contained men's jewelry—tie pins and cuff links of coated brass, little arrows meant to look as if they pierced your necktie, springlike instruments to skewer collars down, buckles to personalize bellies and their heaps of interchangeable letters in plastic mother-of-pearl—this case was smashed and trampled, and the shoddy brightwork spewed down the aisle. Stray neckties were everywhere, brightly coiling and dangling like tropical snakes in a zoo. The coat racks at the rear were all tipped over, and piles of blue and brown material lay heaped in rows, a plowed field sown with buttons.

We advanced, Mr. Hummington in the lead, silent except for the crunch of glass beneath our feet. No sound came from the dark areas at the rear of the store, and we all had the feeling of being watched.

"Got to call Mr. Trotevale," Mr. Hummington whispered.

"We ought to get out of here," Randall Perkins suggested. Though far in the rear, he had either armed himself with or was merely carrying an empty tie rack. Bessie had moved through the door and scared us badly by screaming, "Are you all right?"

Mr. Hummington turned wrathfully, but before he could say anything the ominous presence we had all been conscious of, the author of this terrible derangement rose before us; gathered itself before Mr. Hummington: a great buck with bone-white antlers, thick neck and deep, wild eyes. Mr. Hummington must have been close enough to feel the sharp explosions of wind from the buck's black nostrils.

With his hands slack at his sides, his mouth open, Mr. Hummington stared. All his famous energy had left him, drawn out at a look as awed sighs were drawn from us. The buck's brawny neck trembled with inhuman energy, his black eyes struck away what little nerve we had. In the sudden presence of his fierce strength we were all at once aware of our weakness. The coward's swift insight froze our shy bodies. I, for one, knew in my belly the force of those bony antlers, the power of those sharp hoofs. And the awesome dignity of the huge animal was not dispelled at all by the cheap neckties that flapped from his antlers, gaudy but unfunny: they might have been our own dangling guts.

After the long moment of fear, the deer rose on its hind legs to turn in the narrow aisle. Mr. Hummington fell solidly to the floor and scuttled, with swimming motions, back toward us on the slippery plastic. His head thumped against my shin, and he looked up, without his glasses, astounded at my unmoving presence. His eyes were metallic little beads deep under his forehead. None of the rest of us had run because the deer had—one smooth leap had taken him directly into the banister of the basement stairs. He took the heavy wood downstairs with him as easily as if it had been a spider web across a trail. From the basement we heard a clatter and a thump, then nothing. We had been hearing, but not caring about, Bessie's screams for help. She stood blocking the front door, importuning the town of Leah and the police. Eventually both came.

With the deer more or less safely in the basement, Mr. Hummington took charge. Bessie was led to the elevator and installed in her office on the balcony, Mr. Halperin was sent to his shop, and the rest of us were directed to begin cleaning up. The shoe department hadn't been damaged, and we didn't miss Mr. Brown. While we were sweeping up the jewelry he had been in the basement.

"He's back in the corner by the work shirts," Mr. Brown said. "I'm afraid he'll hurt himself."

"Hurt himself. *Hurt* himself!" Mr. Hummington said.

"He may break a leg if we scare him too badly."

"He may break his goddam neck! He damn well *will* break his goddam neck! I'll do it myself! Look at this place! Look at the hoof marks in my new floor! Look at the glass!" Mr. Hummington yelled.

Mr. Brown looked gravely down at him, a certain amount of contempt detectable in his calmness. Mr. Hummington turned away.

"What's Mr. Trotevale going to say? We can't get any new glass until Monday and he has the shingles again. We'll have to borrow a mattress box from the furniture store and put it over the hole and it'll look just goddam awful!" Some of this was private moan.

People had begun to gather on the sidewalk, and they stood two deep, staring in, steaming the good window so that they had to keep wiping to see. They all seemed to be waving at us. The front door had been locked, but this didn't stop Chief Atmon, who jumped crushingly through the broken window, scattering hats and glass over the floor I'd just swept.

"Where is he?" Atmon yelled, his big hands held open and forward like a wrestler's.

"He's down in the basement and he's as big as a horse," Mr. Hummington said.

"Hah!"

"He's bigger'n you, Harold," Mr. Hummington said. "You're not going to wrestle him out of there."

Atmon looked questioningly at Mr. Brown.

"Three hundred pounds. Ten points," Mr. Brown said.

"Wow!" Atmon's hand dropped tentatively to the butt of his big revolver. On his face was an expression of fierce anticipation.

"Goddam, Harold! You shoot him and you'll ruin half the work clothes. Blood all over the place!" Mr. Hummington cried, "You can't do that! All those chinos! You can't do it!"

"I can drop him in his tracks. One shot. No splatter. Right in the goddam boiler room."

"No! No! You've got to lasso him. Tie him up!"

"I ain't no cowboy," Atmon said. "What about you, Brown?"

"You might tie him up, but by the time you do he'll have wrecked everything down there, and hurt himself," Mr. Brown said.

"Shoot him!" Atmon said. "Only thing *to* do."

"Why don't we just let him go?" Mr. Brown said.

An immediate, wondering silence. We all looked at Mr. Brown as if at a stranger, and from that point on he lost force; he seemed to fade before our eyes, and the more he said, the less his opinion counted. Aside from considerations of retribution for the damage done to the store, and especially the damage done to our equilibrium, the idea was impossible. The deer would have to come back upstairs and leave the store at street level. Then he would have to find his way back to the woods, a matter of a half mile in the best direction. Such gaunt majesty as his would be too alone, too terrible upon the quiet streets of Leah. He'd be sure to get into more trouble somewhere along the line.

"He got in here by himself," Mr. Brown said. "If he isn't driven crazy he might be able to find his way back where he belongs."

"He don't belong *here*," Mr. Hummington said.

"Belongs in my freezer-locker, that's where he belongs," Chief Atmon said.

"Listen," Mr. Brown said, "he isn't stupid. He's big and he's old, and you don't get that way by being stupid."

"So who says he was?" Atmon said.

"He just doesn't belong here. You can't shoot him here. It's

3 7 1

too strange for him. Out in the woods he'd make us all look like fools."

"So who says he wouldn't? Only he ain't out in the woods, by God!" Atmon said, grinning. "He ain't *out* in the woods."

"Why'd he have to come to town, anyway?" Mr. Hummington asked plaintively.

"I'll tell you why," Mr. Brown said. "Because so many brave hunters were out with jack lights last night. I never heard so many shots in the middle of a night. It's a wonder everybody in this town hasn't got his deer all tagged and hung up already. Somebody stampeded this buck. It's not his fault he ran into town."

"So whose fault is it? It ain't mine, but I got to get him out of here," Atmon said.

"How about the game warden?" Mr. Hummington asked hopefully.

"He's out with his thermometer testing to find them deer was jacked last night," Atmon said. "Who could find him?"

Chief Atmon had been edging impatiently toward the basement stairs; Mr. Hummington, who wanted a promise of no bloodshed, was backing away in front. Mr. Brown walked back to his shoe department, turned and stood motionless, watching.

And at that moment, without having to look behind him, Mr. Hummington *knew*. With barely a creak of stairs the buck appeared, whole and majestic. Quick as a squirrel on a tree, Mr. Hummington scrambled around in back of the Chief of Police. Tall and proud, the buck stood over us all, his head high, the magnificent rack of antlers gleaming. He looked from one side of the store to the other, seeming to calculate a mighty leap that would easily clear our heads. His muzzle was dark, yet a silvery fringe of white hairs showed his age. His neck was as thick as a man's waist—a trunk of rigid muscle to carry the great antlers. He held our eyes again—held them absolutely—an invincible magnetism in that wild beauty.

Atmon himself was struck silent for a long time. Then he

had his Colt in his hand, and we all heard three cold clicks as he pulled back the long hammer.

"*MURDERER!*"

For a moment I thought this tearing sound was the expected shot, and then in the shocked silence after this astounding word we saw the tailor on the balcony, his squat legs spread, his stubby hands gripping the rail. His face was black with blood, his eyes burned down upon the startled Chief of Police.

"*MURDERER! MURDERER!* Mr. Brown! Do you see what he is doing? *What are you doing about it?*"

Like the buck itself, Mr. Brown did not move during this outburst. He stood quietly by his wall of shoe boxes, his eyes curiously still, as if he were blind, or in hiding.

The tailor watched him for a second, and then began to stamp his feet, to shriek in German, the words torn by great sobs and sneezes as he hit his disintegrated face with his fists.

The deer took this moment to make his try for freedom, catching us all with our eyes upon the bawling tailor. Chief Atmon's reaction was swift, and had been predicted. He fired, stunning us all, breaking the buck's long back in mid-air as he made his first arcing leap toward the front of the store. He came down upon rigid forelegs, his hindquarters useless, and slid to the feet of Mr. Brown.

"Got him!" Chief Atmon yelled triumphantly. It had been a tremendous, a classic shot from a handgun, yet we were silent, still. The buck still lived. Propped upon his forelegs, his rack still held high, he looked straight at Chief Atmon, waiting. Mr. Brown watched too. "I got him! I got him! I got him!"

"Not quite in the boiler room," Mr. Brown said quietly.

"God damn you! I got him, so shut your lousy mouth!" Chief Atmon screamed. A long sigh from the rest of us, and Chief Atmon whirled around. He seemed to look right at me. *This is what I am good at,* his eyes implored. *And wasn't that a beautiful shot?*

The deer's calm eyes were black and deep. His nostrils

flared at each even breath. His rump lay broken behind him, the long, silky-haired legs splayed across the shiny plastic squares. Atmon came up, his revolver cocked.

"Get the hell out of the way. I'm going to finish him off." Mr. Brown moved away, carefully, quietly. The deer glanced at him once and then turned to watch Chief Atmon and the black gun that was pointed at his neck. He didn't try to move, but held his head as high as the good forelegs could hold it, waiting, breathing steadily, his ears erect and still as if he meant to hear, as well as see, the final explosion.

. . . Which came. Chief Atmon was right: there was very little blood from either wound. The big slug broke the buck's neck and killed him. With a little sigh he dropped his head. An antler rang against the wall and he was very little quieter than he had been alive. His eyes were open, still luminous— but not so deep: those dark wells had silted up.

In the terrible vacuum of Chief Atmon's victory we watched Mr. Brown pace down the squares toward the cloak rack. Each foot precise upon a square, he hit no cracks. His handsome face was as unchangeable as if it were made of wax —the stern, expressionless mourning of waxwork nobility upon a tumbrel. He would look at none of us: whether it was disdain, or the wily ploy of a camouflaged animal who knows his eyes will shine, I didn't know. At the cloak rack he unhurriedly put on his coat and hat, then as proudly, or as carefully casual in the face of danger, he turned around, walked out.

The tailor's long wail of mourning grew above us, its waves and intensifications strangely formal and rhythmical, as if it were a rite of sorrow perfected by legions of the bereaved; as if no one death but the deaths of generations must have called forth such terrible music from the ugly man's throat.

And Bessie, too, her heavy face no longer under the protection of her habit of determination, made the answer to that high litany. She stood at the rail and wept.

Later in the morning, when Mr. Hummington's energy had restored the order of our existence, I found myself with a pair of pants in my hand, making the usual climb to the tailor's shop.

The bursts of his sewing machine were as abrupt as always, and this time he heard my step upon the stairs and turned toward me, dropping a stiff lapel upon his table.

"He is gone?" he asked, grey eyes popping miserably from the brown lids. And without waiting for my reply he asked again, "He is gone?"

"He didn't even say good-by," I said, echoing in the words of Mr. Hummington a disapproval I didn't feel.

"Good-by?" the tailor yelled, bringing his fist down upon the rubber bulb of his chalk-marker. "Good-by?"

A cloud of blue dust rose above the scarred table. Blue chalk hung between us like a mist, and the tailor's eyes began to fill with rage and tears. I backed toward the stairs, feeling for the carved railing, a solid thing to follow back.

"Did you want him to say good-by? Are you still foolish? Do you cry because of this?" the tailor demanded, bringing his fist down on the table so hard the lapel jumped.

I *hadn't* cried. In spite of the tears I'd seen, I hadn't caught them, and I considered this a terrible insult—an unforgivable insult—considered this and suddenly burst out bawling, enraged by the underhanded trick.

"God damn you son of a bitch!" I yelled.

"Ah! That's better," the tailor said calmly, as if my tears had released and strengthened him. "Do you think I don't know you, my funny little one? It is *his* nature to try to escape. He does not know how *we* survive, eh? Never mind! *We* are the slobs who make the world." He motioned with his hand. "Now give me the pants you got in your hand and go back to work. Go on!"

I left him, seeing that shrewd and twisted smile as I fled to my hiding place behind the overcoats, to my private ceremony; the tearful funeral of that thin-lipped version of myself as Tabber, as a Yankee boy of ice and few swift words. I heard again the tailor's long wail as it had grown over the deer's death and Mr. Brown's escape, and now I found the doleful music apt, as if it were part of a ritual some memory of my flesh found anything but alien and strange.

. . . Not so long ago, though Trotevale's and the things of Trotevale's are scattered to the rag bags and the antique shops of Leah.

My son fixes me to here and now, the only place and time there is: he has cornered his apple by the stairs and found that he can break the skin by smashing it against the edge of the bottom step. He sits quietly, his little tongue busy on the split, his eyes darkly watchful. He reminds me of an animal—a young raccoon in some quiet corner of the deep woods —self-sufficient, aware. "You little bastard," I say admiringly, with perhaps too much affection in my voice, those easy tears precariously dammed behind my eyes. "You little bastard . . ." Gently, because he is soft and young. And with fear, for I do not really know what I should hope for him.

The Passion for Silver's Arm

HERBERT WILNER

THERE WAS A WHITE FEROCITY TO THE HEAT OF THE SCHOOL-
yard. It was impossible to ignore the August light on the concrete. Frank Weiss sat on the yellow wooden chair against
the brick wall of the school and tried to read. The little shade
there was no relief from the heat, but the light was darker.

When he looked up from his book to see if the blond fellow
was still squatting near the fence, he saw something he was to
remember for a long time.

It was a simple thing. It was Silver, the blond fellow with
the pink flesh, with the deep torso and the curled and golden
hair. He had been squatting on his haunches for over an hour
watching the few grimy boys at their little game. Now he
had suddenly risen to chase the ball that had gone astray.
Loping after it, the muscles of his back slid under the spotless
white T-shirt. As he moved in the heat, moved beside the
ten-feet-high mesh iron fence topped by four lines of barbed
wire, his brilliant hair darted like a flame.

The fellow picked up the ball and still trotting in that heat
carried it back to where the boy who pitched waited. The
boy was small and dirty. He waited indifferently for the ball
the blond fellow did not throw but insisted on carrying back,
holding it delicately before him, holding it like an egg, or a
chalice. Gently he placed the ball into the soiled hand of the
boy who was already turning to pitch it. For a moment the
blond fellow lingered there beside him. He did not smile, but

he lowered his head. In his hard white-into-pink face, toughened by the prominent bones, the flesh almost luminous in the sunlight, there was for a moment—Frank saw it—a look of care, of hurt, of knowing. Then he backed away a step or two. He turned and strolled to the fence and turned again and then resumed the casual squatting posture which bulged his thighs beneath the khakis. Patient, interested, he watched again as the boys began to play. That was all that Frank Weiss saw.

He tried to go back to his book, but he couldn't. It was more now than the heat and the light.

He had worried that the blond fellow might stir trouble in a schoolyard for children under sixteen. It was an angry neighborhood. But he didn't worry about that now. What kept him from his book was the deepening sense of what he had actually seen. It was the body's act of homage. It was the strong blond fellow's recognition of the small and dirty boy. It was something like that, anyway, he was later to tell his friend Webb when he tried to explain what he had really seen.

This picture would return to vex Frank Weiss. For a long time it would. It would even beyond the few days that followed, days on which Silver—as the dark Italian boys of the schoolyard called the alien man—returned regularly to squat, to watch, and then, at last, to talk. On the fourth day, for example, easier now and friendlier, Silver had said to Frank, closing the ancedote with it as he turned his lyric blond head wondrously toward Frank, said in the casual manner of his narratives: "Yes, he got down on his knees to beg. A thirteen-year-old kid, he got down in the dirt to beg! When I shot, from that close, you know, it about blew the sonofabitch's head all over the path."

II

Frank Weiss was not often the victim of demoralizing poetic insights. Young, having graduated the previous June from one of the city colleges where he had majored excellently in physics, he was already rigid, dogmatic, assertive. If he heard, not even in an argument but simply whispered somewhere, in a subway, on the street, the words Communist, money, Mississippi, his mind clicked with the whole machinery of a fixed view. You could as well have said to him gravity, the refraction of light. Only twenty-two, he was already committed to a set of deliberate renunciations. For almost a year he had been going with a girl from the college. She was intelligent, but indifferent. But in her small and deceptively frail body she concealed enormous physical energy. They had gotten quite involved. Suddenly Frank decided he had carefully to weigh their relationship. He avoided her for two weeks. Then he met with her in the college cafeteria.

"We can't," he said to her, imagining honesty was always kindness. "Webb, for example. That's a part of it too. It embarrasses you that he's a Negro, doesn't it? That we go out together?"

It was hardly fair to her. She had, after all, in her energy, her thoughtlessness, taught him all that he was perhaps ever to know about making love. But he had deliberated, and he had decided.

It was so with his family too. In his senior year he had taken an afternoon job to support himself and had left home for a small room near the college. There was nothing complicated about his motives. He was suddenly in his twenties and he wanted to be away. The clutching family routine was uncongenial to his work. There was no rancor he could admit in what he wanted to do, and he attended regularly the ritual of their Friday night suppers. To his parents the abrupt departure of their younger son was the culminating bewilderment of their lives. Immigrants from Germany, poor, overworked, bitter, Frank had done to them what they had to fear from the moment he had entered college. It pained him that his parents did not understand, as it pained him afterwards about the girl. It was trying on Friday nights when his father was so transparently attentive of his older son Joseph. He had not gone to college. He was a postal clerk and had often been accused by the father for his unambitious ways. Nevertheless, Frank fought the occasional temptation to return home. He examined it and knew that this sort of grief was part of parentage.

So the kind of thing that happened to Frank Weiss during the moment he had watched Silver retrieve the ball was actually a lapse. Now, no matter how he pondered the blond fellow's monstrous tales, all of Frank's proper responses were thwarted. He had to blame it on that foolish image of the first day.

It was troublesome. Occasionally in the last two evenings as he tried to read he might feel Silver's presence in the room, as though a shade of the blond fellow's roseate flesh had passed through the closed door. Frank would have to visualize again the golden hair, the steel-chip eyes that the shy smile could soften to a gentle blue, the high armored ridges of his cheeks, the sharp nose perfectly centered between eyes and cheeks and above the line of the upper lip, the deep scoop of the lower mouth, the square jut of the jaw. He might even begin to hear Silver speak, hear the echo of the afternoon's stories. The voice had all the infectious quality for a New Yorker of Southern speech: drawling, casual, intrenched. Frank would hear, as though he had never heard it spoken before, that single word Silver uttered with all his native casualness, tossed off, if Frank could admit it, charmingly, that one word of almost all the stories, "Nigger. Nigger."

III

"So he went mad, this here nigger. He's runnin' all aroun' the deck and runnin' over to the railin' in the middle of the night way out where we was in the middle of the ocean, the middle of nowhere. It was cold too. And there's this nigger, funny as all hell the way they are, tearin' all aroun' and then gettin' over to the rail and yellin' 'I gotta get me home! Ruby's waitin' up all night for me!' So I couldn't help this fit of laughin' at him and that's where he really went right out of his mind. That's when this happened to my arm, you know, when this crazy nigger came runnin' over like that he—"

"Your arm?"

"This left one here. Ain't no muscle to the top of it. When I hit him like that it went all red of a sudden and the muscle—"

"Hit him?"

"The nigger. He come runnin' over to me and made this grab at my throat screamin' somethin' about I was takin' his Ruby away from him and that's why I was laughin' at him for it. Hell, I couldn't help from laughin', him runnin' around like that ravin' he was gonna swim to Newark right out there in the middle of the ocean on a night so cold it would freeze a nigger's heart. So that's when I hit him, when his hand touched my throat. I caught him here under the jaw and he went about two feet up in the air and his eyeballs sort of popped like a couple of eggs before he come down on the other side of that railin'. That was the last we ever saw of him."

"You left him there?"

"Left him where? He went in the ocean. He wasn't doin' any swimmin' the way I hit him. I caught him right here, you know. What could I do? But that's when it happened to my arm. I couldn't move the arm I hit him with. It just—"

They were, as they had been for the past four afternoons, against the iron fence of the schoolyard. Frank Weiss sat on the yellow chair and Silver squatted. The sun shimmered on the asphalt and it stunned the air. It was even difficult in that light to look across the yard to where the four boys played one o'cat. They played grudgingly, trying to bear the heat, but the ball was coming apart and with only two fielders the batter stayed up too long and the others cursed and scratched their bare, darkened backs. But Silver was immaculate. His white T-shirt was spotless, his khakis sharply creased. There was no perspiration on his face. The curled blond hair was impeccably in place. Beside him Frank, so conscious of the heat, felt dirty and unresourceful. He watched the middle finger of Silver's pale hand as it traced a pattern on the concrete between his feet. His left arm, of which he still talked, he rested on his left thigh. Occasionally he brought the right hand up from the concrete and touched his left elbow in a gentle caress.

They had discharged him, he was saying, after that happened to his arm. He was in a hospital for two weeks, and then they let him go. His voice cracked a little when he spoke of how the maimed arm had destroyed his hope of becoming a fighter. He spoke of the encouragement he had gotten during his service bouts, and of all the delight: "To get in a ring with one of 'em with him sweatin' and smellin' all over you and just put your head down and keep poundin' away at the nigger, poundin' away." Again Frank wanted to turn on Silver, but he did not. He scarcely glanced at him during the telling of tales, though he felt the need to confront him, to declare himself finally.

"Look, you're lying! Even if you lived in Kentucky, in Marlan County even, still you couldn't live this way. You're making it up! I saw you give that boy the ball, what you looked like then. You know anybody will listen to this kind of story, that's why you're telling them."

The stories were all the same to Frank. They were all tinged with a cunning need to lie. Silver had calculated the obvious method by which a Southerner could be anything at all here in Brooklyn. He must have already found at least a hundred Frank Weiss's to tell the stories to, to alarm them with on Brooklyn streets, in Brooklyn bars, in Brooklyn schoolyards. But why he himself should be so victimized by Silver, by a Southerner, that puzzled Frank Weiss. It would puzzle him even after that moment in which he was to bring Webb into Silver's life. He must have already on that afternoon when Silver first spoke of his hurt arm been thinking of Webb. He must have been thinking of him as this story of the arm merged with all the others he had already listened to.

Even the first one had been corrupted by that taint of cunning. After a date, homesick, lonely in the North, Silver had gone into the tavern near the Navy Yard for a drink. Badgered by the sailors, the fight broke out quickly. Hollywood could not have done it better, the story of that fight. Silver had told of flying bottles, of shattered glass, splintered chairs, and the one sailor he had flung over his head, over the bar into the mirror. Frank had to think of how a man would scream when he saw the dagger of glass waiting to puncture his cheek as he dived toward it. And Silver, the one soldier, the one blond perhaps in this Brooklyn tavern, with his back to the bar and standing up for all of them, waiting to be killed, but savage, swinging, feeling damned mean and good, as he said. Then the other soldier was suddenly beside him, swinging also, but hauling Silver at the same time toward the door. The sirens somewhere in the street grew louder, nearer. Around the corner, under the light of a lamppost on a black street, Silver turned to grasp the hand of the soldier who had befriended him. In the dim light he saw the ripe mulatto flesh.

"I hit the sonofabitch! I had to. Up here, you know, ain't a thing no more you can be sure of."

On the second day after the first visit to the schoolyard, Silver had told him of the Negro who had stopped him on the street to ask the time. Without looking at the man, Silver had raised the watch to his eyes. In the same motion, as though it had been some feint of boxing, lashing out from the level of his eye he dropped the astonished man on the seat of his pants to the sidewalk. The few people who had been near simply gaped.

"They don't even sound like niggers, the niggers up here. You can't tell till you look."

"But the police, don't they—"

Silver smiled and shrugged. He peeled away the neck of the T-shirt and revealed the purple welt on his shoulder.

"Yes, I do. I get into a mess of trouble up here."

He began on the neighborhood police. They would pick him up after one of his sieges just as regularly and nonchalantly now as they might write out the ticket for the car beside the hydrant. They would take him down to the station, poke him with the clubs, shout at him the same phrases. That too, by now, was already regular and nonchalant. "You lay off those damned niggers! Where do you think you are? You're gonna get yourself killed up here. Someone's gonna kill you!"

But on the third day Silver told another kind of story. This was the family affair, the courtly heritage. Unfolded with the same splendid naïveté, with the same myth-making necessity, it would be the story longest to intimidate Frank. The more he turned the story in his mind, the more he adorned it with an imagination of his own that was itself ingenuously cunning.

It was back home in Harlan County. Frank had formed already, from Silver's other stories, an image of the place. This was no blue grass Kentucky. There was no grass at all. There were the hills and mountains and woods and black craters in the very middle of the lands where the coal pits were, and over everything the swirling drifts of dust, from the pits, from the land, somehow from the sky. The men rushed home in the evenings. Weary from the pits, they rushed anyway to plunge into the water of some huge bucket and wash from their skin, from their hair, the black chalk of the coal. Then they were very blond and very pink. At night they must have paraded what they called streets, searching for the black men. And the women stayed home and waited and somehow must have understood.

The story began with Silver's father. He had argued on and off for a year with a fellow miner about money. The quarrel was settled one afternoon by the persuasion of friends. Reluctantly the two men went off to the tavern for a drink. Silver's father was the first up the steps. When his hand touched the door, the other shot him. He shot him twice through the neck and once in the buttock. It was then that Silver's mother took him to the woods. She found him the bush to hide behind beside the path the man would have to use on his way to the pits. She left him there with his father's shotgun and the sack of food for the day. She told the thirteen-year-old blond boy, who must have already been the size of a strong man but whose eyes could only have been gentle then, "You wait now. He'll come." She brought him another sack of food on the following morning, and on the succeeding mornings. When the end of August passed into September, she brought him, along with the soiled brown sack, his jacket, his father's muffler and hat, and a blanket. "You wait now. He'll come," she said on every day of those three weeks. And for all that while the boy stayed bound to that bush, except for the short walks he took at night behind the bushes alongside the path and with the shotgun raised. And that was worse than the darkness, the cold, the hunger, the fear. Chained to that one place his mind spun with what he had never been old enough before even to dream. He came to hate the man for whom he waited with particular feeling. It had little to do with his father.

It was a cold morning when the man did finally come. He was obviously drunk. Out on the path, before the man, his shotgun raised, the knees of the boy trembled, but not with fear. The man's arms jerked from his sides, and the lunchbox he carried clattered to the path in the quiet, cold morning. In his drunken memory as he looked at the gun, the face of the boy must have begun to make a sort of awful sense. The boy, expressionless, watched him. When the man began to back away, the boy raised the gun. The man stopped. The man had a heavy stubble of beard that had begun to stain with the tobacco that leaked from his mouth. The man fell to the path and cried.

385

"Yes, he got down on his knees to beg. A thirteen-year-old kid, he got down in the dirt to beg! When I shot, from that close, you know, it about blew the sonofabitch's head all over the path."

That had happened eight years ago. It was a tale for which Frank Weiss never had the experience and ordinarily lacked the attitude of belief. Yet he lingered on its details now whenever he blinked in fascination at that eight years' history of casual violence that was Silver's life. And all of it was muddled by that first vision of a strong and gentle blond man and a dirty little boy. And now Silver lived here in this dark Italian neighborhood of Brooklyn. Perhaps that was the hardest thing for Frank to accept, this end for Silver's life.

Silver worked nights as a mechanic. The pay was better at night, but more important he would not have to, then, in the subways, stand belly to belly with any nigger who had a token to drop in the turnstiles. He worked here now and he lived here now because he was married. He met the girl at an army dance at Fort Hamilton. Her name was Therese. She had been dancing with him and she rescued him from a fight. In her brother's car in which she had come, she slipped him past the guards and took him home to her house. She led him past the old deaf father who sat on a rocking chair with his face a foot from the television screen, and led him upstairs to her room. He was drunk then and she had a difficult time trying to quiet him. He left in the early morning before the brother came home. Overseas he kept a vivid memory of her. He remembered the coal-black hair, the ivory-into-olive flesh. He thought of her often in the hospital. When he was discharged, he found out her house after a full week's search on foot. He accomplished it as a woodsman might. Recalling the general Brooklyn neighborhood, and recalling too the year and make of the brother's car, he narrowed day by day the circumference of his five-in-the-morning walks when he was sure the car would be before the house. After the week, he found the car and the house. He waited until the brother left.

She met him at the door. She must have dreamed often of that blond man, but she would never have expected his return. They were married six days later. Silver moved into the room with her.

Two days ago Frank had seen her. She had come to the schoolyard fence to summon Silver home. Her hair was black and long. Her nose was bent. Her mouth was full and made carmine by the depth of lipstick against the olive shading of the face. Her teeth were very white and perfect. Her eyes were almost black. She wore the black dress of Italians, even young ones, who mourned. She was big, but compact. She seemed capable of an agile sort of ferocity. When she walked away with Silver, she chained his waist with her encircling arm. Against his white T-shirt and below the flaming gold of his head, the arm looked black. She seemed to need, as they walked that way on the Brooklyn street, to claim for anyone who cared to see, how entirely she possessed him, that fair, waxen blond. Frank was certain Silver hated her.

Later Frank was to notice her when she walked the street in the morning. Silver would be home asleep. Often she would be dressed in only shorts and a halter. Her dark flesh glanced with every step. She held her abdomen taut so that her great breasts would raise and thrust. But still there was about her a sense of Silver's presence. It surrounded her. She was showing the neighborhood that stood in awe of Silver how she had done it. It is this black hair and all this dark flesh and this savage walk that brings the blond man here to live and keeps him sleeping now in my room and waiting for me to come back. For the neighborhood must have pondered them. Truly, they feared Silver. It was not only his size, nor that and his quick anger. It must have been, Frank imagined, also the pinkness, the blondness, the ancient fierceness of it.

So the Brooklyn schoolyard was a strange place in which to find him. It was a strange place in which to listen to the drawling, alien, and finally somnolent voice of a blond man from the Kentucky hills who could squat all afternoon, immaculate under the city sun. And Frank Weiss listened. The four dark, half-naked boys suffered their intolerable game with the tearing ball. And Silver casually, contemplatively, pursued his atrocities.

He was still speaking of the veterans' hospital, what they had done to him there, what he had done to them. And still, ruefully, he caressed occasionally with the fingers of his right hand, the elbow of his lame arm. It wasn't even a shock to Frank, what Silver had come to say now. All these past days Frank must have been waiting for this too.

"Here's this Jew doctor then's askin' me all this kinda stuff. I heard about it a little from the other guys, but here this Jew was at the side of my bed askin' me all these things like we'd just done a drunk together. I racked him clear to the wall. I just raised out of that bed and hung it on him with the good arm. And let me tell you that Jew made himself a wide circle anytime he had call to come past my bed again. Even the guy in the next bed, he ends up a Jew too. But a nice sort of little guy, this one. But I guess there ain't much Jew comin' out of a feller with a hole in his belly you could drop a grapefruit in."

He paused now to look at the boy who came toward them, shouting all the while he walked, "Hey, Mr. Frank! Mr. Frank!" He held the beaten ball with the soft yellow kapok oozing out of it. He held it away from his body as a boy would naturally hold some little thing that was dead or dying.

"But the arm's comin' aroun' now a little. I do exercises for it. Some of the strength's comin' back. It don't look none too pretty, though."

He raised the arm toward the sky, turning it, staring at it. The muscles of the forearm slipped under the blond hairs, under the pink skin. The upper arm, what could be seen under the sleeve of the T-shirt, was somewhat less thick than the forearm.

"Too bad about the fightin'," he concluded mournfully.

"I could've made me some dough and then she'd come back home to live with me all right."

The boy dropped the ball at Frank's feet. The others had already left the schoolyard. "It's too hot," the boy complained. He glanced at Silver.

"Hi."

Silver nodded to the boy. He got up without a groan from his squatting. He nodded to Frank, and then, before he turned, suddenly, gently, he smiled. It seemed to Frank more than a smile of parting. It wanted to ask for something, to need something to ask for. Then he strode out of the schoolyard. Along the iron fence on the street side, he moved quickly toward home, toward Therese. The sun found out his golden hair and flamed it like a torch.

And then Frank Weiss, who had lived so long so much without impulse, submitted to an instinctive need. He did not know that then. He thought he was going to ponder it over the weekend, and he did. But the decision that could not be made out of the thinking had been formed before the thought. Perhaps it had formed on that first day when Silver retrieved the ball. Something gentle and equally irrelevant had to be done for Silver. The story of the doctor in the hospital only tested the motive of that need. So Frank Weiss would send Silver to the doctor he knew of. He would restore the blond man's lame arm.

But of this Frank Weiss was not that innocent. He must have known there was no doctor who could do anything for the arm. It was not the arm at all.

IV

"A maniac!" his father said.

"A shame!" his mother said.

"Down at the post office the niggers on the trucks would fix him fast," his brother said.

It was the Friday night supper. The flames of the four candles flickered above the table and the tallow sputtered and dripped, congealing on the brass candlesticks, on the flowered tablecloth. Early in the meal, Frank had broken the reticence he maintained with the family. He had begun to talk with them of Silver. He had not wanted to tell any of the stories, but no sooner had he described the blond fellow than he heard himself going the round of tales. He couldn't stop. "So he killed him . . . He was going to tell him the time and then he hit him . . . The fellow went over the railing of the ship . . . He was only thirteen and . . ." There was a charm in the violence itself which he couldn't escape. Twice, when he saw their faces as they listened, he prepared to tell of Silver chasing the ball for the boy, handing it to him, lowering his head, bowing almost. But he could not. He launched immediately into another of the horrors and felt the scratching on the cord of his back. He left after the dessert. He had expected them to react in the way they did. It was his own resentment of their words that perplexed him.

Webb phoned later that evening. The landlady called Frank to the phone, then she sat down in the chair beside it and peered over her glasses and clacked with her needles at the knitting in her lap. But for the landlady, he might have spoken then to Webb of Silver. They arranged to go to the beach the next day. But it rained. The heat at last broke and it rained on Sunday too. Frank went alone to the movies on Saturday night. Otherwise he remained in his room and read. Occasionally he snatched at the University catalogue and perused the description of courses: critical potentials, molecular beams, methods of particle detection and acceleration, nuclear reactors. The names satisfied him. He glanced at the photos of University dormitories. He had to be pleased too that he and Webb would share a room, the celebrated Calvin Henry Webb. Occasionally interrupting his visions Frank would see Silver with the pink and blond arm raised to the sky, hear him drawl again, "It don't look none too pretty, though."

On Monday afternoon the morning rain ceased and the

sun began to penetrate again. Silver came to the schoolyard. He walked slowly toward where Frank sat against the school wall, the book on his lap. Already on Silver's face there was the shy, abashed smile, the imperceptible lowering of his head. The last time Frank had thought of Silver—which was only moments ago—he had reasoned out finally what he would do.

"You and I have nothing to talk about anymore," he would say. "I have to read now."

But when Silver without a word squatted beside him, preparing, Frank knew, to unlock again the hoard of stories, Frank closed the book and slipped his fingers out of the place. He felt the little shock when he began to speak.

"Listen, Silver, I know a doctor. I mean about the arm. There was a friend of mine could hardly walk once. They said he'd always limp. This doctor did the operation. My friend played football again next year. Maybe he could help you with the arm."

"My arm?"

"Yes."

"He could fix my arm?"

"Maybe he could. You can see him anyway."

"He's your friend?"

"No. I said a friend of mine—I mean he fixed the knee of a friend of mine. His office is right here in Brooklyn."

"How's he gonna fix my arm? They told me I—"

"I don't know about how. Don't you want—"

"Yes. Sure I do. God!"

"Then come in the office with me. We'll look him up in the phone book."

"Now? In the school?"

"Yes. What's the matter with you?"

"I ain't dressed."

"What difference does that make? I'm not dressed either."

"Your shirt's got a collar."

"I don't have a tie."

"It's got a collar."

Silver fingered the neck of his T-shirt. Frank rose from the chair. Silver got up from his haunches. Squatting against the sunlight, Frank looked up for a moment at the blond fellow. Silver was trying not to, but a smile was breaking the hardness of his face. There was the joy in it now a little boy would try to control but could not when the candy he had long cried for was finally handed to him. Frank turned quickly away and brushed past him.

They walked together into the deepening shade of the schoolyard well enclosed by the two dark wings of the old building. Before the iron door at the head of the few steps, Silver hesitated again. Frank looked irritably at him, and Silver moved. Through the dark, school-smelling corridor, Silver walked with his head slightly lowered, his eyes staring. The doors, opened like flaps down the shadowed corridor, revealed the empty rooms, the rows of empty seats and desks. When they stood before the office door, Silver's eyes fastened on the flag which hung limply from the pole that was locked in its socket on the floor beside the door. He ran his tongue over his lower lip. He walked behind Frank into the cluttered room of worn desks and faded filing cabinets. Miss Murphy, who every day at three played "London Bridges" on the piano for the smaller children, was at one of the desks. She had just finished the lunch she always brought in a plastic bag tied at the neck with a red string. She was large and had a puffed, slow face. But she almost jumped from the chair. She looked past Frank to Silver. Her eyes blinked and her head moved quickly.

"Miss Murphy, this is—"

"Yes," she breathed. "Yes, how do you do?"

"Ma'm."

Miss Murphy said she would go for her stroll now. She heaved toward the door in her ponderous stride and Silver, near the door, flattened himself against one of the filing cabinets.

Frank, already at the telephone book, felt his pulse deepen.

He had begun to rehearse what he knew he would soon say to Silver. He could no longer delay it.

"Here's the name. McAdoo. Francis A. McAdoo. I suppose the A's for Aloysius." His voice trailed off with the sound of the foolish name.

He scribbled the information on a pad. He tore off the sheet and held it toward Silver. Light from the windows trapped Silver's hair as he moved away from the filing cabinets and toward the small white leaf of paper. He had begun to grin again. He took the paper and stared at it, his eyes blinking, as if the writing itself were the miracle.

"If you just call him—"

"If he can fix my arm—I mean, if I can fight again—"

He stopped. They didn't look at each other as Silver began neatly to fold, and fold, the paper. The sun pierced the windows of the office. It fell on the two of them there in the light middle of the darker room. Frank turned his face away from the brightness.

"Silver," he said quickly, impulsively, though he had rehearsed it. "Silver, I'm a Jew."

Silver stepped out of the light, moved back against the filing cabinets. When the handles touched his back, he jumped away. His hands fumbled at the paper, unfolding it now. His eyes searched for the door, for the windows, but they did not look at Frank. Frank could scarcely hear him when he began to speak.

"But I thought—I mean—"

"I know. The kids call me Mr. Frank. My name's Frank Weiss. I look Italian."

The words echoed in his ears with their stupidity, their blunder. He could have been saying Aloysius again. He did not look toward Silver, though he heard the muttering from which all the drawl had seemed to disappear.

"They put me in the coal pits when I was ten. He had that hole in him and he never bitched. Maybe you want to come home and meet Therese?"

393

Frank could hear him leave the office, hear his feet down the corridor. He had deluded himself in the fear that Silver would hit him. It was not to end that easily. Frank Weiss would have to ponder for a while the awful advantage from which he had declared his famous words—that slip of paper with the doctor's name, his gesture for the arm.

V

"That's what he does now," Frank said on a final note, trying to get Webb to raise his head. "He's been my protector for three days. Today he nearly scared the life out of one of the kids who answered me back. He grabbed the boy by the collar and— Well, aren't you going to say anything? How much more do I have to tell you!"

"Say what?" Webb mumbled without looking up.

"Say anything. I've been talking to you for over an hour about him."

"He's talked to you for over a week. What have you said to him? What can you say to anyone who talks like that?"

"You're talking to me, not him."

"It's hot in here. You want a beer?"

At last Webb moved. He got up from the bed on which he had all the while been lying crosswise, his head against the wall, the tremendous flats of his feet over the edge. He filled the frame of the doorway as he left the room. Frank turned his face to the open window he sat beside on a wooden chair and looked down through the hot evening darkness at the darker Harlem street.

On every wall of every room in the Webbs' four-room apartment there was at least one photograph of Calvin Henry Webb. His father had put them there. The larger ones were framed, the others simply pasted to the walls like some kind of wallpaper meant to last the life of the walls themselves. In half the pictures he wore the white football uniform of the city college. In some of the others he was behind a table of the college library, the books scattered before him. They had been taken from the various city newspapers in which they had appeared, and from the two national magazines that had taken up the story. For that was the public image of the Negro youth who had overcome, who had demonstrated, who had proved again, and so on. He was the Negro football player who had been offered professional contracts, which offers he had refused, and the Negro student who had graduated from a city college with a straight "A" average, who had majored in physics, who had been awarded and accepted a scholarship for graduate work.

But to Frank Weiss, Webb had been, for the four years he knew him, a friend of sorts, and a mystery always. It was like the pictures they had taken of him. Because the photographers could not persuade him to smile—"What for?" Frank had heard him say in his laconic arrogance—and because the skin was as definitely black as it was, beneath the white helmet there would appear nothing but the polished blur of the features of the huge black head. And so with Webb himself. It was the perfection of his gifts that finally overcame anyone who got near him, and Frank had gotten, he imagined, as near as anyone could. Webb had no attitude toward the perfection, no responsibilities for it. You had at last to wonder what kind of perfections they were, as you wondered from the photographs, even from looking at him, what the face was really like.

He played football, for example, with ferocity that concealed his actual cunning. Webb was massive. He would never get on a scale, so they could only guess at his weight. The programs listed it at 210, but it may have been more. His legs were thick and his chest rolled like an old iron stove. The shoulders sloped deeply and from them the ape-like arms swung to his knees. He could move like a cat. On the field, when the ball was in play, he was terrifying to watch. But when he took his position on the line, while he waited through the other team's huddle, while his teammates went through all the rituals of the varied encouragements, the shouts, the ass-slapping, the scraping of the turf with their cleats, Webb simply rested on one knee and waited, conservative, detached. He could have been merely watching the game. He stayed that way until he could see the different colored helmets lowering opposite him. Then slowly his knee came off the ground, his hand went forward and down to the grass, his legs slid back, the line of his back stiffened, and the machinery of his terrible strength coiled, and coiled, and then unwound.

"Getting hit by Cal," one of his teammates told Frank, "it's not like getting hit by a truck must be. It's like something clean, all at once. Like a whack somewhere from a pipe. A heavy pipe."

"But I don't think you even enjoy playing," Frank had said to him once. "I've spent a whole game in those stands watching only you. You almost looked bored."

Webb shrugged. "It's a silly game in some ways."

"Why do you play?"

"I'm too good at it not to. Some of the game's good enough."

His nonchalance, his sullen unreachable indifference, that was the mystery of Calvin Henry Webb. Sitting together in the college cafeteria, someone would approach with the inevitable petition. Frank would read carefully the declaration at the head of the page. Then he might sign; or he might say, "I would if it weren't for the last sentence"; or, "No. I don't feel that way at all." But Webb, whose signature was a prize, would turn his head away. When the paper was shoved under his face he would turn again his great, gleaming head. Slowly his tiny ebony eyes would move up from the hand of the boy or the girl, move up to the arm, to the shoulder, to the face. Then he would mumble in that bass voice of frightening boredom, "Go away." And they did. They would snatch up their paper and run. Or when Frank and he were double-dating, Frank with the girl he had finally to break with and

396

Webb with any one of the attractive white girls who clung to him, who wanted, Frank knew, only to touch his dark, unfeatured, unresponsive face, then too Frank would be unsettled by Webb's indifference, his incapacity to care, to realize everyone stared. At times like these the words would come that stopped in Frank's throat: How can you ignore all that? Perfect or not, you are black. You are, you know!

And so Frank Weiss had come now and finally to the home of Calvin Henry Webb in Harlem to tell him of the very blond Silver. He did that because he had to see Webb's response, but he knew as he made the subway trip that Webb would only shrug. But he came also because he had in the last three days carefully thought out an arrangement by which Webb and Silver could be brought together. It had become apparent to him this should happen, though he did not know yet for whose benefit it was to be done. There was, after all, nothing Frank Weiss could do for Webb. There was nothing Webb needed done for him. But in Webb's room in the middle of Harlem, staring out the window down to the dark street, Frank knew he would arrange nothing. He would not admit it was treachery, but there was anyway something wrong. It was, at least, unsafe.

But above all Frank Weiss had come here tonight to Webb to talk of Silver because he was baffled. For the last three days he had gone over in his mind what he had wanted to do for Silver. He had given him the doctor's address. It disturbed him now, and sometimes in the image of Webb. He had betrayed his own reason, and he had betrayed Webb. So what he really must have wanted from Webb, perhaps simply from being in his home, was to learn some safe way of betraying Silver.

"Well, what do you think at least of that dark girl he had to marry?" Frank said to him when Webb towered beside him, the black hand hiding the beer it held out. "He's trapped up here by the same—I mean—"

Webb was already stretched again crosswise on the bed.

Above his head was the large framed photograph of himself: white helmet, white jersey, white pants, the black gleaming indiscernible face.

"Don't you think," Frank began again.

"You mean," Webb said, lowering the can of beer, the teeth flashing for a second in what was almost a smile, "you mean the poor blond man?"

Damn him, Frank swore. He got up from the chair.

"I'll call you."

"You didn't finish the beer."

"Forget it."

"Did I disappoint you again, Frank?"

Frank started toward the door. Webb sat up on the edge of the bed. Again on his dark polished face there was the faintest line, the beginning of a smile. His hand almost hid the can of beer it held.

"You want it all both ways, don't you?"

Frank turned at the door. "What do you mean?"

"Like what you did with Evelyn, then with your folks. You want it to be the right thing on paper, you want it to be right the other way. You came here for the paper work, didn't you? You want to find some way of getting back to where you could hate this guy again."

"Hate him?"

Frank took a step back into the room. He wanted to stare at Webb, but his friend's face had unlipped now into a bone-white band as he grinned. Frank glanced above his head to the picture of him on the wall.

"Damn you, Cal, you didn't listen to a word I said. You lie there on your fat ass pretending insights and grinning—stop grinning, will you! But you didn't hear me. Hate him? I told you I want to fix his arm. I gave him your doctor's address, didn't I? I told you about that first day, how he—"

"Prayed to a dark boy?"

"Cut it out! I didn't say that! And you know as well as I do part of the reason I had it out with Evelyn."

"Paper. It was you she'd live with, Weissy, not me."

Frank stared hard at the photograph. From the distance of the doorway, there was no face at all. There was only the white helmet, the white jersey, the white pants, the arrested spring of the form about to dive for the ball, or for another player. So Frank had that inevitable vision of Silver armored also in a football uniform, a black helmet, a black jersey and black pants. The two of them would be racing toward each other from opposite ends of the field. The crowd would see it at once, would be on its feet, hushed, waiting, interested, alarmed. They would collide in the exact middle of the field, in the center of all that watching. The noise of it would boom into the stadium, would rise above its air, would roar out, and out, and beyond.

Frank dove back into the room, into the seat beside the open window.

"Look, Cal, I'll show you how I hate him. This is why I came. What I had in mind. I want you to meet him. I want us to have lunch together. I want you to tell him about the doctor. I want it to come from you too. That you want to help him. He's never known—I mean, he only has to meet you to see— He's all set up for it now, Cal. We can save him. We can take this Southerner and—"

"You're crazy."

"We could do it. It's just like one and one, Cal. Where he was, that's what made him what he is. Now he's here and we can make it something else. He wants it. He's just waiting for someone to do it for him. All afternoon he follows me around the yard and—"

"Where he was? You think they're all like that? They'd pop themselves out of this world so fast—"

"Cal, will you come to lunch with him?"

"What for?"

"I just told you. For him."

"No."

"For me."

"No. Look, Frank, you are trying to hate this guy again. And you're a bloody little bastard too. That's what happens to the paper boys. You ought to be a little bigger. You could play football. You'd like the game."

Frank rose again from the chair. He looked this time into the small, unrevealing eyes of Webb.

"Isn't there anything, a single damn thing in this world you care about, feel responsible to?"

Webb rose from the bed. He towered over Frank. He was grinning again. His fingernails turned rose as his hand tightened around the empty beer can. The sides of it collapsed easily. He turned the can idly as he answered, and it nestled securely in his huge hands.

"But you know I do, Frank. What I care about keeps me all here. Good ol' Calvin Henry Webb, the all-American colored boy. You remember that when we come to room together. Then we'll get along fine. And look," he called after Frank, stopping him once more at the door, "I'll be in Brooklyn Wednesday. I'm modelling again at the Museum. I'll come out for lunch, but with *you*. Same place we met last month. I'll get there about one. But don't bring your golden boy. Don't have him there, Weissy."

VI

"They sure make somethin' pretty of these places up here," Silver said.

Frank shrugged and looked vaguely around the cafeteria. The air was dead and cold as the invisible machinery whirred against the heat outside. Before them on their table, untouched, were the cold salad plates they had gotten at the counter. Frank sipped at his coffee, but Silver kept his hands in his lap. Frank imagined it would have been less difficult if Silver had not worn the newly pressed slacks, the dress shirt, the flowered silk tie.

"That's kind of you. That's sure kindly," Silver had stammered when Frank on Monday afternoon had prepared the Wednesday luncheon.

"He's the fellow who had the knee operation," Frank had said. "He'll be able to tell you more about the doctor." That was all Frank had said.

For the rest of that afternoon and for all of Tuesday afternoon, Silver either squatted beside Frank or followed on his heels through the schoolyard as Frank performed his small duties.

"You heard him, boy. No cards in here!" Silver had glared at the offender, and the stunned boy, without even the gesture at saving face, fled the schoolyard, escaped the blond fellow who distressed a neighborhood.

But now Frank feared it was all pointless. He was beginning to believe he and Silver had both faked what they were doing. It was absurd to sit there and suppose they were doing something for a crippled arm, were going to restore in Silver what had been destroyed long before he had ever used the arm to pile a Negro soldier over the railing of a ship to drown on a cold night. Surely Silver knew the foolishness of it. It was a kind of ritual then, a sort of courtship that involved them both as they waited now for Webb. Silver wanted only to savor what it was for someone to care, to contemplate the servitude of it. He had not, for example, once in the three days of this week uttered the word nigger. So perhaps the luncheon itself would come off. Webb might be finally too indifferent to care. If only Silver had not dressed for the occasion, had at least left off the tie. With his pink, strong fingers Silver kept probing the knot as if it were a noose.

"Maybe we got here too soon," Silver said, his eyes roving the cafeteria.

"He'll be here. He's just bad about time. We might as well eat."

"I reckon we ought to wait."

"We can have the dessert with him."

"I reckon I ought to wait. You say he was able to play football after the operation?"

"Yes. He played at college."

"He went to college?"

"Of course. That's where I know him from."

"Did you learn to be a teacher there? I mean, you gonna do this all the time, teach in the schoolyard?"

Frank had begun to eat hurriedly. He hoped Silver would eat.

"I studied physics. So did Webb. We're going to a University together."

Silver stared.

Frank had directed him to a corner table in the rear of the cafeteria. They sat opposite each other against the wall, an empty seat beside each one of them. It was Silver who faced the entrance and the street. Frank, when he wanted to glance somewhere, looked at the glaring mosaic tiles that composed the back wall of the cafeteria.

"I walloped Vito last night," Silver declared suddenly, nervously. "Therese's brother, you know. I was tellin' her last night about us havin' lunch together and this here friend of yours comin' to tell me about the operation, how it would go and all. We got on talkin' about my fightin' again so then Vito sticks in the way those wops talk, you know."

Silver made a cone of his fingers. Shaking them under his chin, he mimicked the accent.

" 'When a muscle's outa de arm, she's goo'bye. You're a farmer,' the sonofabitch says to me. 'You're a farmer. You ever seen 'em put de head back on a chicken?' I told him ten times before to keep his mouth shut. He was tryin' to tell me someone's takin' me for a ride. You know, gettin' money back from the doctor, or somethin' like that. So I walloped him. Maybe I will have a sip of the coffee, it gets so ass-bitten cold in here. You got to get back to the schoolyard soon?"

"I can come late. There's no one to—"

Silver lowered the cup to the table before it had touched his lips. He stared at the salad plate for a second, then turned his face toward the wall.

Frank looked only at Silver, kept watching for him to turn his head again. But he knew that Webb was there, was standing at the table, was getting ready to sit down beside Silver.

Silver's hands tightened around the edge of the table. His head whirled suddenly toward Webb. He seemed ready to lunge. But he collapsed slowly back onto the chair when Frank blurted:

"Silver, this is Webb! He'll help you with your arm!"

Frank turned to look at Webb. He was sitting now beside Silver, but he was staring at Frank. He did not glance at Silver even as he spoke to him.

"Relax, Silver. I can eat fast. I'll be out of here in a minute."

He began to unload the food from his tray. A black hand went hugely around a glass of milk and all the whiteness disappeared. He began to eat, tearing at the small roll that vanished in a minute. Still the eyes, the small jet eyes set deeply into the great iron skull, stared at Frank. He wore a white crew shirt.

The two of them beside each other were huge. Opposite them Frank felt shrivelled. He tried to look back at Webb, but he had finally to look away. Webb was not indifferent, detached. The anger burned in his polished face, flared the spread of his nostrils. That's what he must always have looked like down on the field, Frank thought, that anger you couldn't see from anywhere in the stands.

Frank turned his eyes to glance at Silver. Silver was staring back at him, but he could not have been seeing. His eyes didn't look, but they didn't blink either. His blond hair flamed beside Webb's head. His right hand, fisted now, pressed the edge of the table. Little beads of sweat gleamed on it, began to run between the knuckles. Frank looked up and the sweat was on Silver's temples too. And still Silver kept his eyes on Frank. They blinked once, then closed for a second. When he opened the lids again, the eyes were vaguer, moister. The blue seemed dull now, grey. He began to hear Silver's breathing, the sounds in his nose a gagged man would make. The sweat was on his cheeks now, and the sweat was above the locked mouth too. At last Webb spoke. The sound of his voice cracked around the table like a whip.

"Well, it's been done now. Just don't go on sitting there like that. I'd like to get up and leave you in peace, Silver. But I can't do that. No more than you can hit me now because of him."

And still, Webb had not looked at Silver. And still Silver sat there, said nothing, stared at Frank, pressed his fist, but did not move. Only a corner of the locked mouth had begun to twitch. But his eyes were clearer, seemed to burn more now and were darker under the blond hair. Frank picked up his fork and plunged it into the salad. But he didn't eat. He began to speak instead.

"Yes, it was me, Silver. I fixed it this way. It's because I want to help you. More than the arm. That's nothing here. I mean it's what's behind the arm. It's—"

"Why don't you stop?" Webb said in that same frighteningly bored voice he would tell a petitioner to go away.

"Yes, and you too, Cal. Help you too. You knew we'd be here, both of us. You had to see him for yourself, this blond. It was you had to learn how to hate him. Because this is what you are inside, what you want to be. This is what you really care about. So the two of you ought to tell each other. You—"

It was not Webb getting to his feet that made Frank sputter and finally quit. It was Silver. Frank had been watching him all the time he had spoken to Webb.

The sweat was coming magically out of every pore of Silver's face. It stained his white dress shirt. There was a circle of it showing on the chest beneath the flowered tie. His mouth had fallen open. He was trying to speak, to smile perhaps. He had put his left hand over the cup of coffee. His fingers tightened like a claw around the rim of the cup. He closed his eyes. His hand raised and the cup came off the table. Then there was the shattering noise, and Frank, expecting it, waiting, could not even jump. The cup and the saucer scattered. Bits of them were over the table, over the floor. Some of the coffee was on Silver's shirt, and on Webb's, who whirled now toward Silver. Silver jumped to his feet and the chair fell away from him. Still he looked only at Frank. The noises he made in his nose were louder now. His face was bathed. Even the blond hair, the curled and golden hair, seemed darker now, and wet. His eyes were clouded again. He stepped past Webb. He did not look at him. He hurried down the aisle of the cafeteria.

Frank turned slowly toward Webb. He could not understand why for Webb and Silver there had not been a fight. It would seem they should have fought. They could not, both of them, have been that much surer, wiser than he. Webb sat down again, and Frank did too, slowly.

"After all those stories," he mumbled, trying to fake what could not for long bewilder him. "After all those bloody stories, he couldn't—I mean, he just ran away from you. As soon as you turned on him he—"

Webb was already eating again. "It was you he ran from, Weissy. I guess he can do for me in a fight well enough. I don't ever need to get that mad."

"Oh."

Frank continued to stare at Webb's polished, featureless, chewing face. He wanted to keep from thinking of the golden hair, the dirty boy, the lame arm. But as Frank stared at Webb, in the wildness of his imagination, he began to see Silver hurrying to some violence somewhere, perhaps with Vito, perhaps even with Therese. Then Frank had to turn from Webb, so strongly did the black face convince him that Silver was going to beat Therese, might even kill her.

A Kind of Scandal

REX WORTHINGTON

WELL ME AND DUMDIE *was playing catch in the alley with an old softball my brother Fred gave me once and when the stuffings came out we got tired and sat down under Henniger's big tree and pretty soon Dumdie thought it would be a good idea to steal some of Mr. Vanderplagg's apples. We didn't really steal them cause they're always green and got worms in them all the time and Mr. Vanderplagg don't want them anyway. Dumdie just liked to say that word so we went and stole a whole bunch and threw them at telephone poles and Dumdie beat me almost every time cause he was older than I was and then he made me stand way back so I couldn't even throw far enough to hit the telephone pole except once when it bounced and Dumdie said I was a sissy and I got mad and went in the house. I told my mother and she said, "That's what you get, I guess you'll never learn," so I went to the toilet and came back in the kitchen and washed my hands and showed my mother before I made a piece of bread with brown sugar on it and when I was eating Dumdie came in our back yard and looked through the screen door. When I got through I went and told my mother and she said, "Well?" and looked at me at the same time so I went in the kitchen and got a glass of water and threw it through the screen door on Dumdie but that made my mother mad and she made me go out and play with Dumdie. Dumdie said we* *ought to steal some more of Mr. Vanderplagg's apples and I said "No," till Dumdie said he could get one of Mr. Turpin's golf clubs and we could play golf with the apples and I said he couldn't so we went down in Mr. Vanderplagg's back yard. Mr. Vanderplagg's back yard is all sunk and cooler than other back yards cause my father said Barbee Creek ran through there before I was born but it's under the ground now and Mr. Turpin lived in Mr. Vanderplagg's red house around in the back where he was. That's not where Mr. Vanderplagg lives though. He lives in his own house on the corner but they got the same back yard only he don't rent that one except downstairs and my mother said we'd never live in a place like that even if Mr. Vanderplagg is rich like all the Belgians cause they got lizards I mean snails all the time and sometimes they wake up in the morning with mold on their shoes. Dumdie could pick up snails like fishworms but they make me want to throw up so we hunted awhile but you can't find them in the daytime except that snotty stuff they make all over the place and Dumdie started digging in some crumbly bricks and found one and I said I don't want to play with any slimy, dirty rotten, filthy lousy lizards I mean snails only I said lizards that time and I said I was going to go home. So Dumdie squashed it and we went over to Mr. Turpin's door and Dumdie was going to go in but the door was hooked so we looked through the wire and it was pretty dark in there for daytime but we could see Mr. Turpin in bed and that woman he said was his maid was in there with him and Dumdie said how about letting us use one of his golf clubs to knock apples with and Mr. Turpin said we was too little and go away and I said to Mr. Turpin, "My big brother said you can't afford a maid." They looked quiet for a minute and then Mr. Turpin laughed and she said, "Oh, for goodness sake, let them have one," only she didn't say it just like that and Mr. Turpin said he'd give us his old putter so he got out of bed and got it for us. After we said, "Thank you," we stole some more of Mr. Vanderplagg's apples and went up where he's going to build a garage for his apartment people but all he's got done is the foundation and that makes the ground there even higher than the alley and Dumdie said that'd be a good place to knock apples so we knocked them across the alley against Mr. Peterson's garage till Dumdie hit one clean over the garage and he said, "I bet you can't do that," and I said, "I can too," and I don't know, I almost forget, but while I was taking a big swing Dumdie bent down to pick up an apple and before I knew it I hit him in the place you call the temple and he held his head with both hands and said, "Oh, Jim," in a kind of old tired voice like if my mother'd said it and he ran down the steps in Mr. Vanderplagg's back yard and I thought first he was going to tell Mr. Turpin but he went up the steps on the other side and headed for home and I got scared and ran home too. Then when I saw my mother—*

"All right, Jim. That's all we wanted to know. That's fine," the big man in the striped suit said. He turned to the lady with fat legs and said, "All right," and she shut her notebook and went out. Then he turned to Jim and said, "And that's just the way it happened, wasn't it Jim. You don't remember any more?"

"No, sir."

"All right. That's fine," he said. He got up and shook hands with Jim's father and grinned with big cheeks at Jim's mother. "Mr. and Mrs. Ryan—you folks have been most helpful."

"Well, we wanted to do everything right," Bill Ryan said.

"That's right. That's fine." Julia Ryan reached down to take Jim's hand and they were going. In the other room the lady had her legs under a little table, and she was running her typewriter and looking at her notebook. She smiled at Jim, who looked at the floor. Then they went down the hall and got in the elevator. Julia leaned back in the corner and grinned because elevators made her feel funny.

Bill Ryan cleared his throat and said, "Why didn't you say, 'Luther'?"

When they got outside, Julia said, "Thank goodness that's over."

It began one Saturday afternoon when Jim came running down the alley and couldn't get the back gate open. Julia, who was weeding the garden, looked up and said, "What's the matter? You have to go to the bathroom again?" For answer Jim began to scream and dance up and down jerkily, like a puppet. "What in the world?" Julia said and went over and unlocked the gate. He squirmed past her and went running up the path. But instead of going in the house he dived under the back porch. When Julia peered into the shadows under the porch, Jim looked like a frightened cat, and she said, "What's the matter?" Jim began screaming again. "Oh, dear," she said, and got down and crawled part way under the porch. "Now what is it? Tell me."

"I hit Dumdie in the head," he bellowed.

"Oh, my. How? Did you hurt him?"

"We was playing golf. And the blood squirted out like anything."

"Oh, merciful God," she whimpered. "Where? Where'd you do it?"

"Vanderplagg's," he got out. Julia backed out from under the porch and struck her head so hard her glasses fell down from one ear. "I didn't do it on purpose," Jim screamed.

"Oh, shut up and stay there," she said, half mad with pain; and she ran down the path and out into the alley. She found the blood sprinkled on the green apples; it led like a string of beads down the steps into Vanderplagg's yard and up the opposite stairs to the sidewalk. When Julia reached the sidewalk, she hiked up her skirts and came swinging up the street revealing her torn petticoat and the tops of her cotton stockings to all the neighbors. There were already several of them out in their yards, bristling in the quickening air like dogs who have smelled something and don't yet know what it is.

What is it?

409

Why, I saw him.
It's the Hiller boy.

Myra Hiller met Julia at the door, standing so handsome and self-possessed there in her beautiful house coat that Julia stopped and smoothed her hands down over her skirt. But then, seeing the flush on Myra's cheeks and a strand of lavender hair askew, she cried, "Oh, Myra. Merciful God."

"There, there," Myra said. "I don't think he's hurt too bad." Dumdie was in his parents' bedroom, and Myra's daughter Doreathy was holding a wet towel to his head.

"Well, you're all right, aren't you, Dumdie?" Julia said. Dumdie smiled thinly.

"I think he's all right," Myra said. "I've seen him come home worse than this."

Julia took this up and thought that there was a lot of truth in it because everybody knew that Dumdie was a little odd, and he must be something like that drunk, Hootie Randall, who was always falling down and never got hurt and came home one time with his face looking like he'd had a run-in with a pack of wildcats. That made her feel better.

"Oh, now hush, smarty. I've already called for an A-M-B-U-L-A-N-C-E," Myra said.

Julia couldn't take her eyes off Doreathy, who was sitting on the bed in only her slip. With her round little figure revealed, her pert face and reddish hair, she looked just like Clara Bow. Then out of the blue, Julia remembered that Hootie Randall had shot himself. "You going to take him to the H-O-S-P-I-T-A-L?" she said to Myra, who nodded. Julia glanced back at Dumdie, who had closed his eyes and was as white as the pillow he was lying on. "I'll get Bill up," she burst out, causing Dumdie to open his eyes.

"Oh, let the poor man sleep," Myra protested. "I haven't even called Frank home yet."

"Oh, now never mind," Julia cried peevishly, running out the front door, "I know what I'm doing." Bill worked nights and had to have his rest in the daytime, but why was he always asleep when something happened, and as Julia struggled up the back-yard path, she cried, "Bill, Bill," with all the breath that was left in her.

Bill, when he woke, couldn't seem to get it straight, and he kept asking who Dumdie was. When he learned that Jim was under the back porch, he went out and asked him where in the world he'd got hold of a golf club. But Jim began to cry and Bill couldn't make heads or tails of what he was saying. "Merciful God, c'mon," Julia said, grabbing his arm and pulling him down the path toward the garage. They drove straight to the hospital and stayed there till late that night, when Dumdie died.

"Well, everything's under control here," Gladys Houston called out the back door when Bill and Julia were no more than halfway up the path from the garage. When Julia came up on the porch, Gladys saw the look on her face and knew what she was going to say, and, as if she had to have her say first, she began, "The girls are both in bed and Jim's been in bed hours ago. What a fine healthy appetite those children have— I've often told Harry I wish I could have had some children of my own just to watch them eat. As soon as you called from the hospital I sent Harry to the store for some ice cream, and those kids tore into that like they'd never seen it before."

"Why, Gladys, there were a lot of leftovers in the refrigerator."

"Oh, now, Julia, you don't mind, I'm sure. I love your wonderful children and I thought a special treat would keep their minds off what happened." Gladys, seeing that this brought Julia back to Dumdie and that she was going to speak, went on quickly, "What a fine handsome understanding young man you have in Fred. Why, when he came home, it was like having a man in the house and he kept the girls in line and went out and got Jim out from under the back porch—the poor little fellow was sound asleep—and Fred cleaned him up and put him into bed. After I got the girls to bed I sent Fred to the movies and while he was gone I just thought I'd tidy up the kitchen a bit." And she stepped back from the door for the first time to let Julia and Bill in their own house. Gladys settled herself by the kitchen cabinet and waited; Julia got it out at last, "Dumdie died." It sounded like the beginning of a nursery rhyme, Gladys thought, and she said, "Oh, Julia, you have a lot to be thankful for. It could just as easily been your boy as not. Mrs. Jordan and Mrs. Kuntz came over tonight and they saw Jim and that Hiller boy out there this afternoon when they were coming home from their shopping and they said they said then, 'Somebody's liable to get hurt.' "

Julia, turning uncertainly in the middle of her polished kitchen, stopped and fixed her eyes on Gladys. "You mean it's all over town already?"

"Well, now, Julia," Gladys said, "you mustn't think I did it. They came over here after I got the girls to bed, and you can ask Fred, he was right there with me."

"Julia didn't mean anything," Bill put in.

Julia, thinking of the blood on Vanderplagg's steps and splattered along the sidewalk in the bright afternoon sun right up to the Hiller place, cried out, "Oh, how could they help but know! I haven't seen so much blood since that motorcycle policeman got hit on the corner."

Gladys looked upset, as if this was in bad taste; and Bill, who had seen Dumdie only in the hospital with a neat bandage around his head, replied, "Oh, Julia, don't dwell on it so. There wasn't much blood."

"Don't tell me what I didn't see," Julia said, turning on her husband. "If I could sleep on a picket fence like you can, I wouldn't see anything either."

"Now, Julia," Bill protested gently, while Gladys said, "Well, I'd better get home. I've got a man of my own to take care of."

Julia watched her go but then ran to the door and said,

"Gladys, I didn't mean anything, really. Don't be angry. But you know how people are."

Gladys turned, a light like triumph on her face, and whispered through the screen door, "Now, honey, I understand, and I don't think there's going to be much talk. It's like Mrs. Kuntz said, everybody knows that Hiller boy wasn't just right and maybe it was an act of God that it was him instead of your boy."

Julia took that to bed with her, and the next morning being Sunday, she insisted that the whole family go to church. But how could it have got round so fast, she wondered, when, getting there late because Jim had had to go to the bathroom at the last minute, the entire congregation turned to watch the Ryans file in. The only bench open was one down near the front on the side. Walking down the aisle Julia thought she was going to faint because Bill didn't seem to know how to act, not having been to church, as everybody probably knew, since he got married over twenty years ago, and kept talking to the children in his street voice just as if nothing was wrong.

The Ryans took up the entire bench by themselves; and when the collection plate came round, Julia discovered that she hadn't any change and Bill had forgot his wallet. The plate was handed to Julia at one end of the row and given by Bill to a monitor at the other end without as much as a red cent being dropped in. By the time Julia got home she was so upset she could hardly get dinner; she crabbed at the girls, who began to cry and pick on Jim, telling him that it was all his fault anyway. That set Jim off, causing Bill to descend on his children; and Fred, being sixteen, said, "You people act like you don't have any sense."

Later in the day the newspaper sent a man over, who asked if he could have a picture of Jim. Julia regretted afterward being so rude, but at the time she was hot and tired and nobody but her seemed to realize how awful this thing was, so that she practically drove him down the steps. The next day there it was in a sub-head right under something about scandals in Washington; and all up and down the street Julia could see the neighbors coming out on their porches after the paper boy had passed, as if he were scattering gold. "Oh, I tell you I'm going to go out of my mind if this doesn't stop," she shouted.

Bill did, in fact, tell her that she wasn't acting at all sensible when she said that Jim would have to go to the funeral. "I don't give a damn what anybody thinks," he said. "It's too much to ask of a little boy."

Julia seemed to have been waiting for this; she breathed a long sigh and said meekly, "You don't think it would be the thing to do then?"

"Damnit, no," he said, feeling his strength, "it's enough that you and me go."

As Julia often told Gladys, "Bill always has to know which way the wind's blowing and who killed Cock Robin, but once he gets everything straight, there's nobody like him." She clung tightly to her husband's arm there in the funeral parlor, when he took her straight up the aisle to view the body past all those eyes like rows of marbles; and she was able to shed a few quiet tears which made her feel as if she had taken a weight off her shoulders and left it on Dumdie's casket. Afterward Myra, looking as smart all in black as an actress, asked Julia and Bill to ride to the cemetery with the Hillers. Then later she had them drop by for cake and coffee and asked several times how Jimmy was taking it all. Julia accepted this with a twinge of guilt, and when she got home, she fell on Jim with so many soft words and caresses that at last he became cross and ended up by crying.

That evening Julia and Gladys talked across the back-yard fence: "They say he's going to marry her," Gladys said.

"Do you suppose this business had anything to do with it?" Julia asked.

"Wouldn't be surprised."

"No wedding ring's going to make a lady out of that

woman," Julia said. They were looking across the Houstons' back yard down into Vanderplagg's; Mr. Turpin was moving, and that woman was helping him. Looking neither to the right nor the left, they hurried back and forth from Turpin's rooms to his car, resembling ants each time they disappeared into the apartment only to emerge with a fresh burden. "They see us all right," Julia said.

Across the alley Mrs. Peterson had stuck her head out of an upstairs window to watch, and Mr. Peterson and Mr. Henniger, who were in the alley smoking, were watching too.

"I'll bet they feel nice," Gladys said acidly.

Mr. Turpin came out of the apartment with his bag of golf clubs covered over with a dark cloth and moved up the steps to his car.

"There," Julia breathed.

"May God forgive them," Gladys said.

While Turpin went over to Mr. Vanderplagg's house on the corner, his woman got in the car and waited; he came back shortly, got in the car, and they drove away.

"Well, good riddance of bad rubbish," Gladys said.

"I don't know," Julia said, "maybe they were instruments of God, as they say."

"Why, how's that?"

"Well, like you said, maybe it was an act of God, Dumdie not being just right, you know."

"Well now, you mustn't say I said that, Julia. It was Mrs. Kuntz. I always give God his due and no more. Dumdie was just like any other boy, as far as I'm concerned."

"Still," Julia insisted, "Myra was so nice and all. I don't know how I'd have acted if it was Jimmy. Why, I don't dare think about it."

"You mean you don't think Dumdie was the same as your boy?" Gladys asked intently.

"Nooo, I don't exactly mean that. But you know how wild he was at times."

"Well, 'Let the dead bury their dead,' I always say."

"It's not that I mean anything against Myra, you understand," Julia said. "Myra's always been wonderful to me. Like last winter, I met her uptown on the street with Doreathy, and you know they're both so pretty and dress so smart that you can't tell mother from daughter, and Myra said, 'God, it's cold enough to freeze the hairs in your nose,' and put me right at ease."

"I've always liked Myra," Gladys put in.

"And besides," Julia said, warming to her subject, "you couldn't ask for anybody to be nicer about all this, and I think it was because of the way she acted that nobody misunderstood. The neighbors go out of their way to be nice to Jim, and I think by the time he goes back to school next month, this will all blow over."

Standing with his back against the school building, Jim refused to meet their eyes. They had him encircled now, and more were coming all the time. He could see his two sisters out on the playground looking on with pale faces, and he felt bitter anger, not because they didn't help but that they should see him like this. He made a sudden dash for freedom, but they pushed him back. Then Petie Hern arrived and made his way to the inside-front of the circle. Petie looked at Jim and spit through the space between his front teeth. "He don't look so tough to me," he said. They shoved Petie forward, and he fell against Jim and dug his fist into his ribs.

"Fight! Fight!" they screamed.

II   Poems

II

Poems

WILLIAM BELVIN

Palermo, Mother's Day, 1943

AMONG THOSE who promised us our honors
Someone said we'd killed a hundred each;
And since our knowledge of events was vague,
We used the digits in our dim additions:
Sometimes I deck zeroes out in lashes
To make crude, comic eyes that will not cry.

Hell's a harbor for the guilty; but
Were we not innocent of the spectacle
In our high and ornamental boxes?
There is no need to say we bluntly murdered;
I memorized the scene in my crossed glasses:
I swear there were not even marionettes.

I could fear the image of a planting;
Yet we knew no sense of sowing (though our seeds
Were miracles that rooted, boled, and bloomed,
Fertilized and fruited in a flash)
For we were timorously tending our ground,
Where rude berries brambled gratuitously.

But at length the sound of women's voices
Will fracture all the sealed rooms of the air,
And all the little rooms that time has bricked
Against my knowledge of that soiled city
Will suddenly sympathize with the vibrations
Of distant propellers meaning no malice but death.

The Geographers

It is of little use to calculate
the hour; and even the most reluctant day,
that promised or loomed, turning in a pool,
breaks at last and suddenly has sounded.
Clockwise or counter clockwise, all pointers swing
into the massive medium: time confirms
more than everything: the flow, forever.
Who questions this backwards-winding verity?
One needs but to address oneself in time
to the ultimate ink-blue whelming of a sea.

But *where* are we? Who has not loosely wandered
the city-less plains of wind, tensely plotting,
without one known stone or dependable instrument,
against his own inevitable disappearance?
Mostly the stiff, pin-pointed creatures, counting,
upon a steeple that they will never see,
currents, where nothing ever comes but currents.
If you're lucky enough, the world has a flock of pigeons
to just for the one time shatter the air to an opal,
before the end, and black-dust ocean for ever.

And thus we count our jewel-perfect clocks
not half so dear as the quaintly desperate
geographies among us: largely illegible
old projections of floating archipelagoes,
of flora and fauna upon the unclimbed mountains—
ornate, ambiguous, arbitrary and contrived
of laws derived from other, stranger, laws,
muttered by the leaves of forgotten forests,
and that incredible voice that speaks to men
alone in the desert or in deserted buildings.

FREDERICK BOCK

A Return from the Wars

A COURTHOUSE in the center of the town
On summer evenings pivots every car
From corn on either side across to corn
And back again though all the tapsters call.

A balmy dusk of gently-riding lights
That dip at Dairy Queens
And still maintain a regular serpentine
Around the Square and around again, each night's
A wreath for the unknown

And makes me glad to come back here and live.
Unhaunted be my mind
By all that in good conscience I forgive
In calling now the vicious circle kind:
I'll save my laughter for the grave—

And drive on summer evenings in my car
Around the courthouse of the living town.

Winter: The Statue of Pomona

FERNS are white fur now, and stub her feet.
She wears frost for willingness
And soot-rimmed eyes for grace of trying.

Starlings anoint her, oak-twigs throw
Uneasy shadows across her breasts
As if the sun would vitiate the crux
Of her co-radiant posture—and not fruits,
Snowballs line her basket.

Yet she knows our coming—knows,
Though dry bowls of fountains foil
Her indefatigable path, we love
By dint of some outlasting nerve . . .

And we—who smile at positive mere iron—
We know her fixed indifference to cold
Makes our living touch the curve
Of waters bearing up an Ark superfluous

To summer's loss. Even in doubt
Of that blithe sandal and black cheek,
We pluck the winter like a proffered rose:
Regardlessness is the summit of all passion.

DONNA BOWEN

The Eggs

LABORING upward through the intricate air
Which proffers under its wings new balance there
Instant by instant, the cardinal, hurled by joy,
Achieves its nest above the watchful boy.

The stalker, wide eyes fiercely striped by lashes
In which each light change flows or motion flashes,
Quivers as he records the passionate flutter,
This homeward bearing through the foliage shutter

Of spring's brief leaves. Respectfully, choosing his time,
He moves within the world of his intent,
Where leafage-shaking, moss-fall and bough bent
Inform his weight with aspect of the climb.

Afterward, after what act? (Dim violence
All coupled with trembling earnestness) which, then,
                                        was real?
The loss, oh the loss in that breast-built gap, or the feel
Of the eggs in his hand, which persists, these almanacs
                                since . . .

Pursuit

For My Father

I CHASED YOU on your blind snow break
Straight down your drift-barred highroad's wake.
Where the wheels spun round in ruts and would not grip,
I faced your strangers, coddled gun on hip.

Kept noting for you continual plausible exits,
Watched corners, walked out often at night
In shoes with echoes, walk that always ended
In banged hotel doors, framing you in light.

I gnawed your snare, and sprung your loop and leaped
With the wild hare to the sewer pipe and lay
And heard the pulse beat in the thin ears bulge,
The collie snuffle at the hole of day.

When cornered in the pew of narrowing churches,
I nailed your figure to the cross with care,
And tried to breathe the attitude of worship
Within the smothering light and bloody air.

Who wants me pulls at me as delicately
As winter grasses pluck at hampering skirts,
Who wants, betrays me avidly in snowslides—
Under my feet the sudden tremor spurts.

And he puts his hand into my hair and bares my throat,
And I bite the hand that slew the grey field mouse
And looped the slip-knot in the sadist's noose,
Then listen to the footsteps of my god picket my house.

JANE COOPER

The Faithful

ONCE you said joking slyly, "If I'm killed
I'll come to haunt your solemn bed.
I'll stand and glower at the head
And see if my place is empty still, or filled."

What was it woke me in the early darkness
Before the first bird's twittering—
A shape dissolving and flittering
Unsteady as a flame in a drafty house.

It seemed a concentration of the dark burning
By the bedpost at my right hand,
While to my left that no-man's land
Of sheet stretched palely as a false morning . . .

All day I have been sick and restless. This evening
Curtained, with all the lights on,
I start up—only to sit down.
Why should I grieve after ten years of grieving?

What if last night I was the one who lay dead,
While the dead burned beside me
Trembling with passionate pity
At my blameless life and shaking its flamelike head?

Morning on the St. John's

(The Chinese character for landscape is mountains-and-
water. A Japanese image of heaven is Fuji reflected in a pool.)

THIS is a country where there are no mountains:
At dawn the water-birds like lines of rain

Rise from the pencilled grasses by the river
And slantwise creak across the growing light.
The sky lifts upwards and the breath of flowers
Wakes with the shadows of the waking birds.

The shadows of the birds, the dancing birds!
With so much freedom, who could ask for mountains?
The heron stands here ankle-deep in flowers,
Wet hyacinths that burn more blue with rain,
And waves of smaller wings hurl wide the light
All up and down the horizontal river.

And now the sun shakes blue locks in the river
And rises dripping-headed while the birds
Go wild in curves of praise at sudden light.
The fire that would flash suddenly off mountains
Bathes this round world in dew as dark as rain
And then strikes green and gold among the flowers.

The dropping heads, the smooth and shaken flowers!
Among the grasses, blue eyes by the river,
And in the garden, fires after rain!
Under umbrella leaves the mockingbirds
Still nestle and trill quietly of mountains,
Then whistle Light!—cadenza—Light! and Light!

While higher and higher streams the opening light,
A rose corona like an opening flower,
More pure than snow at dawn among the mountains;
Paler than any color by the river
Beyond the reach of eyefall flight of birds,
It floods a sky swept innocent by rain.

The assault of sun, the long assault of rain!
Look how our darkness is made true by light!
Look how our silence is confirmed by birds!

The mind that pastured ankle-deep in flowers
Last night, must wake to sunrise on the river,
Graze wide and then grow vertical as mountains.

For even a glimpse of mountains fogged with rain
Or mirrored in a river brings delight
And shakes a man as dawn shakes birds and flowers.

HENRI COULETTE

The Trophies

I KEEP the ornamental dagger,
The diary, and the photograph
For him whose history was so meager
My curse must serve as epitaph,
And for the morrow they may augur.

Black-booted Mars with swagger stick,
He stands there in the Munich noon
—You are the letter of the Reich,
Inscrutable, barbaric rune!
I read you, and your sense is black.

Scanning the diary, though, I find
No meaning stranger than my own.
"Ah, *liebchen*," reads the Gothic hand,
"Ah, *liebchen*, that we were alone,
And Caesar's wars were at an end."

The wicked blade, the gaudy hilt
—What better emblem could I find?
We dangle from great Caesar's belt,
The plaything of his hand or mind,
And ready weapon by default.

Ah, *liebchen*, this is Caesar's night;
His eagles wait upon the sun.
In his campaigns, we cast our lot,
And gather trophies, one by one,
And gather where the losers meet.

Intaglio

I HAVE a picture in my room in which
Four gawky children strike a pose and stare
Out at the world without a worldly care.
Three girls and a boy in a paper hat:
The one too much a mouse to be a bitch,
The bitch, the actress, and the acrobat.

The roles I give them, half suggested by
The poses that they took, are meaningless,
For they are playing games. It is recess
Or summer—we have interrupted them.
They pose for us, with Agile romping by
And dark-eyed Pensive plucking at her hem.

This is my family. I dust them now
And then, and they return the courtesy
By never growing up. Thus, irony
Becomes a kind of family likeness, treasured
Not for the casual sameness of a brow
But for the attitudes one's mind has measured.

I knew an Agile once. To prove himself
The nimbler one, he pushed his books aside,
And crossed to Europe and the war, and died,
And his agility, which I believed a power
Then, then was gone, and his books on my shelf
Harvest the sunlit dust, hour after hour.

And there was Pensive, too, and everything
She touched was touched with fear. She married well,
Her people said, but marriage proves a hell
For those who marry but the flesh alone.
Who would have known a turn of mind could bring
Such knowledge to a girl? Who would have known?

I think of her, the child with heavy heart,
Heavy with child, and, Child, I think of you
And all the follies you will journey through;
I know them as an author knows his book.
Action and thought are nothing if apart.
Love in a gesture, wisdom in a look—

These are the real births for which we die.
Outside, the neighbor children startle me,
Calling, "Allee, alleoutsinfree."
They cut for home. I hear a whirring skate
Fading through the darkness like a sigh.
I dust the frame and set the picture straight.

Cygnets House

THIS is the last retreat that Graciousness
    Can call her own.
      It stands in brick and stone,
    Victorian to the very eaves,
But for the servants who, I must confess,
      Are bloody, modern thieves.

The daughters of the noble and the rich
    Are finished here.
      What polish, what veneer!
    These Helens have their father's nod:
Ledeans know by instinct which is which;
      They know the bill of God.

They learn here what is pleasing to a man.
    From stock exchange
      To modern art they range;
    Of ancient houses, recent horses,
They know the names; and of the Aga Khan
      The size of his resources.

430

I ask you, Mrs. Rennie-O'Mahony,
      You, the Queen Swan,
     Inform me if you can
    What cygnets dream of when they sleep.
Is it the wrinkled faces found on money?
      And do the cygnets weep?

Ignore the beggar, kick the sycophant
      I love the class
      That paddles on its ass!
    The Begum comes, if Aga can;
And if he can't; the Begum speaks of Kant,
     Or quotes the Alcoran.

The Attic

WE HAVE ascended to this paradise,
Make-believe angels hurrying to our choirs.
Imagination is our Sunday vice;
We are alone, alone with our desires.

We are enchanted by the sound of rain;
Darkness, half-light, and light combine and blur:
This is the national treasury of Cockaigne,
Of which we are the keepers, as it were.

Time is our Midas. We are of his line;
His touch descends to us on either side
—That golden touch. One gesture will refine
This dust into such realms as dust would hide.

These beads are pearls disguised as imitations.
This broken chair, my dear? It is a throne
From which you may survey the lesser nations,
Those lands that cannot claim you as their own.

This box contains the music of the spheres;
Its Swiss machinery records the stars.
Ever the listener given to fancy hears
The strings of Venus and the drum of Mars.

Time and imagination—what are they?
They are, my dear, the pseudonyms of Change,
The smooth, indifferent author of our play,
Master of both the common and the strange.

My sister, it is autumn in Cockaigne,
And we are weary for we've come so far
—Too far to be enchanted by the rain.
We are alone, alone with what we are.

ALEXANDER CRAIG

John Smith

THIS old man in the sailor's cap who walks
Beside the tea-tree, waiting on the sand
Now night has come and gaudy towels are gone,
Seems gazing at no ordinary sea
Where holiday-makers swam and splashed while girls,
Buoyed up by sunlit sex, survived the duckings
And children's water-fights.
Say that his eyes
Are watching dark and bitter waters washing
The battered edges of this off-white shore,
The sea that wrecked a myriad ships—they crowd
His mind perhaps: the wind's enormous hands
Wrenched at and tore apart their superstructure.

He'd tell you, if he could, how some were drowned
And some were shattered on the hidden rocks,
Distintegrated in the swollen water—
Old sailing-ships, tramp-steamers, ocean-liners
All equal in the sight of God.
And he
Might show how ships and men limped home to port,
Some twisted, hurt, forgotten,
Or sailing in small circles. You can send
His thoughts afar, make him a kind of symbol
Of anything you wish—of human life,
Of dangerous voyages, de Quiros, Cook,
And man's *Endeavour* foundered . . . He won't care.

He is no statue in the public gardens,
No great man frozen in a famous pose:
His name's John Smith, retired lighthouse-keeper.

He looks nowhere; his mind is drowned and deep
In wise, complete forgetfulness. Good wine
Has made of him the archetype of all
That every meaning moves towards and comes from,
Inheritor and origin and end.

BRUCE CUTLER

The Language of Yes

OUR FIFTH YEAR. And even the heart's highplain
is wound with westering columns of our love,
our body's sod parabled with grain,
mind's aspens opened to mercies of the dove.
We grow in leaf-green mansions toward the sun
and drive our roots with wild-plum discipline;
so colonized, the sky-high West we've won
will outweather ice and alkaline.
And there is a tongue to our frontier
you hear on hummingbirds and talltale youth,
on old-time homesteads where hills confess
the joyful noises of a heyday here,
of love and love for life and living truth,
and all the lessons of that language, yes.

ROBERT PATRICK DANA

Goodbye. Goodbye.

LET redcaps curse and terminal clocks outwit
Young lovers, it does not matter! Sweet Cockaigne,
Your laughter drugs our hearts, and we, half-lit,
March you down the platform to your train.
The sun sinks in the west; in its dying flare,
Children shag the steam along the tracks;
Farewells detain the passengers whose stare,
As we stride past, burns upon our backs.
You climb aboard. Our careful hands propose
No gestures, and in our throats our voices stirred,
But said nothing. As any traveler knows,
The station-master has the final word.
We tell ourselves the necessary lie,
But Time in its treason bells Goodbye. Goodbye.

For Sister Mary Apolline

> " 'How good,' he thinks, 'that she breathes
> in oblivion with every breath she draws! That
> in childhood each night is a deep wide gulf
> between one day and the next.' "
> —Thomas Mann, *Disorders And Early Sorrow.*

I

Now, wrangling bells discipline the day
And the doves, in frenetic scramble, flee
Their steeples. I watch them blown like debris
Over the wind-tormented roofs of town.
On the schoolgrounds, amid children hot for play,
Sisters stroll. You, my sister, hands

436

A-clapping, scold a wild disorder down.
One small boy meets your challenge eye
To eye; who knows from that tall glance
What bells may ring, and what doves fly?

II

When I called "Sister" half the convent turned
And smiled; children touched my blues,
Awed by the bells that swung above my shoes.
I paused, a stranger, in the scuffled dust.
This is a child's world. Here, where love is learned,
You turn to gamy ends these endless days;
Meg jumps rope and only Bob who's lost
His ball knows the size and shape of grief.
You ran to me and we embraced. In your gaze
I saw the season, blossom, blade, and leaf.

III

Sister, we share no common heritage.
A son who does not wear his father's name,
My birth engendered all: the public shame
That rattled mother screwloose in her bed;
Your father, shattering in his rage
The sideboard glass, the radio, and the clock;
Your trembling prayers, and your bowed head.
Above my crib dry birds of paper twirled,
And I, startled by the sounds, the shock,
Woke weeping in the dark and adult world.

IV

When, at seventeen, you took the veil,
I walked and whistled in a Berkshire wood;
As small boys sometimes can, I understood.
Where Christ, half-frozen, legs like sticks,
Hangs in some convent shrine by a rusty nail,
You pray our sins away and ask for grace

And bruise your knees upon the winter bricks.
I am the State's child, now. Being alone
Is something I know better than my face.
The path I walk leads everywhere but home.

V

In those islands of the wise, the Solomons,
The sea salutes the exile. It's Christmas eve;
Drunk as lords, the portside dreams of leave
Tonight, and we, our tin cups full of scotch,
Drink the bloody health of all men's sons.
We carol out of time and out of tune.
Forward, the bos'n bells the starboard watch,
And half the night we watch gulls wheel and flee
Our threatening shape across the moon,
Down the never and forever changing sea.

VI

Now, day's last light dies in the pebbled yard,
And the manic winds of March betray the season.
We stop and listen. The bells, sound without reason,
Summon the sailor seaward, the nun to prayer.
Where there is time, time is its own reward.
We say goodbye. I turn and go, but stay
Fixed forever in your parting stare:
Eastward, the darkness that the doves are bringing;
But in the street, a boy prolongs his play,
Now murmuring to himself, now softly singing.

RICAREDO DEMETILLO

You Laugh Within the House of Me

You LAUGH within the house of me
And all the dark rushes out.
Your hands flick tentative,
Setting my dust to rout.

And I am clean and lit,
Wide open to the sun
Who leaves the signet of his rank,
Gold on my dun.

And you who are the mistress here
Have felt my walls define
Your thoughts' geography
Whose countries are all mine.

The God My Father Chiseled with His Tongue

THE GOD my father chiseled with his tongue
And shaped within the niche of his child's ears,
Offering it the chilled dish of my fears,
On his deathbed was my inheritance.

As in dread shrines the worshipper turns pale,
Daring not touch tabooed things lest he die
Like Uzza by the Ark-wheels, so did I
Who lashed myself before it all night long.

It loomed a fearsome thing. Fiercer than Jah,
Who struck a decalog of stone, the god
My father willed me, held a hissing rod
That struck me who confused the moral score.

I, like the savage that dares not strike
Back at the cobra biting him but placates
The fanged tormentor, lifted no hands; but my hate
Grew, for I wished to dash it to the floor.

My cowardice kept back that blasphemy,
Until a Rabbi hinted in my ears
My vicious idol toughened on my fears
Which, if withheld from it, would make it die.

Since then, I kept away the dish, and I
Have seen my curious heirloom shrink to wood,
Crumbling to pieces where it once had stood,
A Ba-al that devoured its devotee.

WILLIAM DICKEY

The Plot

BEATRICE lay naked on the narrow bed;
"I'm half in love with easeful death," she said.
"And so am I," I said without delay,
"But once you've got him, how will you make him stay?"
"By woman's wiles and by ambitious kisses;
He can't be satisfied with those skeleton blisses,
Those beds on which anatomy reposes.
I'll give him flesh like concentrate of roses.
The change will make a man of him again."
"I grant you that," I said. "What happens then?"
"Then I deceive him carefully," she said,
"I leave him soundly sleeping, and I tread
On airy foot in search of certain potions,
Somniferous drugs and faint, Lethean lotions.
I scatter poppy near him as he slumbers,
I tell off charms and cabalistic numbers—"
"He sleeps?" "He sleeps forever and a day,
He sleeps the ages of the world away."
"He leaves us free for our desired pursuing?"
"He leaves us free for doing and undoing.
Once safe from travelling through that ominous portal
We'll have our pleasure, mortal and immortal."

Part Song, with Concert of Recorders

I

SHE   DOCTOR, I did not see that you were there.

HE   Madam, I've stabbed your husband in his bed.
       He now makes one with the unhouseled dead.
       I come to have you tell me that you care.

SHE   You know I care.

II

SHE I did not know you when you came in there.

HE   I did not then intend that you should know,
     Thought in the dark I'd have my way and go,
     But love has come upon me and I care.

SHE Tell me you care.

III

SHE Who made you come and find the door to there?
     Who made you turn that handle and come in?
     What we have done, what we do, it is sin;
     We shall be punished for it; have a care.

HE   I cannot care.

IV

SHE And I, who lay so warm and quiet there—

HE   And you, who grew excited with my kiss—

SHE Who would have thought that it would come to this?
     Let all be circumspect before they care.

HE   But let them care.

V

SHE And he lies dead—

HE   His blood is seeping there—

SHE Where we have kissed—

HE   Where we have done much more—

SHE I liked it best the way it was before.

HE   You like it now.

SHE   I like it but I care.

HE   No longer care.

VI

BOTH For we have gone a curious way from there,
      But we have love and so we go ahead.

4 4 2

It does no good to think about the dead.
What's dead is dead, it will not ever care
As we can care.

VII

SHE   Come, Doctor, we must fly someotherwhere.

HE   I have my bag full of essential things,
False passports, currency and diamond rings—

SHE   True pledge of love for those who truly care.

HE   Who live and care.

To His Companions in Exile

CLUMSILY the sky grew dark. In the lean doorway
The snow fell like the jerk of a suicide's hand.
Inside, the cat cried, and the meal was planned,
Not in the provincial fashion, but in our way.
The harpsichord was from a familiar land.

But in the world the clang of native quarrels,
The toothbrush man, the broker in hot cry
Asked us to give ourselves, said don't go by,
Don't go to jail, don't go. The plastic murals
Of Elysium-makers stuttered toward our eye.

And Horatio Alger rumbled in his belly
Like thirty couple of questing hounds and said,
"Daddy, you got to make it or you're *dead*."
He climbed the incline of his corporation
And at the top of it unscrewed his head

And threw it at us. Senators in their wisdom
Sang to the lute of deficit finance.
The university asked us to a dance

In its mouth's brick cave. The army wore a system
Of virility-pills suspended from its pants.

And ideas hurt us, made us dangerous
To ourselves. The prostitute voices scorched our minds
Like a dig of a knife, like a mania one finds,
White, hideous, hidden in the underbrush,
Jerking upon the boundaries of minds.

I remind you. Somewhere we have maintained
A kind of humanity to this dead attack.
If the cliffs howl at us, we can answer back.
We are not a pile of animate remains
Nor an ingenious patentable gimcrack.

The snow was clumsy, and the sky with which it fell
Badly proportioned and ignorant. In the room
The music made mention of the laws of home,
Decorous, proud, complete. The essential
Dignity quickened to its metronome.

A ship or a house, it does not matter which,
Holds the careful gods, who are so apt to break,
Whom we must save, in the flood, in the earthquake.
If we do that, we will not suffer much.
The home voyage is the single voyage we take.

Twenty Years Gone, She Returns to the Nunnery

> THE COLOR bleaches from her hair;
> Once black, she is now wholly fair.
> Housewives who cried her out a whore
> Find her not as she was before.

And changed the color of her breast;
Feeling too naked, she has dressed
Herself up over the collar bone
Into a reticence of gown.

Now in her face the smile is white
Like pure transparencies of light,
And disappear the copious red
Kisses she gave in her dark bed.

All is renewed about her form
Since mortal body took no harm,
Moved by an aptitude too clear
For argument to reach her ear.

Finally she comes where she would come,
Enters this house she went out from,
And in the cavern of her breast
Her heart lies like a lamb at rest.

The tall men fade, the dark men dare
No longer to inhabit her
Who is now made the tenement
Of a more masculine intent.

The Answer

I DREAMED I was a ghost
and poised above your pillow.
My desperate, uttermost
need was that you should hear.
I had no tongue or breath.
The night wound through your ear
as through an empty shell
its long sea-silences.
The word I craved to tell
beat formless on the air
it would have made resound
with warning, praise, or prayer.
So you in stillness lay
at one with stones and stars.
For what I could not say
I mourned your death in mine.
And then immediately
you turned, without a sign,
awoke, and answered me.

JOHN ENGELS

The Experimenters

We still wonder if it's true,
The imperfections of the studied man.
We were not very like the two

To whom we posed the puzzle of the salt:
A shallow basin, filled up with the sea
To which they'd bend themselves, and halt

To see themselves and then, deceived,
Self-consciously would smile,
Not knowing of the quick knife in our sleeve.

But still, our greatest interest is the man,
To whom we feed the tenderest of air.
Though we are not alike, our need began

When we imposed and presupposed his fault,
And made the light so alien
He could not solve the problem of the salt.

You Can't Be Wise

DENIED, she screamed in rage, and ran away.
I yelled. She halted, rigid in her going,
Water frozen in the act of flowing.
Then suddenly her fearful face turned gay,
I'll come right back, she called, and laughed. Like wood
Amazed at turning into violin,
At having such a sweet, wild voice within,
She was amazed at turning into good.

Bright as a fragment of the first creation,
Her hand took mine and I could feel it glow,
For love was in her like a lamentation.
What does a mere man do with such surprise?
Don't punish, give your love, and simply know
Wisdom is knowing when you can't be wise.

FROM *For the Iowa Dead*

XIII

CONTRARY century
Where men of plain good will
Must cry out—Enemy!
And teach their hands to kill,
Where earth explodes in space
Shamed with its human life,
Where live tears tear the face,
Where wound slashes the knife,

Where men of peace fought back
War-wanting men, and died

Attacking their attack:
As if on those old sands
The spear leapt from Christ's side
To cut the soldier's hands.

XV

Star-staggerer, old earth, through sullen space,
Lost in looking for some absolute light,
Remember, as history lurches toward its night,
The noblest flame is still a human face.
Searching for their lives' terrible truth, they ran
Over earth's water, air, and bloody ground,
On ruthless hill and ravaged city found
Another word for suffering was—man.

A tree stands up, has branches, birds and leaves.
A man stands up, has children, wars and grieves.
Yet anguished, daily life is consecrated
Where men die to defeat an evil hated.
Such death makes luminous the looking eye,
And makes more radiant God's appalled sky.

Beasts

I

THAT WAS a shocking day
When we watched, lying prone,
The two trout sidle under
The underwater stone:

When we saw there beyond
The hedge of hardy thorn
The sexual touch of summer
Luring the lifted corn:

When down the slope the two
Running red fox dared
Daylight in their need,
Poised, aloof and paired:

When cardinals from green
Willows, with red cries,
Scarlet scream of bird,
Plunged in our pool of eyes:

For we, merely woman
And man, did not believe
Living things could love
Wholly and not grieve:

For love had always been
A nimble animal
That could lure innocence
Or lewd on its belly crawl:

By snarl, by sensual cry,
Love lived, but in a cage,
Barred by my own tight pride
And your rehearsed pure rage:

Pride, pride that would not let
Self give up utterly,
Rage, rage that self would give
Itself up utterly:

They leapt at us like fire
And burned us with our blame,
Defied us with delight,
And shamed our human shame.

II

We have seen animals,
Finned furred and feathered, move
From their straight courses, curve
Into one line of love:

Fish, fox and cardinal,
Unreasoning and quick,
Proved one and one are one
By plain arithmetic.

They shocked us with their proof:
Those pairs of parallel
Loves that met and merged
Our own fused futures tell:

Each in the other's view—
Two lines of living light—
Will bend through the bent eye
One ecstasy of sight:

Our shattered parallels
Of rigid rage and pride
Will bend in one live length
Closer than side by side.

PETER EVERWINE

Soldiers' Woods: Occupied Germany

THESE WOODS were Barbarossa's. Deep in shade
Stone eagles crumble into dust, and rain
Thickens the growth beneath which men are laid.
Here silence guards their slow, corrupting stain.

Forgotten men, they keep the terms of peace:
The horses gone, the clang and bite of steel,
The brazen horns they thought would never cease.
Bone-weary once, their bones are history's seal.

By night we walk these woods. In tangled brush
Lean girls attend the hungers of the state.
In this unstable peace strange lovers thresh—
Their limbs unloosened to love's heavy freight—

Until we think the years mean this: desire
That rages in a wood, alive, unchaste,
And will defy death's emblems, and in fire
Consume the passages of time and waste;

While overhead bright bombers in the air
Amaze the moon and startle from their sleep
Those skeletal, dark heads which, baffled, bear
The sensual earth that they had thought to keep.

On a Photograph of My Grandfather, Paolo Castelnuovo

GRANDFATHER, fortune's child is fair of face.
Watching you now, posed in the granite light
Of some Italian noon. I find no grace,
No radiance to warm this northern night.

A face of small wit, distant and too stern,
Cut by a black moustache, your bristling pride;
The eyes a desert where I might discern
Elusive vineyards that had bloomed but died.

This, then, was your undoing: exiled, old,
Unbent to charity, you found red wine
Thicker than blood and would not once be told
How dogs grow ravenous where misers dine.

You died, alone upon the barren hill
Your pride had built, and in the rootless earth
Found roots at last, cursed for a beggar still.
From failure's purse I must exact my worth.

I owe no recompense: not hate or love,
Allegiance or similitude of brow.
And yet I wear your black moustache to prove
Symbols of pride must be my comfort now.

Waste is the almshouse where I too must live,
Believing in the profit of the mind.
Forged out of pride, pride's coin is what I give.
And will be wealthy in this self I find.

Composed of earth, by private fences bound,
I know the dangers of your distant face.
Aloof, I walk the same unsteady ground,
And will lie down by your impoverished place.

Kinsman, I give this toast to you in wine
As midnight gutters and the cold winds lash:
Out of the earth may spring the burgeoning vine;
The spirit's flame grows from exhausted ash.

To My Father's Ghost

Once more
The rain coerces memory,
And shadows cast upon the door
Love's old encroachment and the face
Of one whose history
Unwinds within this dark, abiding place.

Clocks whir.
The years' residual despair
Sifts downward, gathers to a blur
Of meaning, and the heart is dust.
Who am I? and I wear
Again love's degradation, as I must.

Old mole,
Oh dear, unsponsored ghost, lie still!
The mind, unravelled, would be whole.
I am my own, my own increase!
Yet from your savage hill
The dead still walk where definitions cease.

Winter Stop-over:

Astronomical Clock, Strasbourg

WHIRRING upon their track
In slow processional
Below a zodiac,
Peter and Paul and all
The carven figures lurch,
Come round again to fashion
In Strasbourg's vaulting church
Their prologue to the Passion.

454

Automata of stars,
Treading their measured course,
They move as motion mars
Both axle-tree and source—
A balance wrought in time;
Mass and relation hurled
To echo in a chime.
Here Boyle construed the world
An engine wound in space,
Motion its law and state;
The vestiges of Grace
In weight and counterweight.

I leave through the cold square,
Thinking of Europe's pride
That vaulted stone in air,
And of good men who died—
Some passive, some in rage,
Broken on Europe's plain:
Gaunt emblems of our age
That waste in this night's rain.
And northward, Mainz, Cologne,
Graves settling by the yews;
Berlin, its broken stone;
Munich, whose scattered Jews,
Anonymous in hate,
Smoked in the general will
That drove a manic State.
What pride is with us still?
Compulsive logics grind
In iron necessity;
Dumb matter beats us blind,
And law is energy.
Artificer, what Grace
Moves now on terror's face?

The hour grows late. My train
Speeds for its distant base.
Impersonal, the stain
Of darkness springs to race
Against the window-glass
Obscured by wet and snow.
Blurred terminals we pass
Are nowhere that I know;
While in an empty church
Repeating toward the day,
Small figures grind and lurch
In fixed, archaic sway.

DONALD FINKEL

Braille

THE HAND of an emperor heavy
With rings, beading of rain
Under a black branch, a flat rose
Carved into a frame,
Illuminated monkish prose:
Raised on the bleak flesh, we see
The adorning welts of poetry.

Certain embossings on the pale
Year incite understanding and renew
The faith; the columns of the temple
Are fluted and impractical,
On the altar, clustered angels
Bang unnecessary wings. And Spring, through
Her thin dress, lets her sensual garters show.

The Clothing's New Emperor

SUCH as it is it is. Such as two men
Talking because there is nothing
Easier than to talk. All things
Momentary as that, as the flame

Between two mouths meeting
In simple speech, flame
Clothed in the commonest phrases,
Bent merely, as light bending

457

In water, and shaking. Such
As it is. Lips mouthing vowels
In a vacuum, as in a silent film,
Not empty, rather unheard speech,

Caught at the distance between
Two minds, talking because it is
Easy to talk. Nothing is
Given but the forms. They have seen

The clothes without the emperor.
Deceived by fleas, they see flesh
Under the shirt, blood rushing
Inside the sleeves and out of the collar.

"Danger is the pivot of the sublime life."
                                    D'Annunzio

WHEREAS before the bull's dactylic
Charge, standing with a dry mouth
In all that thunder, man waits in
Man's distinctive sin, the sin of fear.

When first young Theseus went out, with
His father's sword, all haste to hero
He forsook the sea, scorned easy safety,
Went overland, drinking the sweet draught
Of danger.
            Courage is a fascination with
Fear, man preoccupied with his sinful
Belly-button. Not in spite of fear,
Rather because of it, he stands
In front of a great beast neither
Fearful nor brave, and shouts, toro-hoo!

And, in any case, if after the recorte,
The bull has not been properly fixed, he
Is likely to find himself sitting bowel-deep
On a puss-colored horn. Theseus. *Ole.*

E. S. FORGOTSON

Poem at the Hour of Surveyance

HERE in the great passage pause, while shadows and sounds
Cease, palm tight like Theseus' palm on thread,
That from its dullard winding fades before;
Here pause, aware, the brain now bounded least
Within the impure dark, its collocation
Well-made of eddy and flaw and center past
And possible.—Save only in this, that where
At first the curious monster might have risen,
There the strong dream arose and slew, and slew,
Preening to see the nothin'd blood flow down,
And afterward went forward with good hope.

I'll meditate what time the docile day
Ran deep, and in the rank, ecstatic grass
I could see armies. Ah, Ah, the silly sheep
Were dead, but then I knew it not. I was
More instant, and my many tissues grow
More often to a single tissued wonder.
The silly sheep were dead, but I
Knew not.—I mourned them by and by.
For in the stricken years of confidence
And shame, I did uprear and with a beat
Frantic and feathery, quack-quack, tilt most
Against the dark marauder. O Eternity!
O horrid wheel! O Art! and, O, my Love.
Later the evil totter of imperfection,
The fox confused in the wheat, his tail afire,
The sick perception of ungovernment,
And a fresh-scaled emergence, the new names glittering
But slowly worn to use. The brain's dim ball

460

Under his lively lattice will increase
A tidied minimum in the long strife
Of arrow and target. Across the stones advance.

Advance through the excellent dark—does not he lie
With thick-fleshed and bull-skull split and the ridged loins
Riven? With fair and fabled limb before
Have I not shorn him quite?—He cannot lift
His furied visage at that next bend there,
In those eyes yet a frozen blaze and frustrative.

Colloquy

DEATH's sly sea-anger beyond: the nine forced moons
Past for all moons, and breath's harsh exit dammed:
What man upon a crag's locked blaze and dun
Or on the fallen pageant of a plain
Knows then love's press and dark impact, that is
Engendered of no gender, yet of three,
And does not soon the song that harps declared
By Babylon pierce, the "word" Aeneas bore?

Of this, nay what? We see no dull reply
Can find acceptance. Still Thersites culls
Our moods, and by the lightning and crossed fire
Of hope compounds an impotent formula,
Puts burrs under the saddle. The god's old face
Splintered beneath the bright iron many days—
No quarrel thence; but rather where the act
Lies burked, our seed spilled for the hamper's sake,
And that wolf's thrusting leap of life drawn close
With bloodless definition's faery chain
To little good. Even our milder motions,
Love, pity, theft are winnowed for some neat chaff.

—Yet of great thunder the known astounding phrase
Will yield its strong essential to no code.
Death's sly sea-anger's beyond. By no such means,
Upborne on the black, expanding wing, the flock
Pursues the cliff-top's subterranean line
Past the green towers of the cousinly deep.

St. Anthony 1960

BLUE-BLACK, by night the airy roof
Admitted bats, needle-nosed gnats, and worms whose innards
Ran thick like pus; by day the sour sun
Administered at length its wilting stem reproof.

His knees upon the uneven stones took print
Of uneven rock that would have smacked as much
Of food as that green loaf which evening gave
His tic-ing mouth pleased not by teaspoon water's touch.

Yet would that devilish coil of guts he owned
Stop muttering, accept its death, and dry
Vestigial? Hardly, but must forever try
To lord this outcast spot where still he groaned,

And would until his blood's stagnation, form
The way things were, he knew, pursuit of joy
Of body would bring any man to use
Of every ugly means. So evil waited—

And Anthony had a fury to be good.
The way things were. And are: what each one gets
He takes from balking other, therefore desire will
Push all at last to hate, deceive, rob, bully, kill.

But Anthony, moral old scarecrow, does now some whisper
    come
To your bald bones under what coverlet they lie
To notice you that Flesh and Law are fused, from
Which a warm, enormous star glares through the global sky?

Greek Transfiguration

IN THIS AEGEAN ISLAND of white fire
the seas flash with hot brilliance, the waves
eat into the corroded beaches of the bay.

The houses are white in the sun, the cobbled lanes
whitewashed where silly sheep stumble with bells
and black goats drop their black merd in the alleys.

The goatherd's asleep in the vineyard under the fig-tree,
the world is asleep. And I, half-sleeping, sit
on the baked terrace of this hotel over the bay,

dazed in a white flood of fire, wrecked,
on the blurred shore of memory abandoned;
by my side, the cement anti-aircraft enclosure

left by the Germans, now scratched and defiled by hens
and the occasional lizard, hung with the day's washing;
before me hard bread and cheese, a few grapes,

and a sweet white wine staining the tablecloth;
beyond, the bird cries of children as they plunge
like gulls from the hot rocks into the tepid water;

and further, along the deserted esplanade,
its empty coffee-tables and blank arcades,
the village idiot comes, stumbling and halting.

With his right hand he pulls his trousers up
that fall to his knees and trip and entangle him
over and over again; with his left hand he stoops

to gather, in some old newspapers of last night's
public announcements of our private guilt,
the steaming excrement he dropped and drops in the sun,

his mother behind him following, wringing her hands,
calling on the sweet Christ child to exact no sin
of her for this befoulment of the soul's image.

But he, apart, mumbling and stumbling proceeds,
dropping and picking up his soft golden treasure,
his coinage, his artifact, his private and personal poem.

And were I suddenly to rise up out of this trance
compounded of the sun's white fire and the sea's brilliance
and my own and the world's wreck, and take it away

from him, and cast it where it belongs, on the dump
with maggots and rot, the sheeps' and the goats' leavings,
(by which the stony soil of Greece is ever sweetened)

he would weep, I know, as once he wept as a child
trailing into his mother's parlor the salty seaweed,
bits of broken colored glass, pebbles and seashell,

and she snatched them away and cast them with the garbage
and he was taught to know the difference between good and
    evil.
But I am entrapped and entranced in a bright white light

through which the human cries of seagulls swim,
and he is a child skinning his knees on the rocks,
seeking that pebble which does not fade in the sun

but strangely glows with the sea's transfiguration.
And I am dazed with fear in this blind light
that is the darkness of a farther shore

from which I hear the faint sweet cries of love
like drifting foam upon the endless sea's
indifferent and listless sursurration.

JEAN GARRIGUE

A Fable of Berries

For Cornelius A. Yaple and Mrs. Margaret Meeker

THE MOUNTAIN height behind the house goes up
And the wild apple trees still hold a ladder in them.
A birdnest in a pan sits on the window sill
And the white spring is piped through it, runs free
Down rocks as well.
Springs the wild mountain on every side hard up
Softened and laden down with trees, in fissures caught,
And the mist like treks of cloud spumes past,
Dissolves and travels up again,
Ladders of sight against the shagged green sides
As the handsome girl comes out to drive two cows
To pasture where the salt lick stands.

The wheel in the stream and the tool shed
That was going to be moved, and the worm-holed roof
With its roof-nailed ladder and curleycue shingles
And the high bent house amazed on its perch
Like a nailed-up birdcage staggered in wind
And the brown river visible and across up the sides
Like a square in the rocks and bushes a meadow
Where other cows deep in tassels browse
To mark the already marked ascent—
O disturbance great and alien!
The wild gourd grows and one must climb up
To a pitch and an elevation all is so tangled,
Grows without reason, disdains the excuse!

And apples, green, immature, fallen to ground,
And snow balls, white against porous bells of the cloud,
While beyond an uprooted railroad bed

Is a very alley leading, enclosed by trees,
To the spectacular flood of a mountain.
It is this that happens in the wind making morning
When berries are ripe near Gooseneck Hill.
We have come out with wicker and crates
And our ten fingers stained by the sun.
Life is a freshness that milk-mothers know
Bent over cribs to the dark-eyed owl.
Sleep is like casks keeping profundities cool
Though resistance is hooped by steel,
And the cows are led in to pasture out of the moment
The girl comes back from sleepy-licked bolsters.

II

We were here for the night like pedlars or gypsies.
The old man has settled to fire the chimney
Of the lone old woman who's taken us in;
She has doffed us a welcome and pumped the harmonium
And the two sang together like gay-cheeked birds.
Hotcakes and fritters; the spun house settles
Into its spirits and groans with its winds
In the low-eaved bins where I paced and I slept.
Hung the beams with spiders.
I clothed all their work with demented covers
Dead with love, made like a horse on apples.
All night whined the shutters, banged looms
Of footbridge clapping and spectral flying
On the slat bed, in the cupboard room
Sprung by the winds, where I wove ropes
The footwork of riggings, interloped seizures
On the sails of love-crazy loons.

While half through the night the thin sounds broke
Of the lily horn from the dust of its corner
That played the thin water of sound,
Played Harry Lauder and turkey-trot bands
Till the lame-legged ones tried a few turns

And of the old times drank a deep chord
And were revived in the salt-rough water
Where the soul breaks away with a touch or a thread
So delicate-rash is the body sprung—
And half through the night the thin sounds broke
Of the lily horn and their clacking talk
Till the bird saying *day* stood on a stalk
The cows went out and the chipmunk ate
Melon seeds while we dippered warm milk
And were off to the berry-laden mountains.
What were we to do with the berries we got?
The old woodchuck of the party questioned not.
The berries were there and they must be picked.
And into the back country with baskets and crates
Filling jugs with water from springs that he swore
Had the whole liquor of dews from rocks
In a car put together with strings we went.

It was in the grape-valley country of peaches and moles
Small on long spurs full of doors, and ponds
Of green rushes the muskrats delved
And the black-necked goose with its trailing young.
Heights, fulcrums for clouds, and the chipping birds,
Water bushes and long-bladed fields.

III

Much like a long time ago goes this world.
Birds fight in the bush; what is it they say?
Time has strange glasses; take them up.
Seven long years the berries are ripe
And many have married, buried, burned who would eat
Of the dark juice and go mad on it.

The old man is dead, selling bushels and bales
Who had planted a countryside full of elms
And poplars and cedars on occasional days.

469

And the old lady whirled in her chair
with a glee triumphant because it was cracked—
Twice had the lightning played and her hair crinked—
Do they sing from her bones like a daft cat?
In the habitation of each houseghost
It must be certain some do, I think.

For never we got to the mountains that time
And never the berries he bragged
And the wild ladders of foam fell away before
I could get down from them.
How may I think such a time was?
Clouds stream over, all is half seen.
The deep slopes of dark look out at me.

IV

I shall climb up over the other side
By the back of the way we did not know,
Shall climb up, yes, by the new strange track
Up stinted trees the opposite rock
And arise and find them there,
Find neither myself nor they have gone
Though the field has changed from green to brown.

And surprise them there in the glasses I find
By looking thus in the madness of time
And we shall be rocked in the freshets we knew
Though we have fled from the heavens there were
When, like the sensuality of a new rough star
One came, and was revolution.

Shall climb up, yes, by the other side
Though we did not get to the berries that time.
Do I doubt of the berries that the brambles hid?
In this perspective, whatever sense touches
In the form of things will be seen.

The berries in the brambles shall be found
We shall even be among mountains then,
In perturbation I will taste again
And will not come down.

Advice to Travelers

A BURRO ONCE, sent by express,
His shipping ticket on his bridle,
Ate up his name and his address,
And in some warehouse, standing idle,
He waited till he like to died.
The moral hardly needs the showing:
Don't keep things locked up deep inside—
Say who you are and where you're going.

Come Off It

WALKED up a mountain all alone
And stood a while to talk things out
With no one there but tree and stone
To take in what I talked about.
The rocks and woods that I addressed
Looked sympathetically on me,
And what I said there on that crest
Was such a help to stone and tree.

WILLIAM GOODREAU

The Father

THIS ONLY CHILD adjusts the dream you fathered
At your leisure in this clean suburban town.
The room you added, all that décor gathered
For the world of little boys. A kind of crown

Put on your house to show its growing up.
You look upon the public lake, its shore
And pathway neat as brushwork on a cup.
Calm on the screened-in porch you dwell before

That comforting green and breathe a sigh as still
As water on the lake. So much, you say . . .
So much. Your house is white, the windows filled
With antique amber glass. And Saturday

The time's your son's. Night coolness stirs
Great elms which shade the park, a shadow strays
Beyond the lake, across the hills and blurs
Into the blank gold moon. Your hair is gray.

MARTHA GRIMES

The Haunted House

SPIRITLESS STAIR: how much it wanted
One moving, luminous wraith.
In an attic hardly ever haunted
We wasted half our youth.

Dragging old chains up there; and crept
Simply for atmosphere.
We'd scare ourselves to death, except
Games end. We disappear.

I counted ten. Young friend, will you
Never come out? Our game
Is done, our reign of terror through;
Pretending's not the same

Alone. How you'd have died to hear
Steps halting, and the door
Close slowly on the upper stair:
I look back and make sure

Until I feel how I have grown
Beyond this place, until
The dark below the last flight down,
Extravagantly still.

ANTHONY HECHT

A Poem for Julia

HELD in her hand of "almost flawless skin"
A small sprig of Sweet William as a badge
Of beauty, and the region of her nose
Seemed to be made so delicate and thin,
Light of the sun might touch the cartilage
With numerous golden tones and hints of rose
If she but turned to the window now to smell
The lilacs and the undulant green lawn,
Trim as a golf course, where a haze revealed
The sheep, distinguished each with a separate bell,
Grazing and moping near the neighbor field
Where all the clover-seeking bees were gone,
But stood in modesty in full sight
Of Memling, whose accomplished busy hand
Rendered this wimpled lady in such white
Untinted beauty, that she seems to stand
Even as gently to our present gaze
As she had stood there in her breathing days.

Seeing this painting, I am put in mind
Of many a freakish harridan and clown
Who by their native clumsiness or fate
Won for themselves astonishing renown
And stand amongst us even to this date
Since art and history were so inclined:
Here, in a generous Italian scene,
A pimpled, chinless shepherd, whose rough thought
And customary labor lead the ram
Into his sheep for profit and for sport,
Guide their ungainly pleasure with obscene
Mirth at the comedy of sire and dam

Till he has grossly married every ewe—
This shepherd, in a mangy cap of fur,
Stands at the window still regarding her,
That only lady, if the Pope speak true,
Who with a grace more than we understand
Ate of her portion with a flawless hand.

And once a chattering agent of Pope Paul,
A small, foul-minded clergyman, stood by
To watch the aging Michelangelo
Set his *Last Judgment* on the papal wall,
And muttered thereupon that to his eye
It was a lewd and most indecent show
Of nakedness, not for a sacred place,
Fitted to whorehouse or to public bath;
At which the painter promptly drew his face
Horribly gripped, his face a fist of pain,
Amongst those fixed in God's eternal wrath,
And when the fool made motion to complain
He earned this solemn judgment of the Pope:
"Had art set you on Purgatory's Mount
Then had I done my utmost for your hope,
But Hell's fierce immolation takes no count
Of offices and prayers, for as you know,
From that place *nulla est redemptio*."

And I recall certain ambassadors,
Cuffed all in ermine and with vests of mail
Who came their way into the town of Prague
Announced by horns, as history tells the tale,
To seek avoidances of future wars
And try the meaning of the Decalogue,
But whispers went about against their names.
And so it happened that a courtier-wit,
Hating their cause with an intemperate might,
Lauded his castle's vantage, and made claims

Upon their courtesy to visit it,
And having brought them to that famous height
To witness the whole streamed and timbered view
Of his ancestral property, and smell
His fine ancestral air, he pushed them through
The open-standing window, whence they fell,
Oh, in a manner worthy to be sung,
Full thirty feet into a pile of dung.

How many poets, with profoundest breath,
Have set their ladies up to spite the worm,
So that pale mistress or high-busted bawd
Could smile and spit into the eye of death
And dance into our midst all fleshed and firm
Despite she was most perishably flawed?
She lasts, but not in her own body's right,
Nor do we love her for her endless poise.
All of her beauty has become a part
Of neighboring beauty, and what could excite
High expectations among hopeful boys
Now leaves her to the nunnery of art.
And yet a searching discipline can keep
That eye still clear, as though in spite of Hell,
So that she seems as innocent as sheep
Where they still graze, denuded of their smell,
Where fool still writhes upon the chapel wall,
A shepherd stares, ambassadors still fall.

Adam and Eve knew such perfection once,
God's finger in the cloud, and on the ground
Nothing but springtime, nothing else at all.
But in our fallen state where the blood hunts
For blood, and rises at the hunting sound,
What do we know of lasting since the fall?
Who has not, in the oil and heat of youth,
Thought of the flourishing of the almond tree,

The grasshopper, and the failing of desire,
And thought his tongue might pierce the secrecy
Of the six-pointed starlight, and might choir
A secret-voweled, unutterable truth?
The heart is ramified with an old force
(Outlingering the blood, out of the old sway
Of its own fleshy trap) that finds its source
Deep in the phosphorous waters of the bay,
Or in the wind, or pointing cedar tree,
Or its own ramified complexity.

Samuel Sewall

SAMUEL SEWALL, in a world of wigs,
Flouted opinion in his personal hair;
For foppery he gave not any figs,
But in his right and honor took the air.

Thus in his naked style, though well attired,
He went forth in the city, or paid court
To Madam Winthrop, whom he much admired,
Most godly, but yet liberal with the port.

And all the town admired for two full years
His excellent address, his gifts of fruit,
Her gracious ways and delicate white ears.
And held the course of nature absolute.

But yet she bade him suffer a peruke,
"That one be not distinguished from the All";
Delivered of herself this stern rebuke
Framed in the resonant language of St. Paul.

"Madam," he answered her, "I have a Friend
Furnishes me with hair out of His strength,

And He requires only I attend
Unto His charity and to its length."

And all the town was witness to his trust:
On Monday he walked out with the Widow Gibbs,
A pious lady of charm and notable bust,
Whose heart beat tolerably beneath her ribs.

On Saturday he wrote proposing marriage,
And closed, imploring that she be not cruel,
"Your favorable answer will oblige,
Madam, your humble servant, Samuel Sewall."

Upon the Death of George Santayana

Down every passage of the cloister hung
A dark wood cross on a white plaster wall;
But in the court were roses, not as tongue
Would have them (something of Christ's blood grown small)
But just as roses, and at three o'clock
Their essences, inseparably bouqueted,
Seemed more than Christ's last breath, and rose to mock
An elderly man for whom the Sisters prayed.

What heart can know itself? The Sibyl speaks
Mirthless and unbedizened things, but who
Can fathom her intent? Loving the Greeks,
He whispered to a nun who strove to woo
His spirit unto God by prayer and fast,
"Pray that I go to Limbo, if it please
Heaven to let my soul regard at last
Democritus, Plato, and Socrates."

And so it was. The river, as foretold,
Went darkly by. Under his tongue he found

Coin for the passage. The ferry tossed and rolled,
The sages stood on their appointed ground,
Sighing, all as foretold. The mind was tasked;
He had not dreamed that so many had died.
"But where is Alcibiades," he asked,
"The golden roisterer, the animal pride?"
Those sages who had spoken of the love
And enmity of things, how all things flow,
Stood in a light no life is witness of,
And Socrates, whose wisdom was to know
He did not know, spoke with a solemn mien,
And all his wonderful ugliness was lit:
"He, whom I loved for what he might have been,
Freezes with traitors in the ultimate pit."

The Vow

IN THE third month, a sudden flow of blood.
The mirth of tabrets ceaseth, and the joy
Also of the harp. The frail image of God
Lay spilled and formless. Neither boy nor girl,
But yet blood of my blood, nearly my child.
                    All that long day
Her pale face turned to the window's mild
                    Featureless grey.

And for some nights she whimpered as she dreamed.
The dead thing spoke, saying: "Do not recall
Pleasure at my conception. I am redeemed
From pain and sorrow. Mourn rather for all
Who breathlessly issue from the bone gates,
                    The gates of horn,
For truly it is best of all the fates
                    Not to be born."

"Mother, a child lay gasping for bare breath
On Christmas Eve, when Santa Claus had set
Death in the stocking, and the lights of death
Flamed in the tree. O, if you can, forget
You were the child, turn to my father's lips
              Against the time
When his cold hand puts forth its fingertips
              Of jointed lime."

Doctors of Science, what is man that he
Should hope to come to a good end? *The best
Is not to have been born.* And could it be
That Jewish diligence and Irish jest
The consent of flesh and a midwinter storm
              Had reconciled,
Was yet too bold a mixture to inform
              A simple child?

Even as gold is tried, Gentile and Jew.
If that ghost was a girl's, I swear to it:
Your mother shall be far more blessed than you.
And if a boy's, I swear: The flames are lit
That shall refine us; they shall not destroy
              A living hair.
Your younger brothers shall confirm in joy
              This that I swear.

ALBERT HERZING

Canticle I

WHEN LOVE invades the suburbs with a fragrance of oils,
Celery savors and an odor of soap in cellars,
With streamers of saffron locked in the little homes—

When love invades, astonishingly down
On stucco-colored prefabs, soon
Diffusing like a wave his spread warmth,

And the artilleries of love triumphant
On parks, on clothes-lines, on the tentative trees,
Burst flowering out like an oddly beautiful flak:

Then housewives shake their chains, cats roll in sleep,
Pajamaed husbands, startledly waking, see
The flares of love, his gunflash crowning hills;

And even clocks turn traitor: invidious spoons
Devise an end to servitude; they sprint
Like terriers off to the mud and vigor of March!

Dailies unfold and read themselves: the chairs
Infuriatingly berserk, circle the room
Sobbing Hosannas while rushing the stairs.

And what rapes upon their wills, those ones who are con-
quered!
And how sullenly they will bear the great tyrant's yoke
Who clanks through boulevards his damaging pomp,

Causing soft terror when the winged battalions
Shear down old timbers and the house of time
And ruin everything in the name of Love.

The Candy-Man's Art Is the Sweetest Art I Know

THE CANDY-MAN'S ART is the sweetest art I know
Unless the fireworks-man can master him,
Whose spent confections curl in the sky with a glow
Of starry sugar, coloring and cream   I
To dazzle everything—but even so
The candy-man's art were the sweetest of the two

Whose riots of color, stacked on trays in the clean
Cathedral of his counter, bring in to worship
The housewife, the good husband; even the lean
Irreligious urchin proclaims that his religion
Is a wild surging of such masterful rain
As sweetens the tiger and makes fierce the pigeon;

Or holds for us those lollipops like a rainbow
Hinting of all voluptuousness, and even
That fresher nothingness one also knew
As a milk-fed child, his mother singing so
He thought (who could not think) all heaven had come,
Gaudy as cellophane, into his well-scrubbed room.

But "Heaven's my gum-drop, I'll have it all in a bag,"
The child may later cry; then, hiding in words,
A metaphysical taffy comes to swell
The sick and puffy jaw-line of his hours—
No gum-drops then! Nor will he bear an ounce
Of that glib confection he munched on once . . .

Sing *Carpe diem!* the candy-man must come
Himself at last to a narrow room;
The burly, hurling world that whirls in zones
Will hammer out sour epitaphiums
To wall up heaven, all its sweetness gone—
And no more candy under the sun!

THEODORE HOLMES

Journeys

DEATH is a compromise the mind makes between an end it can
    never reach
And all those ends in which it finds existence previous to
    living:
The mind's journeys are journeys begun but never finished,
As when, in understanding, we lift our eyes from a page of
    poetry.
We travel on the journey our love makes as a discovered
    stowaway—
One held in bondage for the payment of his passage; in death,
    the cost
Is a bankruptcy where even the proceedings have been paid
    for.
Each voyage, each journey, must be set out on at least to
    some extent
In terms of the weather: the weather is the condition the
    body imposes on the mind.
Often it makes little difference whether it is mist or rain,
The starting is nowhere. On a sunny day, traveling through
    the country,
The landscape seems to stand out in such strong relief
That each moment is as if waking from a sleep: we are un-
    comprehending.
Roofs sit too squarely on walls and the trees already have
    a life of their own;
It is only what traveling contains of the continuance of sleep
That gives us any chance at all: we live between the dreamer
    and his sleep;
We seek in the depths of a woman's face as we do some
    destination in the sky.

The landscape over which we travel soon becomes our own.
How should we recognize it but through some knowledge
   of it
We have made our own? Passing, we live in the little red
   farmhouse
That sits so small on the hill, when entering it would mean
   passing
More rapidly and in another way. Life leaves little room for
   thought,
And the needs that are satisfied here leave none.
If we walked into the village blacksmith's to see him putting
   a hind shoe on a horse,
Would not the configuration go up in the flame and bellows
   of his forge?
A baby hides in his carriage the softness of the night he was
   conceived.
The landscape on which we live lies between the traveler
   and his sleep,
For it is only in this world that the trip never ends:
Where the picture renews itself each moment is for us another
   trip.
The distance between us and our bodies, in which each at-
   tempt at a crossing
Is a failure, in which our ticket expires before the end of
   the trip,
Affords us at least the chance to recognize the buildings of one
Across the patched squares of the fields in the valley,
As they outline in blue, on the horizon, the destination of
   the other.

Each day we are out traveling in the weather of our soul.
It is probable that even as we are entering church,
With its spire rising against the sun like a mote in the eye
   of Infinity,
We are not ever able to get quite all of ourselves in under
   the roof.

A woman's face is the part of her that grows above the clouds,
Toward which we, in our noblest desire,
Can hardly rise further than the highest tree on a wooded hill:
At night, when the foliage grows cold, our sap needs too much
  the warmth of a root.
The fire we cook our food over rises and the smoke hangs
  in the leaves;
When we've finished, the face that looks up from our dish
  is our own.
And the clouds that once floated between our head and our
  hopes,
Have come down to darken the green of the leaves; a journey
Held long enough on the earth, always brings us back to
  the start:
The weather of our lives falls from the ceiling of our birth.
If we look up in the knowledge that Heaven is there,
Then the blue we see may be just the color of the failure
  of our eyes
And our lives, our loves waiting below for this cloud to pass.

The Life of the Estate

A WOMAN inherits the proprietorship of her estate:
That though the land belongs to someone else,

Those that live as they are accustomed to in the house on the
  hill,
She feels in the same slow tread of the caretaker,
Under his straw hat, that the right of possession lies at the
  finger tips
And that the land we feel beneath our feet is part of ourselves.
The lands she cares for have been so long the living of her
  family
That every man is considered an intruder, though some excuse
  themselves
In that their needs lie beneath the perpetuation of the estate.

The house sits up on the hill; and has that satisfied look
Of a head taking credit for the comfort the body enjoys in
    bed,
While below, on the green sloping lawns, its history is daily
    re-enacted:
The gardener with his tools, breaking the earth for the new
    root to grow,
Or tying up plants grown too high for their stem to support;
The delivery boy walking toward the rear with the food
    in his arms;
And the guests, having motored up the long drive, chat awhile
    on the porch
And are taken around to see with what pains the grounds are
    cared for:
On lawns kept too short to show for long any marks where
    they have been stepped on.

From below, in the town, where crops are raised and goods
    paid for,
Her estate looks like El Greco's *View of Toledo* in which
    the lights have gone out:
The soft green slope of the hill itself betrays a consciousness
That would keep a common man from violating it without
    business;
As if they knew that a woman becomes wholly the feet that
    tread on her land.
And I, who, as a boy, worked there one whole summer in
    an open field,
Replanting it as lawn that keeps green between the profusions
    of the tree,
Am satisfied now that I know my attentions, along with
    others',
Are hung up in the barn with the rakes.

DOMINADOR I. ILIO

Diplomat Listening to Speech of Another Diplomat

THEY cannot go to the summer sea this year,
Where on the boardwalk, in no more than shorts
And bare feet, he can toss platitudes
Without much mind to the next fellow, perhaps,
Or to his nervous wife all ears beside him.
And watch the silly antics of the children,
Long unloved, in the carefree stretch of sand,
Or, perhaps, with anonymous paunch and goggles,
Foolishly try to execute a handstand
In wrist-deep water, and make it,
Though with much awkward kicking in air.
It will be fun there in the summer sea.

But with this, he cannot hint a word
To the little woman. His hands are firmly chained
To bulky paper-weight on his polished desk.
And his nights will be crammed with not merely silence.
It shall need greater diplomacy, though,
To tell the children why they cannot go
Than answer back this shrill-voiced speaker. O,
These talks shall drag on many long seasons yet.

CAROL JOHNSON

Sonnet

LET US FORGET the horn's end of the year,
Orion marching inconclusively;
out-Heroded of individual fear,
recall Odysseus apprised of Circe,
a name that burns. O Christ, we who relied
on quiet heaven and revengeless water
shall, like the friend of Dante, have descried
a strand unknown to Vergil, naked water
as salt upon our exile as the world.
(Turn backward, Alice. Is the Queen in tears?)
The mirrored senses separately curled
cannot reverse the circumscriptive years.
How should the Will we fail abstractly win
sevens of light for us except for sin?

From a Book of Hours

A LUMPISH Virgin in a cloud
of muffled angels rides
on gold: the praising crowd

are deaths we might have died
denying grace for grace
the insubstantial tide

absence of time will efface,
or lauds and matins prime
the hours' annealing pace.

Here spiky halos mime
the presences of love
the stasis of that climb

in green and cobalt mov-
ing on hypostatic red.
The lines our eyes remove

in these clear colors' stead
are tensile filaments
to us seem parented,

kept home from all offence
or married like this bride,
enceinte, indifferent.

DONALD JUSTICE

Beyond the Hunting Woods

I SPEAK of that great house
Beyond the hunting woods,
Turreted and towered
In nineteenth-century style,
Where fireflies by the hundreds
Leap in the long grass,
Odor of jessamine
And roses, canker-bit,
Recalling famous times
When dame and maiden sipped
Sassafras and wild
Elderberry wine,
While far in the hunting woods
Men after their red hounds
Pursued the mythic beast.

I ask it of a stranger,
In all that great house finding
Not any living thing,
Or of the wind and the weather,
What charm was in that wine
That they should vanish so,
Ladies in their stiff
Bone and clean of limb,
And over the hunting woods
What mist has maddened them
That gentlemen should lose
Not only the beast in view
But Belle and Ginger too,
Nor home from the hunting woods
Ever, ever come?

Tales from a Family Album

How shall I speak of doom, and ours in special
But as of something altogether common?
No house of Atreus ours, too humble surely,
Our family tree the simple chinaberry   I
Such as springs up in Georgia in a season.
(Under it sags the farmer's broken wagon.)
Nor may I laud it much for shade or beauty,
Yet praise that tree for being prompt to flourish
Spite of the worm and weather out of heaven.

I publish of my folk how they have prospered
With something in the eyes perhaps inherent,
Or great-winged nose, bespeaking an acquaintance
Not casual and not recent with a monster,
Citing, as an example of some courage,
That aunt, long gone, who kept one in a birdcage
Thirty-odd years, in shape of a green parrot,
Nor overcame her fears, yet missed no feeding,
Thrust in the crumbs with thimbles on her fingers.

I had an uncle, long of arm and hairy,
Who seldom spoke in any lady's hearing
Lest that his tongue should light on aught unseemly,
Yet he could treat most kindly with us children
Touching that beast, wholly imaginary,
Which, hunting once, his hounds had got the wind of.
And even of this present generation
There is a cousin of no great removal
Or whom the mark is printed of a forepaw.

How shall I speak of doom, and not that shadow
Caught on the famished cheeks of those few beauties
My people boast of, being flushed and phthisic?
Of my own childhood I remember dimly

One who died young, though as a hag most toothless,
Her fine hair wintry, from a hard encounter
By moonlight in a dark wood with a stranger,
Who had as well been unicorn or centaur
For all she might recall of him thereafter.

There was a kinsman took up pen and paper
To write our history, whereat he perished,
Calling for water and the holy wafer,
Who had, ere that, resisted much persuasion.
I pray your mercy on a leaf so shaken,
And mercy likewise on these other fallen,
Torn from the berry tree in heaven's fashion,
That there was somewhat in their way of going
Put doom upon my tongue and bade me utter.

Sonnet

THE WALL surrounding them they never saw;
The angels, often. Angels were as common
As birds or butterflies, but seemed more human.
As long as the wings were furled, they felt no awe.
Beasts, too, were friendly. They could find no flaw
In all of Eden: this was the first omen.
The second was the dream which woke the woman:
She dreamed she saw the lion sharpen his claw.
As for the fruit, it had no taste at all.
They had been warned of what was bound to happen;
They had been told of something called the world;
They had been told and told about the wall.
They saw it now; the gate was standing open.
As they advanced, the giant wings unfurled.

On a Painting by Patient B of the
Independence State Hospital for the Insane

I

THESE SEVEN HOUSES have learned to face one another
But not at the expected angles; those silly brown lumps,
That were probably meant for hills and not other houses,
After ages of being themselves, though naturally slow,
Are learning to be exclusive without offending;
The arches and entrances (down to the right out of sight)
Have mastered the lesson of remaining closed;
And even the skies keep a certain understandable distance,
For these are the houses of the very rich.

II

One sees their children playing with leopards, tamed
At great cost, or perhaps it is only other children,
For none of these objects is anything more than a spot,
And perhaps there are not any children but only leopards
Playing with leopards, and perhaps there are only the spots;
And the little maids from the windows hanging like tongues,
Calling the children in, admiring the leopards,
Are the dashes a child might represent motion by means of,
Or dazzlement possibly, the brilliance of solid-gold houses.

III

The clouds resemble those empty balloons in cartoons
Which approximate silence. These clouds, if clouds they are—
And not the smoke from the seven aspiring chimneys—
The more one studies them the more it appears
They too have expressions; one might almost say
They have their habits, their wrong opinions, that their
Impassivity masks an essentially lovable foolishness,
And they will be given names by those who live under them
Not public like mountains "but private like companions."

494

Anniversaries

GREAT LEO roared at my birth,
The windowpanes were lit
With stars' applausive light,
And I have heard that the earth
As far away as Japan
Was shaken again and again
The morning I came forth.
Many drew round me then,
Admiring. Above my bed
The tall aunts prophesied,
And cousins from afar,
Predicting a great career.

At ten there came an hour
When, waking out of ether
Into an autumn weather
Inexpressibly dear,
I was wheeled superb in a chair
Past vacant lots in bloom
With goldenrod and with broom,
In secret proud of the scar
Dividing me from life,
Which I could admire like one
Come down from Mars or the moon,
Standing a little off.

By seventeen I had guessed
That the "really great loneliness"
Of James's governess
Might account for the ghost
On the other side of the lake.
Oh, all that year was lost
Somewhere among the black
Keys of Chopin! I sat,

All afternoon after school,
Fingering his ripe heart,
While boys outside in the dirt
Kicked, up and down, their ball.

Thirty today, I saw
The trees flare briefly like
The candles upon a cake
As the sun went down the sky,
A momentary flash,
Yet there was time to wish
Before the light could die,
If I had known what to wish,
As once I must have known,
Bending above the clean
Candlelit tablecloth
To blow them out with a breath.

JOSEPH LANGLAND

Pruners: Conca di Marini

PRUNERS have come again among the vineyards;
They ride the terraced mountain on their ladders
To clip the grapevines hanging in these arbors.
                I heard their winter shears
                Go cleanly by these stairs.

Among the wild disorder of our twigs
Over the outer edges, frugal snips
Devour half the vines, and willow slips
                Bind up the bloodless stems
                In greys and gold reds.

Someone must train the vines (no spring has come)
Trying a few pale tendrils in the air;
Now they are clean, stripped to a winter stare.
                In less becoming more,
                Consider what is lost.

This shock will keep the vines asleep till March.
They would not dare affront their keeper's eyes
Though he is full of wine, in nothing wise
                Except these ritual chores,
                Economy of words.

For who would let a senseless love of sun
Updraw him, or a warm unseasonal rain,
Only to gaze at winter once again?
                The mild unsparing grooms
                Keep the essential roots

And pile the clippings on their women's backs
To ride the hearths and ovens of these hills
Where food and wine and fire have their wills
            And the rank autumn grapes
            Rise in their winter flames.

The Amalfi Grotto

WATER IS LIGHT. It blooms from dipping oars
    In huge lilies with golden tongues
        Echoing in green caves,
            A lost home.
Even stalactites sing of sudden jewels
        Dropping from bright eyes.

Just for a moment, let us dispel this charm.
The sun plunged down far undersea
Enters this cave, reflects,
Surprising us
Upon these emerald waters. Filtered light
Illuminates this world.

We cup our hands among the waves of light.
    We drip a quick florescence from
        Our watery fingers. Bells
            Ring from our arms.
The fleeting ghost of daylight everywhere
        Taps on the bones of night.

Forget these explanations that I give;
I would not have you think that I
Did not know how it was,
Or thought it was.
We have to know the things we have to know,
Then, if we can, forget.

I walked on water in a field of light
  And heard the dark tides of the world
    Tell, with a bell of tongues,
      The inland sea.
I do not tell you all, but who can be
    Complete with miracles?

Beside My Grandmother

MAM-MAW'S LOSING touch at last: her face
is neutralizing in the early gloom
of mid-November. But hanging on because
    of drab & milky bottles her room
withdraws into, she croaks for doctors whom
    the pinpricks in her junkie's arm
retired by calming her coronary storm.

Her eighty years become twelve hours today.
Clustered diamonds weigh upon her hands.
No one but me attends her as the gray
    outside & in her walls extends
across her muzzled eyes until she bends
    into her heyday froth again.
Her tears are salty on her sandy skin.

Her second husband's home & coughing blood
like a lame house dog choking on a tack.
Her bachelor youngest son dusts off the road
    & calls it quits, wobbling back
with his tail between his legs, down on his luck
    at 51, & mama cries
to see her brother slink like a lost cause.

"Lie back & rest! I am your fair-haired boy.
Everything I've touched has turned to gold,"
I tell this woman bedded with a noise
    inside her ears, which are as filled
as her bed is violent & deathly cold.
    Her memory becomes a cell.
"Stop it," she says, "the hammering in the hall."

PHILIP LEGLER

Landscape for a Wife
(After the death of the first son)

DEAR LOVE, how of the seasons made
Your body is, and holds the seed—
   The waiting supplicant in need
Of grace. Nor is the heart afraid
   Of winter's deluge, lost of light.
Yet memory, like a truth and blight
   Of snow, descends on April's bed
In drifts of shrouded fear to freeze
Your wounded crib of flesh, confuse
   Summer and winter, still unwed.

Asleep and weatherblind you claim
Your vision's dream again. A sign
   Of dust upon the leaf and vine,
Like Sunday's flowers upon a tomb,
   Suggests in any glimpse of yours
That loss to feed upon; but tears
   And calendars are useless, mark
Those days on walls, as if a pin
Could turn the weather back to win
   A winter's refuge of the dark.

Here in the darkness of these arms
In days like shadows that surround
   The body's wishes, weatherbound
To veil a summer's temper, harm's
   A weather vane to tell the heart
How weather keeps the months apart.
   And I, who feel the seasons, reap

Scattered chaff and turn to touch
A flower, where only seasons teach
   A lesson in the turn of sleep:

Let all month's weeping of a prayer
Be offered. May you hear and find
   That beauty in your womankind
Of drifted nights of snow; or flare
   From rain in root and dying toil
Of sun that startles frost of soil.
   For all the summers of your wish,
Though Adam's generation, thrive
To breed and bear that wish alive
   In all the winters of the flesh.

Dear love, how of the seasons blest
Your body is, and who must grieve
   Or praise the gift we lovers give.
Though we, snowblind again, lie lost
   In silence, may your sleeping take
A comfort from the darkness, wake
   Close to my breathing, knowing of
Summer in winter. Take this hand
Which cannot help you. In the end
   Body and blood are all we have.

PHILIP LEVINE

Mad Day in March

BEATEN, like an old hound
Whimpering by the stove,
I complicate the pain
That smarts with promised love.
The oilstove fails; the rain,
Forecast, licks at my wound;
Ice forms, clips the green shoot,
And strikes the wren-house mute.

May commoner and king,
The barren bride and nun
Begrudge the season's dues.
May children curse the sun,
Sweet briar and grass refuse
To compromise the spring,
And both sower and seed
Choke on the summer's weed.

Those promises we heard
We heard in ignorance;
The numbered days we named,
And in our innocence
Assumed the beast was tamed.
On a bare limb, a bird,
Alone, arrived, with wings
Frozen, holds on and sings.

Green Thumb

SHAKE OUT MY POCKETS! Beckon to the call
Of that calm voice that makes no sound at all!
Take of me all you can; my average weight
May make amends for this, my low estate,
But do not shake, Green Thumb, as once you did
My heart and liver, or my prostate bid
Good Morning to—leave it, the savage gland,
Content within the mercy of my hand.

The world was safe in winter; I was spring,
Enslaved and rattling to the slightest thing
That she might give. If planter were my trade
Why was I then not like a planter made:
With veins like rivers, smudge-pots for a soul,
A simple mind geared to a simple goal?
You fashioned me, great-headed and obscene
On two weak legs, the weakest thing between.

My blood was bubbling like a ten-day stew;
It kept on telling me the thing to do.
I asked, she acquiesced, and then we fell
To private Edens in the midst of hell.
For forty days temptation was our meal,
The night our guide, and what we could not feel
We would not trust. Later, beneath the bed,
We found you taking notes of all we said.

At last we parted, she to East Moline,
I to the service of the great unseen.
All the way home I watched a circling crow
And read your falling portents in the snow.
I burned my clothes, I moved, I changed my name,
But every night, unstamped, her letter came:
"Ominous cramps and pains." I cursed the vows
That cattle make to grass when cattle browse.

Heartsick and tired, to you, Green Thumb, I prayed
For her reprieve, and that our debt be paid
By my remorse. "Give me a sign," I said,
"Give me my burning bush." You squeaked the bed.
I hid my face like Moses on the hill,
But unlike Moses did not feel my will
Swell with new strength. I put my choice to sleep.
That night we cowered, choice and I, like sheep.

When I awoke I found beneath the door
Only the invoice from the liquor store.
The grape-vine brought the word. I switched to beer:
She had become a civil engineer.
When I went walking birds and children fled.
I took my love, myself, behind the shed;
The shed burned down. I switched to milk and eggs.
At night a dream ran up and down my legs.

I have endured, as Godless Nazarite,
Life like a bone even a dog would slight;
All that the dog would have, I have refused.
May I, of all your subjects, be excused.
The world is yours, Green Thumb; I smell your heat
Licking the winter to a green defeat.
The creatures join, the coupling seasons start;
Leave me, Green Thumb, my solitary part.

Small Game

IN BORROWED BOOTS which don't fit
And an old olive greatcoat,
I hunt the corn-fed rabbit,
Game fowl, squirrel, starved bobcat,
Anything small. I bring down

Young deer wandered from the doe's
Gaze, and reload, and move on
Leaving flesh to inform crows.

At dusk they seem to suspect
Me, burrowed in a corn field
Verging their stream. The unpecked
Stalks call them. Nervous, they yield
To what they must: hunger, thirst,
Habit. Closer and closer
Comes the scratching which at first
Sounds like sheaves clicked together.

I know them better than they
Themselves, so I win. At night
The darkness is against me.
I can't see enough to sight
My weapon, which becomes freight
To be endured or at best
A crutch to ease swollen feet
That demand but don't get rest

Unless I invade your barn,
Which I do. Under my dark
Coat, monstrous and vague, I turn
Down your lane, float through the yard,
And roost. Or so I appear
To you who call me spirit
Or devil, though I'm neither.
What's more, under all, I'm white

And soft, more like yourself than
You ever would have guessed before
You claimed your barn with shot gun,
Torch, and hounds. Why am I here?

What do I want? Who am I?
You demand from the blank mask
Which amuses the dogs. Leave me!
I do your work so why ask.

Night Thoughts over a Sick Child

NUMB, STIFF, broken by no sleep,
I keep night watch. Looking for
Signs to quiet fear, I creep
Closer to his bed and hear
His breath come and go, holding
My own as if my own were
All I paid. Nothing I bring,
Say, or do has meaning here.

Outside, ice crusts on river
And pond; wild hare come to my
Door, pacified by torture.
No less ignorant than they
Of what grips and why, I am
Moved to prayer, the quaint gestures
Which ennoble beyond shame
Only the mute listener.

No one hears. A dry wind shifts
Dry snow, indifferently;
The roof, rotting beneath drifts,
Sighs and holds. Terrified by
Sleep, the child strives toward
Consciousness and the known pain.
If it were mine by one word
I would not save any man,

Myself, or the universe
At such cost: reality.
Heir to an ancestral curse
Though fallen from Judah's tree,
I take up into my arms my hopes,
My son, for what it's worth give
Bodily warmth. When he escapes
His heritage, then what have

I left but false remembrance
And the name. Against that day
There is no armor or stance,
Only the frail dignity
Of surrender, which is all
That can separate me now
Or then from the dumb beast's fall,
Unseen in the frozen snow.

Joy of Man's Desiring

NEEDLE sliding in the groove,
Resurrect undying love:
Shining metal, turn again—
Past the whisper in the brain
Of its own destruction—
Thought to intuition:

You have reason, Reason none,
For it filters coldly down
Towers black with soot this light
That is neither day nor night
But darkness rational, late star
Of him who shall be Lucifer

Nevermore, and underground,
Mathematically bound,
Fractions all till nova brim
White light over Bethlehem.
Still emerge from the machine
Light that Satan has not seen

On land or sea; and needle probe
Time's resistance until Love,
Born again in the dull cave
Of our imagination, prove—
Fidelity in more than wiring—
Jesu, joy of man's desiring.

Three Ladies

MY FIRST is rare and gracious, courtesy
And light and darkness mingle in her face:
She dwells at day's end in a most luminous place:
Food, wine, and lanterns of civility.

My second scorns such gross and bodily
Clinging to houses and rich provender,
Saying it ripens like a yellow pear
Only for others, rots for itself; and she

(My second lady) hunts a dangerous prey
Through harsh, unsettled pastures where burdock
Sticks to her clothes but cannot bar her way
And eats wild grapes, a native of the rock.

My third, in blue, sits on a stone nearby
A little covered basket. The babe in her lap
Lifts in his fists a bunch of grapes which she
Plucks as she will and feeds him grape by grape.

None are for her. Her husband for their fare
Hurls his long staff up into a nut tree
To knock a handful down. The donkey there
Stares at the infant lovingly, sadly.

My first is rich; my second, fleet of foot,
Outstrips the world; my third pities its care.
And all the three are one; the one is three.
There are no other ladies anywhere.

The Factory

THE THING that cannot be spoken,
And you who involved me in it,
And she too—she whose person
Burns like a banner of fire
So that I cannot shun it,

And the boy with the bad face,
He with the fish-blue eye and the tow hair
Whom I met in the alley later, wholly lost,
Answering, with malice in his answer:
"That way if you can sir, can, sir, can, sir";

And you with the briefcase, who involved me in it,
There by the water cooler, neat as ever
When I came back in rags, burning with fever,
Smiling so reassuringly your: "Never
Shall I believe for a moment you will not win it";

And the knowing that she who burns like a banner of fire
And the boy with the bad face and the glittering leer,
And the courteous gentleman with the briefcase
Are but disguises that I chose to wear
To warn and dissuade myself from coming here.

For I failed completely, for all my mastery of time;
Discovered I should not listen, though not why;
And now as first light milks the Eastern sky
I quit the blacktop, stop the car, and see
Looming in this ploughed field, the Factory

That made me. I have found it. Overhead,
Million windows blue with sunrise.
Smelling the earth, I tread
Afraid of furrows onward to the wall
Stiller than a hospital.

KARL KIMBER MERKER

Poem for Con

THE GARDEN held wet weather.
You teased me to find in this,
The sign, confirming the gains
Three doctors thought you'd gather.
"Your garden quickens; the rain
Shapes fox-glove, phlox, late iris . . ."

But conceits stopped at the weeds
Which cramped our yard all season,
Though for you nothing was spoiled.
Some nettles bloomed toward seed;
I pointed; you only smiled,
A planter's act of treason,

Then said what you thought I'd known:
No judgment of kinds could suit
Your dreams on the child you'd bear,
Though the plants' growth was your sign,
Past weed or flower your care
Was held by the clench of roots.

But the roots grew past rumor;
Afraid your dreams could be changed
By all the people I'd found
Walking the streets since summer—
The crippled; the dumb; the blind;
The mad, whom birth had deranged—

I damned them to hidden hells.
You laughed, and asked when I'd learn
The time for fretting was past;

"Verse may be shaped by the will,
But a child grows as it must,"
And growth was your one concern.

Now, as we wait for the child,
Though I've hardly learned, I feel
That calm which you bring to birth,
And fears turn formal and mild;
No need for worry seems worth
The peace you shape with your smile.

ROBERT MEZEY

The Lovemaker

I SEE YOU in her bed,
Dark, rootless epicene,
Where a lone ghost is laid
And other ghosts convene;

And hear you moan at last
Your pleasure in the deep
Haven of her who kissed
Your blind mouth into sleep.

But the body, once enthralled,
Wakes in the chains it wore,
Dishevelled, stupid, cold,
And famished as before—

And hears its paragon
Breathe in the ghostly air,
Anonymous carrion,
Ravished by despair.

Lovemaker, I have felt
Your hungers in my heart,
But lacked your constant fault
And something of your art,

Unwilling to bend my knees
To such unmantled pride
As left you in that place,
Restless, unsatisfied.

Pakim Pond, New Jersey

I

THE WATER of Pakim Pond is red.
From a distance, the sky's in the pond
And the pond's blue.
But scoop some in your hands.

The sky blue, the water red:
That would be loud, and rather incongruous.
But no—
It has brown and a little blue in it like blood.

It is not cherry or flamingo or rust,
It is the wet darkness of blood
That stains
Always the bridal- and sometimes the death-bed.

II

One might imagine
That crocodiles had feasted, ferociously.
But not so,
For there are no crocodiles in New Jersey.

You might think that a drifting corpse
Had bumped against a rock, or even coral,
And been punctured
Like a gigantic blood vessel.

But even that would not color a large pond.
(It is almost a small lake)
It would make
Only a brief floating island.

And it would be unlikely:
They would drag the floor and pull it up;
(It would be missing)
They do not leave corpses around in New Jersey.

III

It is not foolish to conjecture like this,
Even if we know the origin of the color
To be the roots,
The roots, bleeding, of the shore trees.

IV

But such an animal red!
Is it a miracle, or a sigh?
Martyrs maybe,
Nailed to the rough-hewn bed.

A school of martyrs and saints,
Drowned like Patrick Spens under the sea . . .
But then, I don't know—
Do they have saints in New Jersey?

The Funeral Home

IN THE ENVIRONS of the funeral home
The smell of death was absent. All I knew
Were flowers rioting and odors blown
Tangible as a blossom into the face,
To be inhaled and hushed—and where they grew
Smothered the nostrils in the pungent grass.

Hyacinths of innocence, and yellow-hammers,
That beat the air at dawn, at dusk, to metal
Immortality, that flush where a bee clamors

For wine, are blooms of another color. See
How the flush fades as it descends the petal,
How deep the insect drinks, how quietly.

And curious, that among these ferns and rocks,
The violets flying a silver and blue elation,
And flapping ruffles of the white lilacs,
Shaking the air to tempt the golden bee,
Stiffen at the moment of consummation,
Swayed with guilt and weight of the bee's body.

These flowers, when cut and used, will remain ruddy,
As though made deathless in the very way
Their cutter kept the hue in the human body
That they were cut to celebrate and mourn.
The coffin has sprouted in dark mahogany
Out of them—edged, and shining like a thorn.

Against Seasons

WHY SHOULD WE PRAISE THEM, or revere
The stations of the Zodiac,
When every unforgiving year
Drives us hence and calls us back?

The expectations we invent
Drift bodiless on the drifting air,
And who conceives them but must rent
The dark apartment of despair?

Days come and go, and we suppose
The future will bring something big;
But season after season throws
Rhomboids of sunlight on the rug.

They say a heavenly horn will blow,
They say we must not be afraid,
But they are fools for saying so.
Endless meridians swing and fade,

All bodies in their orbits go,
The sky has nothing left to give.
We in this clash of circles know
Only the vicious ones we live.

Waiting for nothing, still, I wait,
Tired of God and of God's work;
Change is illusion—yet I hate
The silence and the changeless dark.

RAEBURN MILLER

For Megan Hall Merker, Newly Born

ONE DAY OLD and you have already learned
How to glance aside to see your tears' effect
Through glass on our unknown faces. You are stubborn,
I decide, but coy. I go back to your mother.

> Last night I thought a long time about love,
> How any choice is mostly a denial,
> Even holding hands, how there is no way out
> But holding hands—or else going in the kitchen
> To lean your head against the wall a moment,
> Wanting tears, but no outside comfort. And either path
> Is a narrowing of the horizon, a descent.

A couple of times this morning I slipped and called you
My nephew, but then I hadn't seen you cry
With such obvious delight in your own noise
That you had to stop occasionally to chuckle.
I am not likely to forget now you are a woman.
But until you have grown awhile and been hurt,
Your pleasure in tears is too simple. It frightens me.
I go back gladly to your intricate mother.

> Holding hands can be a satisfaction
> Like having the whole apartment to oneself
> Can be a satisfaction. Neither lasts.
> Hands part to light another cigarette
> And beautiful faces in a theatre lobby
> Reappear on the refrigerator door
> Or over the sprawled pages of a fallen book.

Yet be coy, my dear, and cry. It will get you far,
Though not far enough. But if you learn

Truly skillful tears and to open your eyes,
You need never want for salads and cosmetics.
I know one who once needed such things
And gathered them from air, who is now a mother.

    I know what it is like to fear summer
    And the lost touch of separated hands
    Or to think of getting supper alone at sixty
    With an unwashed fork and too much grease, on a table-
        top
    Stacked with newspapers and catalogues.
    And I know what it is like not to decide,
    To wait at night for one trustworthy hint
    Past thirty and past forty and past waiting.

You will learn that pearls are lovelier than oysters,
Poems than poets, how to choose stationery,
When to change the subject. And you will be unhappy.
And that is the time to learn another crying,
Silent and dry inside from the long fear
Of knowing and enduring what is yours
Here and no more and inescapable.
That birth-pains should go hard through all Easter
Reminds us, yet is only one granite shiver
From the quarried slope where nothing grows except
The prospect of superior distance, where I have seen
Your mother climbing in the thin sunlight.

    To be alone or not to be alone
    Or not to be. And our choices are made for us.
    It is vain to sweat and calculate at night
    Looking for theories in the tangled stars;
    And whether at last the hands slacken, or never
    Never have touched, what is important for our life
    Is not the given stone but the long carving
    To jewelry sets or garden walls or grave markers.

You were born from two who are in love, who live
Hand in hand, and I, who sulk in a corner
And fidget and complain and eat cake,
Should not instruct you in how and when to cry.
But it does seem certain that pain ultimately
Is the secret, and I would have you grow at last
Beyond mere coyness into knowledge. For that time
I entrust you to your mother and to Our Mother.

And Our Mother of Good Counsel, pray for us.
Empty into our cradled narrow bed
The stubborn light that rushes for your palms
To steal an apple and a rose for love.
Give us our weariness and indecision,
Give us our pain. And help us learn to cry
In coy, genuine tears as winningly
And glance as simply as a one-day girl
Beyond the pane to where all choice is home.

JOHN MONTAGUE

Speech for an Ideal Irish Election

THEN the visionary lady
Walked like a magician's daughter
Across green acres of Ireland;
The broad bright sword
Of the politician's word
Summoned the applause in every square.

The unseen inhabited
A well, a corner of a field;
Houses assumed magic light
From patriots' memory;
Assemblies knelt in awe before
The supernatural in a shaking tree.

The light that never was
Enlarged profile, gun and phrase:
Green of the grass worn
On shoulder as catalytic token;
Acrid speech of rifle and gun
Easing neurosis into definite action.

The house subsides into stillness,
Buried bombs ignore the spade.
The evening light, suitably grave,
Challenges renewed activity.
The transfigured heroes assume
Grey proportions of statuary.

Now the extraordinary hour of calm
And day of limitation.
The soft grasses stir

Where unfinished dreams
Are buried with the Fianna
In that remote rock cave.

Who today asks for more
—Smoke of battle blown aside—
Than the struggle with casual
Graceless unheroic things
The greater task of swimming
Against a slackening tide?

WILLIAM M. MURRAY

Little Boy Blue's Father Speaks

YET, PRETENCE TOUCHED some high desire you had,
Child, in that exercise of early mind
Playing with toys. A headstoned plot preserves
Your name against an earth you stamped on once.
Today, an old rain scoots along the streets;
Odd gusts of wind drive up against the house—
Movements of impulse born, they say, each time
Nature loses balance. She, too, designs
Her weather: seagulls inland, swallows high,
A mist around the moon, a red sunset.

A cupboard atmosphere surrounds the toys.
If they could suffocate they'd know close space
As men do when by chance they're buried alive.
But peeling paint and manufactured stance
Display the leaden nature underneath.

Time was you set toy feet to imitate
The steps of your imagination, taught
And practiced them in drills to pass the hours:
Now, they have lost the manners of your mind
And have outlived pretending, like the rain.
Here, I hold doors wide and keep black shadows
Cornered; the motion your hand made remains
In toys. My own hand moves and shadows leap;
I shut the doors. And now, the spider moves
Like God among the dead in pitch-black space.

DOUGLAS NICHOLS

Of Spinster Ladies and Flowers

AROUND A ROSE the elderly ladies spin,
Like witches now, and now like powdered lovers,
Like ancient mothers, bewhiskered and very wise:
Grey-haired Miss Gertrude, with terrifying eyes
To match her down-east voice, I see deliver
The witches' lines at table and make me cringe.

She scared me out of sense another time:
I saw her lean from her chair and never move,
Wide-eyed and drooling. . . . She was hospitalized:
I brought her violets, remembering how she prized
Her flowering beds and bushes. She asked of love
Only a blanket of roses at burial time.

Old ladies fall in love with younger men:
Miss Lucy wheezed from asthma but never wearied
Of summer playing. Up in Maine we'd skim
The lake in a green canoe and then come in
For luncheon in her garden. I gave her merely
A sprig of lilac once—which still could win

Her kindergarten heart. And now in Rome
The plump *padrona*, busying herself like Mother,
Brings flowers daily. Today she overflows
With pinks and a French saying, "*J'aime deux choses,
Toi, et la rose.*" . . . She bids me pledge one other
Heart with a rose before I leave for home.

O rose, O heart, O ladies with the ache
Of love remaining: I am bewitched by you.
Out of the air you spin your charms and fears

Of all depriving, muttering, smiling—in tears
For would-be love, for love that is not true:
I honor the rose for you and the heart's sake.

The Island Queen

I REMEMBER straddling my father's head and shoulders
To watch the Island Queen ride the Ohio
As though on a slide-rule point, its course so smooth
I didn't suppose anything could stop it.

Later I read the ancient steamer exploded
—Just like that. I was miles from Cincinnati,
But I saw it puff its smoke and fly to pieces
Like a purplish dragon, bursting its fury of steam.

It's years since that newspaper trauma. More years
Since Dad, lifting me from the honeysuckle, pointed
Through trees of Eden Park to the ship's strung lights,
More brilliant than my fifth-year Christmas tree.

Father, those baubles, reflecting a star and candles,
Decked out the tree of life. And when the river
Showed us its sparkling promise, it seemed the tree
Became a bright queen mother, making her progress.

YOSHIE OSADA

FROM *Hiroshima*

INTO SUMMER'S HEIGHT over Hiroshima climbs
The gay sun of inland cities. In a dug-out
Starving Kosaku, haunted by the idea of hope,
Whispers to Oyae-chan, "Should I throw
These thirty useless yen in the mud?"
She, that hare-lipped woman, eats her hidden
Rice and replies only her huge and crooked smile.
Judge Chiba in his uniform with the tight collar
Slaps his wife for cooking black-market rice,
Swearing the Empire would die with honest hunger
Before the dry Yamato River drank a woman's tears.

Snowy heron, four, five, seven, huddle and peck
In the rice field. Was it you who saw in Shikoku
Three cherry blossoms in the pine tree of Matsue shrine,
A miracle meaning victory? Did you shout
When the bamboo spear exercise was over at school,
Laughing through the salty sweat, jonquils
Bound on your forehead? And then did you line up
For a bucket relay in the neighborhood campaign,
To quench incendiary bombs raging in streets
Or secretly burning in attics?

Did you run with your small bucket under that great bomb,
As if you encouraged the clamor yourself, by sharing,
Undefiled, in the blood of that doomed city?

DONALD PETERSEN

Going Back

JUST WHERE my long road started out, it ends.
I stand alone and see my childhood town
Calling its kids and saying goodnight to friends.
And now the ruffled window shades draw down.

Old men and women, slumped in easy chairs,
Fold up their papers, yawn, and cease to talk.
I know that only a tireless streetlamp cares
Where I, a ghost with fisted pockets, walk.

Shadow and I, we play a little game
Of hide-and-seek, as we have always done.
Ten years ago I had a boy's nickname,
Voiced in the streets and known by everyone.

That name, those years, companions that I had—
Channing the fiddler and the girls next door,
The roughneck gang that drove my father mad,
Trampling his flowers in their relentless war—

Where are they now, so dear and out of date?
Old men and women yawn but do not stir
The burned-out embers, and the hour is late.
Someone is calling but I can't see her.

"Sneakthief!" she cries. "You've waited here too long,
Thinking of them, beside an old streetlamp.
Shadow will fall on you, and he will throng
Your reckless head and beat you for a tramp.

"And when you go back home—to your own home—
No one will know you. Peering through a crack,
Familiar eyes will say, 'Too bad you've come,'
Familiar lips will mutter, 'Don't come back.' "

On Several Landscapes by Van Gogh

This is our world, imperfect by design,
Living beyond our power to explain—
The farmhouse all entangled with the vine,
The farmer overshadowed by his grain;
A field run rampant through divine neglect;
A sanctuary for the rapacious crow
In bristling, golden blades that resurrect
As much of life as anyone may know.
We cannot see how far the road extends
That twists away to nowhere in the field.
Night falls on everything. It comprehends
The road, the traveler, and the cypress tree.
The moon and stars, like searchlights ranked and sealed,
Blink their dear radiance for eternity.

In Defense of Colds

SICKNESS heals the world. I lie in pain
thermometers would quiet as a cold
and think of all the men I might have been.

The sun comes in and mocks me, drawing squares
upon the dazzling sheets in which I see
the faces of the incandescent dead
framed in dark, and one blank frame that stares
as if it knew my name. I shut my eyes.
The Red Bear blunders through the gathering wood
ploughing up the earth. The Dragon's tail
lashes out in war its thousand scales.
But comfort will not come. I am the man.

Chaillot jumps up. I stroke her back and press
my burning fever in her fur. She purrs
and purrs, in thoughtless pagan joy. "O God!—
(I push her off the bed)—Where is the way
to ask for what I want unselfishly?"
The left hand and the right hand, counter worlds
in inconsiderate scales. I turn my face.
The Yankees win. The world will never end.

At noon my wife comes home, erupting smiles
and confidence. I spill my soup and groan.
Incompetent to breathe I will not speak.
She fusses with the covers, lifts the shades,
and leaves for work at last with puckered eyes.

It cheers me up. I think of how the dead
outnumber all the living; how the cat

will massacre the rocker in despair;
the black-spined volume bearing Blackmur's words
around the globe: "A promise he fulfilled."
It cheers me up, and up; but pleasure dies.
By afternoon the covers are convinced
that I will live. They twitch and take offense.
The sun assumes a slant that hurts.
The children play too loud. I rise and look
over the autumn rooftops tiled with gold
to where the river loops its tail in joy.
Swallows sing for their supper to the wind
that sways infectious leaves. The world is good.
The Dodgers lose, and Russia will not wait
for argument. The prophets sing like birds
twittering on the wind: "The sun must die."
But being sick, I know the world is well.

Elegy for an Unrelated Cousin

I MET YOU at our wedding, shook your hand
and bowed to the laughing smile that was your wife.
You were a jokester, affluent of life.
You decked the bumper, siphoned out our tank.
Now, on a swaying trolley, in a foreign land,
I hear that you have played your final prank.

At first the cancer struck a private vein.
At night, in bed, what stifled speech, what tears,
one world of love split to neuter spheres,
what cries of unbelief, what vows till death!
The knife cut in and took away all pain.
And then—the moths crowded the rooms of breath.

The day the doctors told you you would die
you took the long way home, through Fairley Park,

and watched the elm trees sift the growing dark,
the streetlights in the pond swell out and spill,
and bought three orange custards and a pie.
The stones you walked on echoed and were still.

Now you are safe from echoes, darkness' friend.
The hand I grappled has unclasped the world
and lies upon the lap of time uncurled.
A graver cancer eats away all trace
of that strong heart, and all your humours end
in just two furrows on a woman's face.

The trolley bucks and shudders—you are gone—
and I get off to face the city's night.
Shadows crowd around each naked light,
and echoes of my footsteps fill the street.
Cousin, goodbye—I know you—we are kin.
The heart admits another small defeat.

Bridge Park

THIS is the place where summer comes to sleep:
the men bare-necked; the women dressed for bed,
their hair in snarls, their children half in tears,
to stand, or sit, or lie at river's edge
and catch the breezes, fanned by burning steel.
The bridge is there—opening other lands,
its lights upon the waters, spilling moons,
but few regard the bridge, or watch its lines.
Most strain their eyes on spider strings of lights
that look like shore, but move, unlike the shore,
upstream, or down, and on, and out of sight
where still the horns give substance to the past.

I think of Avalon and Arthur's barge,
of how the horns bring loneliness to bear,
of how the lights might fit on Christmas trees
though white and far from shore, of going somewhere—
and wipe my sweating head. They watch the ships—
their lights, names, motion, and feel the heat
leave their clammy skins and go inside.

CYNTHIA PICKARD

Light on the Water

THE RIVER IS MUDDY? In the main, utility?
You see it as it is, in the realistic shade?
Granted it works for the roots, even makes a trade
For some of the richness just to flush it on to the sea.

The river is for drowning you and me?
Yes, it's deep, and where's the whirlpool hid?
I'll wait to argue death with the experienced
But this is quick, over at the count of three.

The sun is raining on the wrinkles, and they don't die.
That slow flow is alive on down your way.
Why, it's Christmas! It's the Fourth of July!
Sparklers right out of heaven celebrate me.
(Blackbird, I know your noisiness. Fly, fly.
I'll have only the silent silver today.)

VERN RUTSALA

The Institution

SOMEONE, working steadily at night
by dropping water from his canteen,
has worn grooves in the steps
leading to columns pitted as chewed pencils.

The windows are like deep-set eyes;
the door is a leather-bound book no one has read.
A commemorative plaque is worn smooth
as an old coin by many kisses—

just as, inside, the leaders have lost their toes
from wading in the blind reverence
of the people. Terra-cotta statues of them
line the entrance hall; they each have slots

in the top like children's banks.
A former hero dozes on a folding chair
chasing the wounded cats of his sleep.
Feet on marble sound like spoons tapping eggs.

Large, furtive insects like pageboys
stare from the shadows and run along
the baseboards. Outside the meeting chamber
a justice of the peace bandages his eyes.

Inside the chamber a school of vagrants
studies leisure or rolls endless cigarettes.
A special subcommittee is in session
scheduling obscure illnesses for us.

SATORU SATO

On the Bridge

I STAND on the bridge,
Looking into the mirror of the sky, wiped and wet
In soapsud blue of the dawn,
Feeling a rascal breeze sneak through my head
And kidnap half-shaped thoughts back into the innocent ob-
    scurity.

Without sorrow, without delight,
Without intimate daily-life-reality,
I stand alone in a small town far
From my home, which hangs
Upside down on the other side of the globe . . .
I, who just happen to be I,
Who just happen to be here,
Am nothing but a position like this moment
Which is, in itself, timeless time.

Water moves, but never moves.
What is a moment is an illusion.

Let it be asked
What I have done hitherto.
Let it be remembered
That I am always as I have been; and
Let the river run softly as do the old sayings . . .
Should I leave then such tedious paradox
To come and go with the dead,
When the light is stabbing the truth,
Nails, stretched, in the flank of the last darkness?

Making a fool of mannerisms
Of traffic signals, red and green,
Birds, innumerable but invisible, are
Animated in the aged woods, chattering and calling.

Harvest

ALL THAT WAS FALLEN, all that had to fall.
With brooms and rakes we set upon the trash;
The cackling leaves revealed a child's blue ball,
An apple core, a scarecrow, last year's ash.
The scraps of summer were all hauled away
To shifty piles out back and left to rot;
We carved and lit fat pumpkins to portray
The fire within, the sickly grin without.
Then children trailed in through the open door;
We recognized high heels and cast-off dress,
Nudged each other, laughed at masks they wore—
The very things we'd tried to dispossess.
Yet whiter seasons made us blink our eyes
At pieces of snowmen falling from the skies.

Evening in the Park

PAPER BOATS soon sank in midlake
And *crackerjack* icons turned to tin;
Balloons went limp. At precisely what point
Desire atomized I do not know, but they
Were restless gathering the bowls and cups,
Had expected too much probably.

As colored lights went off one by one
Things lost fixity and the whole park
Seemed adrift on a darkened excursion
And they were ghosts in a sea of debris.
They hurried to waiting cars and could have slapped
Their children whose hands smelled of crushed fireflies
And shone with a greasy green light in the dark.

On My Twenty-first Birthday

I STARED WITH my brain's furrowed eye
To the long limbed boy I left behind,
The teeth of my mind . . . a keyboard locked
To his dreaming skin and floating hair;
Glared through his eyesockets
                              old nests
Where robin's eggs dazzled like empty waiting snares.

How long I had tried to clear
The stables of his heart; working
Like some gray Hercules to rout
The orphan beasts which formed
His chain of flagellating shadows
While hurt's sparrows filched
Dried dung from chinks I had not searched.

I despaired; said, "Keep your hothouse to yourself,"
And forsook his eyes for a remote mirror
Bright with madness, in which I stripped him naked
And so unmanned myself.
Now I turn the key and await the roar
That I will make my music with help
Of new beasts rushing up a bone-dry stair
And a dark bird with a bleeding breast
Returning to its lair.

An Athlete Dying Old

(The octogenarian, who had avoided doctors and considered
old age a bad habit, died today. —NEWS ITEM)

Down at the medical center
   the nurses remember the day
when the sculptor who modeled in sinew
    left nothing but clay.

The intestine complained of the bile duct,
   the liver distended with rage,
as the boy who played tennis at eighty
    acted his age.

The bile was absorbed in the system
   till tissues were stained as with dye
from the laboring bowel to the languid
    and jaundiced eye.

Attendants walked softly in whispers
   putting the temperature down
and noting in keen expectation
    if his urine were brown.

Now he feels the support of subscribers
   applauding the pose from afar
as the thrust of the chin, well extended,
    is crossing the bar.

And he feels that the bowl of his belly
   spills into a liquid abyss.
The parachute jump in the Hudson
    was nothing to this.

They looked at, remarked, and admired
   the color of physical flaws,
relieved now to see the transgressor
    obeying the laws,

but nobody saw through the features
   into the yellowing sleep,
and nobody saw the last breath
    he tried to keep.

These Trees Stand . . .

THESE TREES stand very tall under the heavens.
While *they* stand, if I walk, all stars traverse
This steep celestial gulf their branches chart.
Though lovers stand at sixes and at sevens
While civilizations come down with the curse,
Snodgrass is walking through the universe.

I can't make any world go around *your* house.
But note this moon. Recall how the night nurse
Goes ward-rounds, by the mild, reflective art
Of focusing her flashlight on her blouse.
Your name's safe conduct into love or verse;
Snodgrass is walking through the universe.

Your name's absurd, miraculous as sperm
And as decisive. If you can't coerce
One thing outside yourself, why you're the poet!
What irrefrangible atoms whirl, affirm
Their destiny and form Lucinda's skirts!
She can't make up your mind. Soon as you know it,
Your firmament grows touchable and firm.
If all this world runs battlefield or worse,
Come, let us wipe our glasses on our shirts:
Snodgrass is walking through the universe.

April Inventory

THE GREEN catalpa tree has turned
All white; the cherry blooms once more.
In one whole year I haven't learned

A blessed thing they pay you for.
The blossoms snow down in my hair;
The trees and I will soon be bare.

The trees have more than I to spare.
The sleek, expensive girls I teach,
Younger and pinker every year,
Bloom gradually out of reach.
The pear tree lets its petals drop
Like dandruff on a tabletop.

The girls have grown so young by now
I have to nudge myself to stare.
This year they smile and mind me how
My teeth are falling with my hair.
In thirty years I may not get
Younger, shrewder, or out of debt.

The tenth time, just a year ago,
I made myself a little list
Of all the things I'd ought to know,
Then told my parents, analyst,
And everyone who's trusted me
I'd be substantial, presently.

I haven't read one book about
A book or memorized one plot.
Or found a mind I did not doubt.
I learned one date. And then forgot.
And one by one the solid scholars
Get the degrees, the jobs, the dollars.

And smile above their starchy collars.
I taught my classes Whitehead's notions;
One lovely girl, a song of Mahler's.
Lacking a source-book or promotions,

I showed one child the colors of
A luna moth and how to love.

I taught myself to name my name,
To bark back, loosen love and crying;
To ease my woman so she came,
To ease an old man who was dying.
I have not learned how often I
Can win, can love, but choose to die.

I have not learned there is a lie
Love shall be blonder, slimmer, younger;
That my equivocating eye
Loves only by my body's hunger;
That I have forces, true to feel,
Or that the lovely world is real.

While scholars speak authority
And wear their ulcers on their sleeves,
My eyes in spectacles shall see
These trees procure and spend their leaves.
There is a value underneath
The gold and silver in my teeth.

Though trees turn bare and girls turn wives,
We shall afford our costly seasons;
There is a gentleness survives
That will outspeak and has its reasons.
There is a loveliness exists,
Preserves us, not for specialists.

FROM *Heart's Needle*

II

LATE APRIL and you are three; today
We dug your garden in the yard.

To curb the damage of your play,
Strange dogs at night and the moles tunneling,
   Four slender sticks of lath stand guard
      Uplifting their thin string.

   So you were the first to tramp it down.
      And after the earth was sifted close
   You brought your watering can to drown
All earth *and* us. But these mixed seeds are pressed
   With light loam in their steadfast rows.
      Child, we've done our best.

   Someone will have to weed and spread
      The young sprouts. Sprinkle them in the hour
   When shadow falls across their bed.
You should try to look at them every day
   Because when they come to full flower
      I will be away.

VI

   Easter has come around
  again; the river is rising
     over the thawed ground
  and the banksides. When you come you bring
     an egg dyed lavender.
   We shout along our bank to hear
our voices returning from the hills to meet us.
   We need the landscape to repeat us.

   You lived on this bank first.
  While nine months filled your term, we knew
     how your lungs, immersed
  in the womb, miraculously grew
     their useless folds till
  the fierce, cold air rushed in to fill

them out like bushes thick with leaves. You took your hour,
  caught breath, and cried with your full lung power.

    Over the stagnant bight
we see the hungry bank swallow
    flaunting his free flight
still; we sink in mud to follow
    the killdeer from the grass
that hides her nest. That March there was
rain; the rivers rose; you could hear killdeers flying
    all night over the mudflats crying.

    You bring back how the red-
winged blackbird shrieked, slapping frail wings,
    diving at my head—
I saw where her tough nest, cradled, swings
    in tall reeds that must sway
with the winds blowing every way.
If you recall much, you recall this place. You still
    live nearby—on the opposite hill.

    After the sharp windstorm
of July Fourth, all that summer
    through the gentle, warm
afternoons, we heard great chain saws chirr
    like iron locusts. Crews
of roughneck boys swarmed to cut loose
branches wrenched in the shattering wind, to hack free
    all the torn limbs that could sap the tree.

    In the debris lay
starlings, dead. Near the park's birdrun
    we surprised one day
a proud, tan-spatted, buff-brown pigeon.
    In my hands she flapped so
fearfully that I let her go.

Her keeper came. And we helped snarl her in a net.
   You bring things I'd as soon forget.

   You raise into my head
a Fall night that I came once more
   to sit on your bed;
sweat beads stood out on your arms and forehead and you wheezed for breath,
for help, like some child caught beneath
its comfortable wooly blankets, drowning there.
   Your lungs caught and would not take the air.

   Of all things, only we
have power to choose that we should die;
   nothing else is free
in this world to refuse it. Yet I,
   who say this, could not raise
myself from bed how many days
to the thieving world. Child, I have another wife,
   another child. We try to choose our life.

VII

Here in the scuffled dust
   is our ground of play.
I lift you on your swing and must
   shove you away,
see you return again,
   drive you off again, then

stand quiet till you come.
   You, though you climb
higher, farther from me, longer,
   will fall back to me stronger.
Bad penny, pendulum,
   you keep my constant time

547

to bob in blue July
    where fat goldfinches fly
over the glittering, fecund
    reach of our growing lands.
Once more now, this second,
    I hold you in my hands.

IX

    I get numb and go in
though the dry ground will not hold
    the few dry swirls of snow
and it must not be very cold.
A friend asks how you've been
        and I don't know

    or see much right to ask.
Or what use it could be to know.
    In three months since you came
the leaves have fallen and the snow;
your pictures pinned above my desk
        seem much the same.

    Somehow I came to find
myself upstairs in the third floor
    museum's halls,
walking to kill my time once more
among the enduring and resigned
        stuffed animals,

    where, through a century's
caprice, displacement and
    known treachery between
its wars, they hear some old command
and in their peaceable kingdoms freeze
        to this still scene,

Nature Morte. Here
by the door, its guardian,
   the patchwork dodo stands
where you and your stepsister ran
laughing and pointing. Here, last year,
      you pulled my hands

   and had your first, worst quarrel,
so toys were put up on your shelves.
   Here in the first glass cage
the little bobcats arch themselves,
still practicing their snarl
      of constant rage.

   The bison, here, immense,
shoves at his calf, brow to brow,
   and looks it in the eye
to see what is it thinking now.
I forced you to obedience;
      I don't know why.

   Still the lean lioness
beyond them, on her jutting ledge
   of shale and desert shrub,
stands watching always at the edge,
stands hard and tanned and envious
      above her cub;

   with horns locked in tall heather,
two great Olympian Elk stand bound,
   fixed in their lasting hate
till hunger brings them both to ground.
Whom equal weakness binds together
      none shall separate.

   Yet separate in the ocean
of broken ice, the white bear reels

beyond the leathery groups
of scattered, drab Arctic seals
arrested here in violent motion
    like Napoleon's troops.

Our states have stood so long
At war, shaken with hate and dread,
    they are paralyzed at bay;
once we were out of reach, we said,
we would grow reasonable and strong.
    Some other day.

Like the cold men of Rome
we have won costly fields to sow
    in salt, our only seed.
Nothing but injury will grow.
I write you only the bitter poems
    that you can't read.

Onan who would not breed
a child to take his brother's bread
    and be his brother's birth,
rose up and left his lawful bed,
went out and spilled his seed
    in the cold earth.

I stand by the unborn,
by putty-colored children curled
    in jars of alcohol,
that waken to no other world,
unchanging where no eye shall mourn.
    I see the caul

that wrapped a kitten, dead.
I see the branching, doubled throat
    of a two-headed foal;

I see the hydrocephalic goat;
here is the curled and swollen head,
        there, the burst skull;

    skin of a limbless calf;
a horse's foetus, mummified;
    mounted and joined forever,
the Siamese twin dogs that ride
belly to belly, half and half,
        that none shall sever.

    I walk among the growths,
by gangrenous tissue, goiter, cysts,
    by fistulas and cancers,
where the malignancy man loathes
is held suspended and persists.
        And I don't know the answers.

    The window's turning white.
The world moves like a diseased heart
    packed with ice and snow.
Three months now we have been apart
less than a mile. I cannot fight
        or let you go.

                    x

The vicious winter finally yields
    the green winter wheat;
the farmer, tired in the tired fields
    he dare not leave, will eat.

Once more the runs come fresh; prevailing
    piglets, stout as jugs,
harry their old sow to the railing
    to ease her swollen dugs

and game colts trail the herded mares
    that circle the pasture courses;
our seasons bring us back once more
    like merry-go-round horses.

With crocus mouths, perennial hungers,
    into the park Spring comes;
we roast hot dogs on old coat hangers
    and feed the swan bread crumbs,

pay our respects to the peacocks, rabbits,
    and leathery Canada goose
who took, last Fall, our tame white habits
    and now will not turn loose.

In full regalia, the pheasant cocks
    march past their dubious hens;
the porcupine and the lean, red fox
    trot around bachelor pens

and the miniature painted train
    wails on its oval track:
you said, I'm going to Pennsylvania!
    and waved. And you've come back.

If I loved you, they said, I'd leave
    and find my own affairs.
Well, once again this April, we've
    come around to the bears;

punished and cared for, behind bars,
    the coons on bread and water
stretch thin black fingers after ours.
    And you are still my daughter.

WILLIAM STAFFORD

For the Grave of Daniel Boone

THE FARTHER HE WENT the farther home grew.
Kentucky became another room;
the mansion arched over the Mississippi;
flowers were spread all over the floor.
He traced ahead a deepening home,
and better, with goldenrod:

Leaving the snakeskin of place after place,
going on—after the trees
the grass, a bird flying after a song.
Rifle so level, sighting so well
his picture freezes down to now,
a story-picture for children.

They go over the velvet falls
into the tapestry of his time,
heirs to the landscape, feeling no jar;
it is like evening; they are the quail
surrounding his fire, coming in for the kill;
their little feet move sacred sand.

Children, we live in a barb-wire time
but can follow the old hands back—
the ring in the light, the knuckle, the palm,
all the way to Daniel Boone,
hunting our own kind of deepening home.
From the land that was his I heft this rock.
Here on his grave I put it down.

Walking West

Anyone with quiet pace who
walks a gray road in the West
may hear a badger underground where
in deep flint another time is

Caught by flint and held forever,
the quiet pace of God stopped still.
Anyone who listens walks on
time that dogs him single file

To mountains that are far from people,
the face of the land gone gray like flint.
Badgers dig their little lives there,
quiet-paced the land lies gaunt,

The railroad dies by a yellow old depot,
town falls away toward a muddy creek.
Badger-gray the sod goes under
a river of wind, a hawk on a stick.

Along Highway 40

Those who wear green glasses through Nevada
travel a ghastly road in unbelievable cars
And lose pale dollars
Under violet hoods when they park at gambling houses.

I saw those martyrs—all sure of their cars in the open
and always believers in any handle they pulled—
wracked on an invisible cross
and staring at a green table.

554

While the stars were watching
we crossed the Sierras in our old Dodge
letting the speedometer measure God's kindness,
And slept in the wilderness on the hard ground.

Written on the Stub of a Paycheck

GASOLINE makes game scarce.
In Elko, Nevada, I remember a stuffed wildcat
someone had shot on Bing Crosby's ranch.
I stood in the filling station
breathing fumes and reading the snarl of a map.

There were peaks to the left so high
they almost got away in the heat;
Reno and Las Vegas were ahead.
I had promise of the California job,
and three kids with me.

It takes a lot of miles to equal one wildcat
today. We moved into a housing tract.
Every dodging animal carries my hope in Nevada.
It has been a long day, Bing.
Wherever I go is your ranch.

ROBERT S. SWARD

The Poetry Workshop

SEATED, against the room, against the walls
Legs extended, or under chairs
Iambs, trochees & knees . . .
We surrender, each of us, to the sheets
At hand. The author swallows his voice. Still.

Page two—page one is saved (and for the last).
The poet has here been impressed
By the relationship
Between BLUE birds and black. In the octet
We note the crow. And its iambic death.

On page three, "The Poet Upon His Wife,"
(By his wife) *we note the symbols*
For the poet—the bird
In flight, the collapsing crow, the BLUE bird . . .
(Note too the resemblance between sonnets.)

We vote and stare at one another's crow.
Ours is an age of light. Our crows
Reflect the age—Ike-Dick—
Colored stripes, rainbow-solids, blacks & whites.
(Ruffling their wings, the crows refuse to vote.)

Page four, "Apologies to William S."
Apologies—the third sonnet.
(And those who teach, who write—
And teach—the man at hand, apologize
For themselves, and themselves at hand; themselves.)

The "love" is *his*. The form, the words, the love.
Epigraphs—footnotes—transitions.
It is all a matter
Of course, of one's course: "The Collapsing Crow."
Chaucer—Shakespeare—Donne, Self . . . *Apologies*.

Poets buy their socks at "Brooks & Warren"
Like Du Pont—like Edsel—like Ike.
—Anecdotes, whispers, cliques
Whispering—then aloud into prominence.
Brooks & Warren—Du Pont—Edsel & Ike.

Order is resumed. *We have been here, now*
Forever. From the beginning
Of verse (one has written
Nothing—and it is inconceivable
That one would, or will ever write again).

A class has ended:—they pass by, gazing
In. The poets gaze out, and grin.
They gaze out, and through the
Electric voice, the ruffled sonnet-sheets
That stare against the faces staring in.

Page one. Walled-in glances at the author;
And then the author disappears
(The poem anonymous).
Voice. Voices—there are voices about it:
Anonymous. The self. A sonnet's self . . .

The room is filled with it. It is a bird.
It sits beside us and extends
Its wings. Someone squirts it
With a fountain pen. Blinded, it shrieks, dies
And sprawls upon the floor. We surrender

We surrender to its death—the poem breathes,
Becomes its author and departs.
We all depart. And watch
The green walls take our seats—apologies.
Brooks & Warren—Du Pont—Edsel & Ford.

JOHN A. TAYLOR

The Bat

A GENTLE BEATING at the wall
Mixed with the sigh of troubled air
Was all the warning which a soul
Had of this soft noctambular.

Through some uncovered crack or cranny
He flew into our darkened room,
And warm in bed we heard his many
Attempts to find the way he'd come.

My wife insisted something more
Was in the house with us; I laughed
Until the lamp shone on the fur
Which blindly whirled and tacked about.

Unclothed, and flourishing a broom
I thrashed the air with harmless strokes
To play the fool in pantomime
Against that scorner of hard knocks.

Sliding round the room, he flapped
His fingers in a knotted way
In air, misleading each inept
Recalculation of my eye.

Afraid, he fled me through the house
Into my attic den and vanished
Before I saw which way he'd use
To keep his flight from being punished.

I looked the books and rafters over
And found no sign of the black imp,
All empty of his live cadaver
As graves will greet the final trump.

Since then the bat has made a haunt
Within my dreams until I feel
I am the hunted and the hunt,
I am the bat whose screams are still.

EDITH TIEMPO

Lament for the Littlest Fellow

THE LITTLEST FELLOW was a marmoset.
He held the bars and blinked his old man's eyes.
You said he knew us and took my arm and set
My fingers around the bars, with coaxing mimicries
Of squeak and twitter. "Now he thinks you are
Another marmoset in a cage." A proud denial
Set you to laughing, shutting back a question far
Into my mind, something enormous and final.

The question was unasked but there is an answer.
Sometimes in your sleeping face upon the pillow,
I would catch our own little truant unaware;
He had fled from our pain and the dark room of our rage,
But I would snatch him back from yesterday and tomorrow.
You wake, and I bruise my hands on the living cage.

ROLANDO S. TINIO

Gentle My Song

GENTLE MY SONG and slip us like the night.
Early morning lambent on the floor sprawls white

As the shapeless moon of temporary summers
In the tropic city. Our narrow cave is dumber

Than the egg-shell closing. Love lies speechless
On her salt-bed, head wounded by the nearness

Of the rooster's antedated crow. So gentle . . .
Our sculpturing of beauty in the ancient shell

Is a daring thing. Fingers like pins move
In a labor of telepathic love. The witch's dove

Caught in her hand is cushioned against the breast
With a tarnished pin. The reeling echoes of the past

Dovetail with the egg-shell echo of the cove.
Down in the probed deep, we are minute from above.

The bottom is as comfortable as the dark
And, liquescent, we seek our own levelled mark.

Go like a bird on paper wings, like the winds
On our sunken foreheads, thin like the mind's

Partitioning. Temples are exhumed from the flat
Earth silent and healed. The Mayas who have sat

On twisted twigs are bruised in the new
Destruction. Confident as men loving, they knew

Nothing of the history of twigs and wounds,
The recklessness held in stone and bound.

Silence moons on the broken stones. The last
Stir on the pointed crag is a poisoned bat's.

EMMANUEL TORRES

Song for a Dry Season

IT IS A WONDER how on a fine day like this
With the sun spilled on the hardstained planks of walls,
The wind lolloping, the birds singing and singing,
We pick up broken pieces and are poor.

Though nothing has changed our lean and hardwood house,
We still can bear our faces on the cracked glass
And be glad that our pain is personal, be glad
The bed is in one corner, the table nailed in place.

No special feast lies on the breakfast table;
It is rice and fish and coffee steaming and steaming.
There is no wine but a china jug of water
Will do to make us relish appetite.

Everything is spare and useful to keep alive
Talk—such as the rough-grained texture of table,
The stove burning, the floorboards creaking and creaking.
Familiarity still fails to blunt our senses.

Somewhere rich relations are fattening and fattening
On surplus, yet ours is the nearer country of plenty
As your full breast tames that babe's loud hunger, and
Your thighs conceive of islands green with legend.

This lot may not be worth a curse. All is
Within reach of want as long as love is able.
That sunhammered tree outside our crooked window
Manages a few flimsy leaves in a dry season.

LEWIS TURCO

Raceway

MY RACEWAY of sheets last night became
a cool trotter, unwinding with grace. Today,
    autumn peeps imponderably out of
        the soggy drought July had posted
            on the foothills. It is August

            here in Saratoga; the races
open tomorrow. Yesterday a filly
    worked out her own odds, snapping two of her
        ankles while we watched. She was done in
            by a green syringe. She lounged on

            the turf, staring from one farthest eye,
both her forehooves angled like ballerina
    slippers. With her, summer has staggered: it,
        too, soon will drop and the jockey sun
            grow grey above the world's brown hide.

            When a thoroughbred loses its
        pins, there's no more running. Snort if you
    will, but reason, too, exhausts itself when
cause falters. Men have run down when barred from the
        race. Summer is a fragile courser

            here in the north; our racers are
        all imports from the southland. Summer
    will not slow for falling leaves, nor haul our
sleighs: it will linger, pawing its reluctance
        to leave, but its strength is of only

short will, meant for one swift effort.
Watch the summer run its oval, it's
a winner now—nothing can stop it! The
stands urge their encouragement upon open
air: shouts fall and rise like the fall wind

that moves out of the foothills now, sure,
pervasive, wild.
Blooded summer shies.

LEONARD UNGER

Forgetful

REMEMBER AGAIN the early morning faith
In her wise and deliberate conspiracy for you,
The fairy godmother plotting a good surprise—
You didn't know what, but something good would come true.

And ponder now the old talent for design
That knew with ear and eye to frame about
Breasts and thighs embellished with freshening darkness
And something which now you cannot quite make out.

For you would recall to the dim and echoing head
The trappings and bustle of that delicious game
Which rang with the accurate phrase that seemed to hold
Indelibly your once familiar name.

But do you remember whether it came to pass,
The good surprise which daily you hoped to own?
And have you no dream to unbury the eyes that saw
That light with which the drifting body shone?

It will do no good to go and ask your mother
Who moves among outworn worries, unaware
You don't remember that, really, you did tell her
Those forgotten words you imagine you would not dare.

She is spelling the words of a fragment of a story,
And it is beautiful—if she could only know.
And you are plotting fables for the disenchanted
Who wait in unbelief for what they know.

CONSTANCE URDANG

The Madman

AT FIRST, he wondered why he should be spared;
Observed, of all the windows, none was barred,
And every door swung open at a word.

The garden welcomes him; the angel's sword
Flowered before his eyes like Aaron's rod;
At first he wondered that he should be spared.

The beasts had grown so tame they hardly stirred;
The wall uncoiled its length without a guard
Where every door swung open at a word,

And trees bowed low to offer all they had.
The woman swore he was her only lord
Although, of all the windows, none was barred.

He called it Eden (but it was the world),
And so, until it was too late, ignored
The lucid glass that sealed the windows hard;

No longer troubled to pronounce the word.
But at the end, when towering clouds hurled
Boomerangs at him, and the thunder roared

At him one terrible and final chord,
He knew at last that he had not been spared,
Ran screaming from the mirror, and was mad.

MONA VAN DUYN

Three Valentines to the Wide World

I

THE CHILD disturbs our view. Tow-head bent, she
stands on one leg and folds up the other. She is listening
to the sound of her fingernail on a scab on her knee.
If I were her mother I would think right now of the chastening
that ridiculous arrangement of bones and bumps must go
    through,
and that big ear too, till they learn what to do and hear.
People don't perch like something seen in a zoo
or in tropical sections of Florida. They'll have to buy her
a cheap violin if she wants to make scraping noises.
She is eight years old. What in the world could she wear
that would cover her hinges and disproportions? Her face is
pointed and blank, the brows as white as the hair.

"Mother, is love God's hobby?" At eight you don't even
look up from your scab when you ask it. A kid's squeak,
is that a fit instrument for such a question?
Eight times the seasons turned and cold snow tricked
the earth to death, and still she hasn't noticed.
Her friend has a mean Dad, a milkman always kicks
at the dog, but by some childish hocus-pocus
she blinks them away. She counts ten and sucks in her cheeks
and the globe moves under the green thumb of an Amateur,
the morning yelp, the crying at recess are gone.
In the freeness of time He gardens, and to His leisure
old stems entrust new leaves all winter long.

Hating is hard work, and the uncaring thought is hard;
but loving is easy, love is that lovely play
that makes us and keeps us. No one answers you. Such absurd

charity of the imagination has shamed us, Emily.
I remember now. Legs shoved you up, you couldn't tell
where the next tooth would fall out or grow in, or what
your own nose would look like next year. Anything was
     possible.
Then it slowed down, and you had to keep what you got.
When this child's body stretches to the grace of her notion,
and she's tamed and curled, may she be free enough to bring
mind and heart to that serious recreation
where anything is still possible—or almost anything.

II

I have never enjoyed those roadside overlooks from which
you can see the mountains of two states. The view keeps
     generating
a kind of pure, meaningless exaltation
that I can't find a use for. It drifts away from things.

And it seems to me also that the truckdriver's waste of the
     world
is sobering. When he rolls round it on a callus of macadam,
think how all those limping puppydogs, girls
thumbing rides under the hot sun, or under the white moon

how all those couples kissing at the side of the road,
bad hills, cat eyes, and horses asleep on their feet
must run together into a statement so abstract
that it's tiresome. Nothing in particular holds still in it.

Perhaps he does learn that the planet can still support life,
though with some difficulty. Or even that there is injustice,
since he rolls round and round and may be able to feel
the slight but measurable wobble of the earth on its axis.

But what I find most useful is the poem. To find some spot
on the surface and then bear down until the skin can't stand

570

the tension and breaks under it, breaks under that half-
    demented
"pressure of speech" the psychiatrists saw in Pound

is a discreetness of consumption that I value. Only the poem
is strong enough to make the initial rupture,
at least for me. Its view is simultaneous
discovery and reminiscence. It starts with the creature

and stays there, assuming creation is worth the time
it takes, from the first day down to the last line on the last
    page.
And I've never seen anything like it for making you think
that to spend your life on such old premises is a privilege.

III

> "Your yen two wol slee me sodenly;
> I may the beautee of hem not sustene."
> *Merciles Beaute*

When, in the middle of my life, the earth stalks me
with sticks and stones, I fear its merciless beauty.
This morning a bird woke me with a four-note outcry,
and cried out eighteen times. With the shades down, sleepy
as I was, I recognized his agony.
It resembles ours. With one more heave, the day
sends us a generous orb and lets us see
all sights lost when we lie down finally.

And if, in the middle of her life, some beauty falls on
a girl, who turns under its swarm to astonished woman,
then, into that miraculous buzzing, stung
in the lips and eyes without mercy, strangers may run.
An untended power—I pity her and them.
It is late, late; haste! says the falling moon,
as blinded they stand and smart till the fever's done
and blindly she moves, wearing her furious weapon.

Beauty is merciless and intemperate.
Who, turning this way and that, by day, by night,
still stands in the heart-felt storm of its benefit,
will plead in vain for mercy, or cry, "Put out
the lovely eyes of the world, whose rise and set
move us to death!" And never will temper it,
but against that rage slowly may learn to pit
love and art, which are compassionate.

TENNESSEE WILLIAMS

Little Horse
For F. M.

Mignon he was or *mignonette*
avec les yeux plus grands que lui.
My name for him was Little Horse.
I fear he had no name for me.

I came upon him more by plan
than accidents appear to be.
Something started or something stopped
and there I was and there was he.

And then it rained but Little Horse
had brought along his *parapluie.*
Petit cheval it kept quite dry
till he divided it with me.

For it was late and I was lost
When Little Horse enquired of me,
What has a bark but cannot bite?
And I was right. It was a tree.

Mignon he is or *mignonette*
avec les yeux plus grands que lui.
My name for him is Little Horse.
I wish he had a name for me.

CHRISTOPHER WISEMAN

Magnets

SAFE ENOUGH, you think, a field
    Like this, decently wide,
And you, like poles, at an even distance.
So the slow current is concealed,
    Attraction seems denied,
And space intrudes in case you yield.

Who could foresee that sudden start,
    The force that set these two
On their frantic headlong course, the shock
Of contact, such fierce pressure? Whose art
    Can hope to free them now?
Coupled so close, yet poles apart.

LEONARD WOLF

Florentine Easter III

I

THE CITY OF FLORENCE in the marble seen
Palazzos shows and sunlight, ponderous
As massive gold, shines heavily between
Red balustrades. In alleys, perilous
With beauty, Cleveland glows, a nebulous
And distant structure in Italian air;
A reasonable town, not dangerous
At Easter time. Its traveller, shy, takes care
Of Florence with its God and His imposing snare.

II

The city of Florence is a broken stone
That shines in fragments on the Arno plain.
A ruined crypt that may be looked upon
By any tourist at the risk of pain.
The godless Clevelander, in towers, vain
With the besotted vanity of years
Explores the wreck of the intense inane.
The city printed on a card, brings tears;
Its print in stone brings love and grave religious fears.

III

He wants no god. In Florence where he turns
Are mumbling priests, and on the butcher's hooks
Hang lambs adorned with roses. Florence burns
The thickest incense; prints the fairest books
Of prayers for her cathedrals. There, Christ looks
Compassion crudely from a monument
And cherubs, grimy in their dusty nooks

Adore him, simpering, from a pediment
Where all the knees of Florence in His praise are bent.

IV

Who eats this eats wrath, or perfect life,
Or else the crumbs that fall from it betray
The baker's weakness, or the baker's wife
Who makes thin wafers that too soon decay.
The Clevelander is glad the rich array
Before the altar's tarnished, and a rent
Is in the altar cloth. He tastes the clay
That's in the bread and knows no god is pent
In musty wafers waiting with malign intent.

V

The queen of Sheba is another queen!
But Christ in Florence is an emperor, wan,
Denied her presence. Busy Florentines
Have time to watch her, and her purple swan
Making their progress. Who has looked upon
That Negro lady with her leopard's eyes
May not be saved. Unless his soul outrun,
With heaven's help, her Abyssinian sighs,
He'll trip in luxury and lose his paradise.

VI

Imagination's paradox. To sin
Where we adore, and by remote decree
To maim the god we have salvation in.
The north is brutal; from the nearest tree
The Norsemen hang him; in the south, we see
Him clinging gently. From his side, a dew
Like ichor flowing, while humility
In every picture more intense than true
Sustains him where he hangs, his palms pierced through
    and through.

He'll have no gods; the Cleveland tourist, now
A wide-eyed truant from a safer shore
Is still erect. No image sees him bow,
Except his head, rebelliously, before
The beautiful. His lips will not implore
A resurrection. Swiftly, swiftly flows
The stream of his impiety. The more
The church in satin and in triumph goes,
The deeper roils his current and more fierce it grows.

VIII

The traveller lives in Cleveland O. How shall
He bear such knowledge gracefully; he stands
Amazed before these icons that appall
His reason. Yet his intellect commands
Lake Erie's troubled and ungracious strands
Without much shock. There, limestone slakes the ore
Unhelped by attitudes of praying hands.
In Florence, it makes fountains from which pour
Out streams of grace and glory at the church's door.

IX

Die down! The church is a presumption torn
Out of the mouths of babes. Belief must die,
And prayer too. He's bought a missal, worn
By an Italian hand, whose pages lie
In soft black letter to his heart and eye
And lovely, with the classic innocence
Of lies that are believed. Abashed, he'll buy
Tomorrow, on the grain of a pretence
A gaudy rosary and count him out of sense.

Why will the stones rise up and Duomo build
Whose source is beauty, peril and decay?

Poor Clevelander; he's busy, and has filled
His notebooks sternly for a later day
When his emotions, after long delay
And recollected, like a dream appear
Which there impelled him, while he could, to pray
Away from Cleveland. In a single year
He will deny that too; and he denies it here.

JOHN WOODS

On Genius, Interrupted

DRIVEN TO HIS GARDEN, his woodworking tools,
From the blaze of his own work, making his study
Uninhabitable, he pulled terrible anchors.
Always, in the rout beyond his hedge
Where even dust had lost its innocence,
Were those who'd write down everything he said
And sell it back to him, as news, as truth.
What could he command outside the fence?
All the lovely causes. Once, outside
His gate, he found a golden podium.
Once, when steel went up, he found a sigh:
Love thy neighbor as he loves himself.
Outside his lawn, he thought, were many truths.

But after mitres, varnish, and rottenstone,
After pruning, peatmoss and a cross of roses,
After Israel, after mail, and after dinner
Where he fed on his own, crisp lettuce hearts,
There was the burning corridor, the smoking door,
The desk, flaring with his own great vision,
Which he must seize and strike with bare hand,
Or drown with tears for the ordinary world.

In My Darkest Age

IN MY darkest age
I loved your medieval
Lips that dripped with gall
And honey in their rage.
I hung upon their feast
And gorged like any beast.

In a duel of tongues
Your kisses let out blood.
Beneath your falcon's hood
I urged such tender songs
That, gentled by such pap,
You fed me from your lap.

But last night in your cell
I heard the shadows speak
That others, drawn and weak,
Had swung within your bell
And made the armor boom
Across the freezing room.

I lie this lonely hour
And hold you, ignorance.
I know what renaissance
Is knocking at the tower.
But when the towers spill,
I'll swing, your clapper still.

When Senses Fled

I AM CUSTODIAN of close things.
Even winter trees have blurred
To leaf, and faces come upon me
Suddenly. I am a startled man
To half the town, and half my yard
Is blunderland. First, I lost
The violets, then the grass,
And now, the red and wren white fence.
Farewell, the bright decay of oak,
The crewcut water, the black assizes
Of the night. Farewell, the visual.

Today, the wind began to lag
And all its freight of season drained
Into the neighbor trees. And all
The smoking, sideburned streets
Dropped ashes on the muted playground.
Let lightning slam the screen, I cry,
Let neighbors war, a shop of cats
Tear metal. O stone me with shouting.
But the grating thunderhead suspends
Its buzzing nest beneath my bough.
Farewell, the audible.

       Touch,
Tell me what the world displays
For now I rain behind my eyes.
If you would hurt me, gather close,
For in the last deception, skin,
I must be broken by a kiss.
Love is a cave of scrolls, and I
Have thrown away all spectacles.
I roll horizons like a hoop
Among the mufflered trees, and see
Nerve ends crackling in the dark.
Farewell, the tangible.

       Inside,
I stand, a coalescent dust.
When I sing, my voices turn
To stone, and where I touch, veins
Stand out. When I am alone, the forest
Swarms with nakedness, and where
I point, pole stars waltz along
My finger. Look, the fence appears,
Then grass. And all my senses step
On naked feet into the garden
To ring, an anvil of the storm,
To name the kneeling animals.

BIOGRAPHIES

WILLIAM BELVIN was born in Dante, Virginia in 1918 and grew up in Tennessee where he took his B.S. degree at East Tennessee State College. After the war, in which he served as a bombardier, he received an M.A. in English at Northwestern University. He taught there at that time and later at the State University of Iowa, where he attended the Poetry Workshop. He also taught at Alabama Polytechnic Institute and Coe College. In 1953-54 he was awarded a Rockefeller Foundation grant. At present he is an advertising copywriter. His poems have appeared in *Botteghe Oscure, Prairie Schooner, Kenyon Review* and elsewhere.

WILLIAM BERGE writes: "I am a bachelor of thirty-one years of age, a teacher of English in Ely Junior College, and my hobbies are chiefly reading, hunting and canoeing in the Minnesota lake country." The story by which he is represented in this collection was a prize winner in the Knopf-Furioso Fiction Contest and appeared in *The Best American Short Stories of 1952* collected by Martha Foley.

GEORGE BLUESTONE was born in 1928 in New York City. He says his "diplomas, degrees, tales and braces came from Harvard, Iowa and Johns Hopkins." The year 1956-57 he spent abroad, mostly in Florence, working on a novel "while my wife went off daily to the USIS library to work on Sartre (she had the grant)." Since that time he has been on the staff of the University of Washington and has published a number of stories in *The Atlantic* (a "first" prize), *Epoch, New World Writing, Contact, San Francisco Review* and *Virginia Quarterly Review*. His first novel, *The Private World of Cully Powers*, was published last year by

Doubleday. A critical book, *Novels into Film*, came out in 1947. He has also done a number of articles, chiefly on the motion picture medium, and these have been published in *Sewanee Review*, *Western Review*, *Film Culture*, *Film Quarterly* and *Tulane Drama Review*.

FREDERICK BOCK has been an Assistant Editor of *Poetry* magazine since 1955. He was enrolled in the Iowa Poetry Workshop a year earlier. His poems have appeared in a number of literary journals, including *Partisan Review* and *Yale Review*, and he has given readings at the Poetry Center in New York City.

DONNA BOWEN was born and raised in Minnesota. She received a B.S. degree in Art and, in 1950, an M.A. degree in English from the University of Minnesota where she studied with Robert Penn Warren. After attending the Writer's Workshop at the State University of Iowa she came to New York and held a variety of jobs, among them the editorship of a political-social journal. In 1953 she married Wallace Kaminsky, now an English professor at Auburn University. She has two children and is finishing a first novel. Her poems have been published in *Poetry*, *Botteghe Oscure*, *Mademoiselle* and other magazines. In 1948 she was named a Fellow of the American Association of University Women.

JAMES BUECHLER grew up in Schenectady, New York, and went to Harvard at eighteen. After graduation, he lived in Europe for a year, in Iowa for a year while attending the State University Workshop, and a year in Schenectady. He now teaches at St. Bernard's School in New Jersey where he makes his home with his wife and two children. The story which appears here was first published by *Mademoiselle*.

R. V. CASSILL writes: "That I was born in Iowa seemed to me once a highly fortuitous circumstance, but in my middle age it looks more like a fatality, an originally neutral event which comes more and more to have the force and color of choice. When I first went to the State University of Iowa, I had no good reasons for registering there, but the good reasons emerged—as if they

had been the basis for my prior decision—in the course of time."
During the war he was stationed in the South Pacific. Back in his
home state now, he has "two children, boy and girl." His novel
The Eagle on the Coin was published by Random House in 1950.

JANE COOPER was born in 1924, spent her childhood in Florida
and her adolescence in Princeton, New Jersey. She has taught at
Sarah Lawrence College since 1950. Her poems have appeared in
*Poetry, The New Yorker, New World Writing, Harper's Maga-
zine* and *Voices*; also in the Borestone Mt. Poetry Awards' *Best
Poems of 1957*. She was awarded a Guggenheim Fellowship for
creative writing in poetry for 1960-61.

HENRI COULETTE loves to play games. He has invented one and
refined others. Born in 1927, he is married, teaches creative writing at Los Angeles States College and has already memorized the
colors and nicknames of all the major colleges in America. His
verse has appeared in *The New Yorker, Hudson Review, The
Paris Review* and *Mademoiselle*. At present he is preparing a
book of poems and writing a detective story.

ALEXANDER CRAIG is a native of Australia. He has published his
work in the leading magazines of that country and has reviewed
Australian verse for *Poetry*. He holds degrees from the University
of Melbourne and the State University of Iowa.

BRUCE CUTLER was graduated with a B.A. degree from the State
University of Iowa writers' program in 1951. He worked for
four years in Mexico and Central America with the American
Friends Service Committee, and in 1957 received his master's
degree from Kansas State University. He was a Fulbright scholar
in Italy in 1957-58, became a member of the English Department
of Kansas State University in 1958, and now teaches in the English Department of the University of Wichita. His book, entitled
The Year of the Green Wave, was published in 1960 as the first
selection in the University of Nebraska Press *First-Book Poetry
Series*, with an introduction by Karl Shapiro.

ROBERT PATRICK DANA was born in Allston, Massachusetts thirty-one years ago. He served as radioman in the Navy. His academic record includes a B.A. degree from Drake University and an M.A. from the State University of Iowa. He is now on the faculty of Cornell College while working on his Ph.D. at Iowa. His poems have been published in *Poetry* magazine.

RICAREDO DEMETILLO was born in Panay, Philippines, where he attended native schools and American missionary colleges. He took his B.A. from Silliman University and his M.F.A. from the State University of Iowa. At Iowa he studied under Paul Engle and Robert Lowell; at the Indiana University School of Letters, under Allen Tate and Richard Blackmur. He has won two major literary awards in the Philippines and has published two books of verse: *No Certain Weather* (1955) and *La Via, A Spiritual Journey* (1959). At present he is an Assistant Professor at the University of the Philippines and an editor of *The Diliman Review*.

WILLIAM DICKEY was born in Bellingham, Washington in 1928, and educated at Reed College, Harvard University and State University of Iowa. He is a former managing editor of *Western Review*, assistant editor of *Civil War History* and editor of *Epoch*. His book *Of the Festivity* was published by Yale University Press in 1959.

HARRY DUNCAN was born in Keokuk, Iowa in 1916, was graduated from Grinnell College and did graduate work at Duke University. He has managed The Cummington Press from its beginning, and his *Poems and Translations* was published in the first POETS OF TODAY series by Scribner's. He has written librettos for three one-act operas, one produced on NBC Opera Theatre, another at Spoleto and a third in New York's City Center. He has taught at the State University of Iowa since 1956 and directs the Typographic Laboratory there.

JOHN ENGELS grew up as the son of a faculty member at Notre Dame University, which he also attended as a student. Later he was a member of the Poetry Workshop at the State University of Iowa, after a brief interlude in Dublin. His work has been published in *Poetry, Commonweal, The Literary Review* and elsewhere. He now teaches at a Roman Catholic college in northern Wisconsin.

PAUL ENGLE, a former student in the Iowa Writer's Workshop, now directs it. His latest book is *Poems in Praise* (1959).

PETER EVERWINE is a graduate of Northwestern University. A Stanford Poetry Fellow in 1958-59, he is now on the faculty of the State University of Iowa. His pamphlet entitled *The Broken Frieze* was published by the Hillside Press in 1958.

DONALD FINKEL, born in New York City in 1929, received his B.S. and M.A. degrees at Columbia University. He has been a ticket seller in Grand Central Station and an instructor in English. He now teaches at Bard College and is an editor of *The Shasta Review*. His first book, *The Clothing's New Emperor*, is part of the POETS OF TODAY series.

E. S. FORGOTSON was born in Alexandria, Louisiana in 1916, and composed his first poem at the age of four: "Uncle Bill, you're a pill." He took his B.A. degree at Louisiana State University in 1939 and his M.A. at Vanderbilt University in 1940. He studied at the State University of Iowa between 1940 and 1942. His work has appeared in *The Southern Review, The Nation, American Prefaces, Poetry, Signets, Kenyon Review, The Nashville Banner* and *The New York Times*.

KIMON FRIAR has been a director of the Poetry Center in New York City and chairman of presentations at New York's Circle in the Square Theatre. His translation of Nikos Kasantzakis' *The Odyssey: A Modern Sequel* was published in 1958 with enormous success. Since then he has been doing a film treatment and scenario of the poem for Twentieth Century-Fox. He is editor of *The Charioteer*, a quarterly review of modern Greek culture, and last year served as a judge for the National Book Award in poetry. Besides the Kasantzakis translation, he has edited, with introduction, *The Poetry Center Presents* (1947); co-edited (with John Malcolm Brinnin) *Modern American and British Poetry* (1951);

and translated, with introduction, *The Saviors of God: Spiritual Exercises* (1960). He is now at work on two other projects, one a translation of Homer's *Odyssey* into iambic hexameter, and the other, *Contemporary Greek Poetry*, an anthology of about forty moderns. Following study at the University of Wisconsin, he won a scholarship to the Chicago Art Institute and became a Zona Gale Literary Scholar. He continued at the Yale Graduate School of the Drama, under George Pierce Baker, and at the University of Michigan, which granted him an A.M. degree and a Hopwood Award in the Essay for his study of Yeats. He has taught English at the State University of Iowa, the University of Minnesota, Adelphi College, Amherst and New York University. He is a contributor to *The Atlantic, The New Republic, Poetry* and *A Little Treasury of World Poetry*, among others.

JEAN GARRIGUE was born in Evansville, Indiana and grew up in the Middle West where she attended the University of Chicago and State University of Iowa. She has since lived in and around New York City. Her books of verse include *The Ego and the Centaur, The Monument Rose* and *A Water Walk by the Villa d'Este*. She spent two years in Europe on a Rockefeller Foundation grant. Her published writings include criticism, articles, stories, a novella and sections from a novel, which have appeared in various journals in the United States and abroad.

WALKER GIBSON was raised in Albany, New York and was graduated from Yale in 1940. During the war he was with an Air Force squadron in the Caribbean. After the war he studied at the State University of Iowa and later at Amherst, where he was a member of the faculty for eleven years, including one year spent in New Mexico on a Ford Foundation fellowship. He now teaches at New York University. He has published two books of verse, *The Reckless Spenders* (1954) and *Come As You Are* (1958).

WILLIAM GOODREAU is a native of Maine and a graduate of Bates College. He has an M.F.A. degree from the State University of Iowa and is a member of the English Department at the College of Saint Teresa in Winona, Minnesota. His poems have been published in *The Hudson Review*, *The Commonweal*, *The Critic* and *The Colorado Quarterly*.

MARTHA GRIMES is a native of Maryland. She received her M.A. degree from the University of Maryland. Her poetry has appeared in *Western Review* and *New Orleans Poetry Journal*, as well as other publications.

JAMES B. HALL teaches at the University of Oregon. He has published many stories, several novels since his first, *Not by the Door*, and frequent poems. His verse has appeared in *Perspective*, *Harper's Bazaar*, *Epoch* and *Western Review*. He served in the Army during World War II.

CARL HARTMAN was born in Austin, Texas in 1923 and was graduated from the University of Illinois, thereafter spending three and a half years in the infantry during World War II. He took his M.F.A. degree from the State University of Iowa in 1950. Since then he has taught at A. and M. College of Texas, Cornell University and, currently, at Washington University. He has edited, and published poetry in a number of journals, including *Accent*, *Western Review*, *Epoch* and *Perspective*. He is married and has one child.

ANTHONY HECHT was born in 1922. After leaving the State University of Iowa, he studied with John Crowe Ransom at Kenyon College. His first book, *A Summoning of Stones*, was published by The Macmillan Company in 1954 and received wide critical acclaim.

ALBERT HERZING studied at Kenyon College and the State University of Iowa. He now teaches at Fairleigh Dickinson University where he is associated with *The Literary Review*.

THEODORE HOLMES was born thirty-three years ago in New Jersey. He attended Princeton, where he received his B.S. degree in biology. He was the *Kenyon Review* Poetry Fellow for 1958-59. He has taught at the University of Oregon and is currently on the staff of Harvard University. His first book was published in the series POETS OF TODAY IV by Charles Scribner's Sons.

DOMINADOR I. ILIO has an engineering degree from the University of the Philippines. He studied hydraulics and poetry at the State University of Iowa where he was a Fellow in 1950. Now an Associate Professor in mechanics at the University of the Philippines, his verse appears in *Poetry, Botteghe Oscure, Diliman Review, Comment* and elsewhere. His first book, *The Diplomat and Other Poems*, was published in 1955.

DAVID CLAY JENKINS was born in Alabama and attended school in Birmingham. At the end of the war, and during part of the occupation, he was a battalion sergeant-major in an infantry unit in Germany. At the University of Alabama he studied writing with Hudson Strode. There he received his B.A. and M.A. degrees in English. Later he became a member of the Writer's Workshop at the State University of Iowa, working toward a Ph.D. He wrote his dissertation on Welshmen (including Dylan Thomas) writing in English, a research project begun while he was a Fulbright Scholar for two years at University College of Wales, 1949-51. Since receiving his Ph. D. in 1956 he has taught English at the College of William and Mary in Virginia and is now an Assistant Professor. His stories have appeared in *Prairie Schooner, Points* (Paris) and other publications. He also writes poetry and criticism. Of the story in this collection he says: "As the reader will see, I am spiritually a Southerner, but my expatriate years at Iowa were pleasantly spent among the other expatriates."

CAROL JOHNSON has taught at Marquette University and the State University of Iowa. Her poetry has appeared in *Sewanee Review, Commonweal* and *Hudson Review.* Two years ago at Iowa she won the Academy of American Poets Prize. She now teaches at the Woman's College of North Carolina.

DONALD JUSTICE won the Lamont Prize for 1960 with his first book, *The Summer Anniversaries,* which was published that spring. He studied at the University of Miami, the University of North Carolina and Stanford University, as well as the State University of Iowa. Born in 1925 in Florida, he now makes his home in Iowa City and teaches in the Iowa Poetry Workshop.

CALVIN KENTFIELD has done many kinds of work since the age of seventeen, chiefly maritime. Born in 1924 at Keokuk, Iowa, he now lives in Sausalito, California, where he is co-founder and editor of *Contact: The Western Review*. He has traveled about the world and, while in London, married Veronica Humble Bernard, who is co-founder and managing editor of two small Kentfield publications, one of each sex. He has published two books, *The Alchemist's Voyage* (1955) and *The Angel and the Sailor* (1957), plus many short stories. He is at work on a novel, *The Small Rain*.

KIM YONG IK, a Korean, has returned to his native land after study at the State University of Iowa but continues to publish his work widely in this country.

JOSEPH LANGLAND was born in 1917 at Spring Grove, Minnesota, and grew up on a farm in Iowa. *The Green Town* was his first book of poems. He is co-author of *The Short Story*, an anthology-text. His work has appeared in many magazines, including *London Magazine*, *Accent* and *Harper's Bazaar*. He teaches at the University of Massachusetts.

ALFRED M. LEE was born in 1938 in Louisville, Kentucky. He received his B.A. degree from Yale College, where he won the Academy of American Poets and Berkeley prizes. He is now studying at the State University of Iowa. His poems have appeared in *Poetry*, *The Yale Review* and *Susurrus*. He has sold antiquarian books in New Haven and began writing poems in 1958 while working in a refrigerator plant at Gennevilliers, France. His last job was tending bar in St. Tropez.

PHILIP LEGLER was born in 1928 in Dayton, Ohio. He had two years' service as a Marine sergeant at the close of World War II. Later he attended Denison University, where he received his B.A. degree, and took his M.F.A. degree at the State University of Iowa. Since 1953 he has taught literature and writing at Ohio

University, Central Missouri State College, New Mexico Highlands University, and currently, at Illinois Wesleyan University. His poems have appeared in the *New Mexico Quarterly*, *Poetry*, *Prairie Schooner*, *Western Review* and other publications.

PHILIP LEVINE teaches at Fresno State College. He was born in 1928 in Detroit. He holds B.A. and M.A. degrees from Wayne State University, and an M.F.A. from the State University of Iowa. "From 1949-53," he says, "I worked as a machinist. I first attended the Writer's Workshop at Iowa in 1953, then went off for a year to the mountains of North Carolina and the swamps of northern Florida. I returned to Iowa in 1955 as an instructor of English and left in the fall of '57 for Stanford University, where I received the Jones Fellowship in Poetry. I am married to a beautiful woman and have three wild sons." His first volume of poetry was published recently by The Leavenworth Company of San Francisco. His poems have appeared in *Commentary*, *The Paris Review*, *Poetry*, *New Campus Writing*, *Western Review*, *The New Yorker* and other magazines.

ROBIE MACAULEY comes from Grand Rapids, Michigan, where he was born in 1919. He studied at Olivet College under Ford Madox Ford; at Kenyon College under John Crowe Ransom, and did graduate work while teaching at the State University of Iowa, where he was on the staff of the *Western Review*. He is now editor of the *Kenyon Review*. He has published a novel, *The Disguises of Love*, and a collection of short stories, *The End of Pity*.

WILLARD MARSH was born in Oakland, California in 1922, and grew up expecting to be a chemist. "Upon flunking math, I switched to music and, with a group of crew-cut young hoods known as Will Marsh and the Four Collegians, perpetrated musical crimes in a nearby gin mill." After his graduation from high school he attended Chico State College until he became an Air Force radio operator in World War II. Later he returned to college, "flunked English and thereupon became interested in writing," which he now teaches at Winthrop College. He says he "owns one wife, no children, and stories in *Best American Short*

Stories (1953); *Best Saturday Evening Post Stories* (1954); *The Antioch Review Anthology* and *The Year's Greatest Science Fiction and Fantasy Prize Stories of 1957.*"

E. L. MAYO has published three volumes of verse, the latest being *The Swimmers*. He has published poetry in numerous journals and teaches at Drake University.

KARL KIMBER MERKER was born in New York City in 1932. While he still considers it home, he has lived in the Caribbean, Florida, Illinois, California and Iowa. His undergraduate work was done at Illinois College where he received a B.A. degree after two years in the Air Force. Following a short period in San Francisco, he came to the State University of Iowa. There he has done part-time graduate work for several years and has run The Stone Wall Press (until recently with Raeburn Miller). The press prints "fine" limited editions of contemporary poetry. He is married and has two children.

ROBERT MEZEY was born in 1935. He attended Kenyon College before coming to Iowa, and spent two years in the Army. His poems have appeared in *The Paris Review*, *The New Yorker*, *Kenyon Review* and *New Campus Writing #2*. Recently he won the 1960 Lamont Poetry Selection Award for his book *The Lovemaker*.

RAEBURN MILLER is currently enrolled in the Writer's Workshop at the State University of Iowa and has been co-editor and publisher of The Stone Wall Press.

WARREN MILLER has written several novels, including *The Way We Live* and *The Cool World*, the latter being made into a musical. His stories have been published in *The New Yorker* and *Harper's Bazaar*.

JOHN MONTAGUE was born in Brooklyn, New York in 1929, and was brought up in Ireland on an Ulster mountain farm. Educated at Armagh College and University College, Dublin, he spent three years thereafter in the United States, traveling and studying at

Yale University, the State University of Iowa and in California. He has contributed to the *Faber Book of Irish Short Stories* and published, in 1958, a collection of poems, *Forms of Exile*. He manages to survive most climates and occupations by a combination of timidity and truculence; trusts this process will continue.

WILLIAM M. MURRAY, born in 1929, in Miltown Malbay, County Clare, Eire, was educated at St. Flannans College and Southern Connecticut State College. He became an American citizen after two years in the U.S. Army. He taught at the State University of Iowa and now lives in San Francisco.

DOUGLAS NICHOLS teaches at the University of Colorado. His work has been published in *Kenyon Review* and *Boetteghe Oscure*, among others.

FLANNERY O'CONNOR has published her work virtually everywhere, in most distinguished magazines. She lives in Georgia and raises fowl.

YOSHIE OSADA was born in Kyoto, Japan's city of temples and gardens. She writes verse both in Japanese and English. At present she is living in Tokyo.

DONALD PETERSEN was born in 1928 and grew up in Wisconsin. He received his B.A. degree from Carleton College, his M.F.A. from Iowa. His verse has been published in *Furioso*, *Poetry* and *Western Review* under his own name as well as a pseudonym, Peter Hald. He teaches at Oneonta State Teachers College in New York.

PAUL PETRIE has B.A. and M.A. degrees from Wayne University, and a Ph.D. from Iowa. His poetry has been widely published. His personal interests center about a great record collection. He is now on the faculty of the University of Rhode Island.

CYNTHIA PICKARD had her first book of verse published recently. Its title is *Woman in Apartment*. She makes her home in Nashville, Tennessee.

RICHARD POWER was born in 1928 in County Kildare, near three of Ireland's best-known racetracks. As between two gambles he chose to write rather than follow the horses. He was educated in two conflicting schools of Irish culture, the Irish Christian Brothers and Trinity College, Dublin; his degree, in English and Celtic literature, is an attempt at a compromise between them. Bilingual, he writes in Gaelic and English. His English work has appeared in several English and Irish magazines, including *The Bell*, *Poetry Ireland*, *Icarus*, *The Saturday Book* and, in America, *The Dial*. Two of his plays were produced by the Abbey Theatre, and his book describing Aran Islanders at home and as exiles in industrial England won a £200 award for the best Irish book of 1957. He spent two years in the Writer's Workshop at the State University of Iowa and returned home in the fall of 1960. Like many Irish writers who prefer to live in Ireland, he earns his living in the Irish civil service. He is married and has three sons, the youngest of whom is an American citizen.

VERN RUTSALA was born in McCall, Idaho in 1934 and after a somewhat nomadic childhood attended high school near Portland, Oregon. He then studied at Reed College, receiving a B.A. degree in 1956 and the annual creative work prize for his thesis, a collection of poetry. Following graduation from Reed, he was drafted and spent most of the next two years in Munich where he edited an Army newspaper. He was married in 1957. Since first publication in *Epoch*, his work has continued to appear in such magazines as *The Paris Review*, *The Beloit Poetry Journal*, *Texas Quarterly*, *San Francisco Review*, *Perspective*, *Inland* and *Northwest Review*. One of his poems was recently published in pamphlet form by The Stone Wall Press in Iowa City. Since September, 1958 he has been doing graduate work at the State University of Iowa, and in June, 1960 he received an M.F.A. degree in writing.

BIENVENIDO N. SANTOS, a native of the Philippines, took his B.S.E. degree in 1932 from the University of the Philippines; his A.M. in English from the University of Illinois in 1942. He has also done graduate work at Columbia University, Harvard University and at the State University of Iowa on a Rockefeller Foundation grant. He has won numerous writing awards in his homeland and is president of Legazpi College there. His published works include two collections of short stories: *You Lovely People* (1955) and *Brother, My Brother* (1959), as well as a book of poems, *The Wounded Stag* (1956).

SATORU SATO is the son of a Tokyo doctor. He studied at the First Higher School and later at Tokyo University. He was an officer in the Imperial Japanese Navy in 1944-45. His home was burned during the war. He has worked in the Foreign Section of the Yomiuri Press, and in the Poetry Workshop wrote verse in Japanese and English, the latter being original poems rather than translations. He edited a special issue of *Poetry* on modern Japanese poems, translating and writing notes as well as an introduction. He was aided on this project by Constance Urdang, a fellow Workshop poet. Today he paints in watercolor and teaches English at the Tokyo University of Art and Music. He feels that English is "more functional for simultaneous operation of the senses and the intellect than the recent Japanese" language. He is sometimes a little homesick for the warm attitude of Iowa City toward poets, foreign and domestic.

ROBERT SHELLEY came to the Poetry Workshop from St. Louis, Missouri, where he received his B.A. degree from Washington University. At the time of his early and unfortunate death he had already given promise of a brilliant career. His play, *Now Falls the Shadow*, performed at Washington University, received the Wilson Memorial Award in 1947. He was a member of the editorial staff of *Western Review* and his poems were published there, in *Poetry*, and in other magazines. *New Directions 12*, which appeared in 1950, contained his monologue, "A Young Prince to the Dying King." His poems have some of the lyrical liveliness of his English namesake.

KNUTE SKINNER was born in St. Louis in 1929. He received his Ph.D. degree from the State University of Iowa in 1958, and for two years lived in Europe where he wrote a novel. His poetry has appeared in *The New Republic, The Literary Review, New*

Campus Writing #3, *Antioch Review*, *New Orleans Poetry Journal* and other magazines.

W. D. SNODGRASS won a Pulitzer Prize in May, 1960 for *Heart's Needle*, his first book of poems, published by Knopf. It has gone through several printings, and British rights have been sold. The same volume won the first Ingram Merrill Foundation Award. He was born in Wilkinsburg, Pennsylvania, attended Geneva College in Beaver Falls, that state, and was graduated from the State University of Iowa, receiving M.A. and M.F.A. degrees from the latter. During the years 1955 to 1958 he taught at Cornell University and the University of Rochester; also at Morehead (Kentucky) and Antioch writers' conferences. He was a *Hudson Review* Poetry Fellow in 1958-59. Last year he received a $1,500 award from the National Institute of Arts and Letters. At present he is teaching at Wayne State University in Detroit.

JEAN STAFFORD was born in Covina, California in 1915. She received her A.B. and A.M. degrees from the University of Colorado in 1936. The following year she studied at the University of Heidelberg. Her novels include *Boston Adventure, The Mountain Lion, The Catherine Wheel* and *Children Are Bored on Sunday*. She has contributed short stories to *Kenyon Review, Partisan Review, Sewanee Review, Harper's, Harper's Bazaar, Vogue, Mademoiselle* and *The New Yorker*. In 1945 she received an Academy of Arts and Letters grant and has had two Guggenheim fellowships, in 1945 and 1948. She is married to writer A. J. Liebling and lives in Long Island.

WILLIAM STAFFORD, who has been called "the most prolific poet in America," received his Ph.D. from the State University of Iowa in 1954. He teaches at Lewis and Clark College in Oregon. His publications include poems in *The Atlantic, Hudson Review, The Nation, New Republic* and *Poetry*.

WALLACE STEGNER was born in Lake Mills, Iowa. He received his A.B. degree from the University of Utah (1930); his A.M. (1932) and his Ph.D. (1935) from the State University of Iowa. He also studied at the University of California from 1932-33. He has taught English at Augustana College, University of Utah, University of Wisconsin, Harvard University and, since 1945, at Stanford University. He began writing about 1934 and was awarded a Guggenheim fellowship in 1950, renewed in 1952. He received the Little, Brown & Company prize for a novelette, *Remembering Laughter*, in 1937. His most recent publications are: *Second Growth, The Women on the Wall, Preacher and Slave, Beyond the Hundredth Meridian* and *The City of the Living*. He has also edited (with Richard Scowcroft and Boris Ilyin) *The Writer's Art*, in 1950. He is a contributor to literary magazines. He married in 1934 and has one son. His home is Los Altos, California.

RICHARD G. STERN was born in New York City in 1928 and has degrees from the University of North Carolina, Harvard University and the State University of Iowa. He is now Assistant Professor of English and General Studies in Humanities at the University of Chicago. His first novel, *Golk*, was published last year. His fiction, criticism, translations and verse have appeared widely. Editor of the anthology *American Poetry of the Fifties*, he has completed a second novel and two plays. He is married, the father of four children.

LAWRENCE STURHAHN has been working in motion picture production in New York City for the past five years. His stories have appeared in *Mutiny, The Paris Review* and *Quixote*.

HOLLIS SUMMERS teaches contemporary fiction and other courses at Ohio University and has served on the staffs of a number of writers' conferences, including Bread Loaf and Antioch. His poems and stories have appeared in numerous publications. He has written three novels: *City Limit* (1948), *Brighten the Corner* (1952), *The Weather of February* (1957); one book of poems, *The Walks near Athens* (1959), and co-edited the anthology *Kentucky Story* (1954).

BETTY SUNWALL was born in Waterloo, Iowa in 1925. She was graduated from the State University of Iowa and did graduate work in writing under Robert Penn Warren at the University of

Minnesota. She is married, the mother of a ten-year-old son and is now living in Gainesville, Florida, where her husband teaches at the University of Florida.

Robert S. Sward published his first collection of verse, *Advertisements*, as an Odyssey Chapbook in 1959. His poems have appeared in *American Poetry Magazine*, *A Huoyhnhnm's Scrapbook* and elsewhere. He taught at Connecticut College for Women recently and spent several months in 1959 at the MacDowell Colony.

John A. Taylor has a B.A. degree from the University of Missouri, subsequent M.A. and Ph.D degrees from the State University of Iowa. He spent two years in the Army and now teaches at the University of New Hampshire.

Edith Tiempo was in the Iowa Poetry Workshop during the years from 1947 to 1950. She teaches English at Silliman University in the Philippines. Her verse has appeared in *Poetry* and *Western Review*.

Rolando S. Tinio was born in Tondo, Manila, the Philippines in 1937. He took a B.Phil. from The Pontifical University of Santo Tomas and an M.F.A. in creative writing from the State University of Iowa. At present he is teaching English, acting and dramatic arts simultaneously at various places in the Philippines, and is serving on the staff of *The Apostolate of the Rosary*. He has won writing prizes in the Philippines and has been active in several dramatic productions.

Emmanuel Torres was born in Manila in 1932. He received his B.A. degree from Ateneo de Manila, a Jesuit College, in 1954. He studied at the State University of Iowa in 1955-56 under a Fulbright grant and a Smith-Mundt Award.

Lewis Turco, born in 1934, periodically affirms his vow to beat the academicians at their own game, which they perniciously refuse to play. From 1952 to 1956 the Navy sent him on a world cruise. He took a B.A. degree in English, did graduate work and taught at the University of Connecticut, where for three years he was editor of *Fine Arts Magazine*. He spent the summer of 1959 at Yaddo and is now working on an M.A. in English at the State University of Iowa. He has a diploma in creative writing from Palmer Institute and has published plays, reviews and verse in eight anthologies and a number of magazines, including *The Beloit Poetry Journal*, *Carleton Miscellany*, *Kenyon Review*, *Magazine of Fantasy & Science Fiction*, *The Mid-Century* and *Sewanee Review*. He has recently put together a book of verse entitled *Raceway and Other Poems*.

LEONARD UNGER has degrees from Louisiana State University and the State University of Iowa. He has written brilliant criticism of T. S. Eliot and now teaches at the University of Minnesota.

CONSTANCE URDANG is a native New Yorker. She has worked for military intelligence, and edited crossword puzzles, mail-order catalogues and an encyclopedia. With Satoru Sato she translated and edited the 1956 Japanese issue of *Poetry*. She has published verse and criticism in many leading periodicals.

MONA VAN DUYN, co-editor of *Perspective*, is a lecturer in University College of Washington University. She has won the Eunice Tietjens Prize. Her poems and stories have appeared in such magazines as *Kenyon Review*, *Sewanee Review*, *Poetry* and *Epoch*.

TENNESSEE WILLIAMS is one of America's leading dramatists. New Directions recently published a collection of his poetry under the title *In the Winter of Cities*.

THOMAS WILLIAMS is the author of the novel *Ceremony of Innocence*. His short stories have appeared in *Esquire*; his poetry in *Accent*. He has had Army service in Japan.

HERBERT WILNER was born in 1925. He took his B.A., M.A. and Ph.D. degrees at Brooklyn College, Columbia University and State University of Iowa, respectively. He is married and has two children. He teaches creative writing at San Francisco State College. His stories have appeared in *Esquire*, *Western Review*,

Sewanee Review, Furioso, Epoch and the O. Henry Collections of 1954 and 1958. He is currently at work on a collection of short stories and a novel.

CHRISTOPHER WISEMAN was born in Hull, England in 1936, and was educated at Manchester Grammar School and Cambridge, where he read English and played far too much football. He started writing poetry in 1956, after two years in the Royal Air Force. He has also worked as a baker and a schoolteacher. He is now in his second year of study at the State University of Iowa.

LEONARD WOLF, Rumanian-born, grew up in Cleveland, Ohio. He was educated at Ohio State University, the University of California, the State University of Iowa, and now holds a Ph.D. degree. He is currently teaching in Shiraz, Iran as a Fulbright professor, but his regular post is at San Francisco State College. His poems have appeared in *Accent, Western Review, Commentary, Commonweal, Hudson Review* and *Contact*.

JOHN WOODS was born in 1926 in Martinsville, Indiana. He took a B.A. degree and did graduate work at the State University of Iowa. During the war he served with the Air Force in Panama. At present he is Assistant Professor of English at Western Michigan University. He is married and has two sons. His poetry has appeared in *Kenyon Review, Poetry, Prairie Schooner* and *Western Review*, and his book, *The Deaths of Paragon*, was published in 1955.

REX WORTHINGTON has degrees from Indiana University and the State University of Iowa. At present he teaches at the University of Virginia. He served three years as an enlisted man in World War II, two of them overseas.